fundamentals of civil engineering graphics
for construction,
land planning,
and aesthetics

Robert S. Ketzner
Robert M. Rights
Department of Mechanical Engineering
New Jersey Institute of Technology

STIPES PUBLISHING COMPANY
CHAMPAIGN, ILLINOIS   61820

FUNDAMENTALS
OF
CIVIL
ENGINEERING
GRAPHICS

for construction, land planning, and aesthetics

third edition

FUNDAMENTALS OF CIVIL ENGINEERING GRAPHICS
for construction, land planning, and aesthetics

THIRD EDITION

by

Robert S. Ketzner
Robert M. Rights

Copyright © 1972, 1975, 1992
BY ROBERT S. KETZNER & ROBERT M. RIGHTS

Stipes Publishing Company
10-12 Chester Street, Champaign, Illinois 61820

Library of Congress catalog card number: 72-86543

Current printing (last digit)
10 9 8 7 6 5 4 3 2 1

OTHER BOOKS BY THE AUTHORS:
Fundamental Problems of Civil Engineering Graphics,
   1st edition, Edwards Brothers, Inc., 1973

PREFACE

The principal objective of this book is to present fundamental graphical concepts and related material as they apply to the technology of our present society, particularly in the field of civil engineering. This includes, first the general category of "communication and construction." Second, there is the area of "aesthetics thru sketching" which uses graphical means to represent principles of pleasing design. Third, there is a considerable amount of graphical representation employed thru location plan design, site planning and subdivision layout, and cluster development. This might be called "graphical supplementation."

It is not a simple matter to separate formally these somewhat arbitrary classifications, and no attempt to do so has been made in this text. The reader will do well to think of the ideas and methods described as an integral part of the general technological endeavor of today's industrial complex rather than to treat them as separate entities. Graphical work, of necessity, overlaps many scientific and engineering fields, actually becoming a part of them. It is this vein of thought that has prompted what is contained in the chapters of this text.

In addition to the text book, a complete workbook has been prepared especially for use with this text: *Fundamental Problems of Civil Engineering Graphics*, by Ketzner and Rights, 1975.

Most of the problems in the workbook are designed for 8½" x 11" sheets, which are most suitable for filing. However, in the areas of Topography, Location Plan Design, Site Planning and Subdivision, and Cluster Development larger sheets are required.

Additional objectives of the text are as follows:

1) develop the students' ability to apply the fundamentals of Civil Engineering Graphics useful in the communication of engineering information through freehand sketches and working drawings in the areas of construction, land planning and aesthetics.

2) to train the student to recognize the geometrical and analogous elements in civil engineering and to apply the graphical method to his solution.

3) to develop the students' vocabulary of technical terms pertaining to the field of civil engineering.

Our interest is in helping students to achieve the objectives of this text, and continued feedback on the use and effectiveness of this book is most important to us. We invite all users--students and teachers--to send comments and criticisms on both the general aspects and the details of both *Fundamentals of Civil Engineering Graphics* and *Fundamental Problems of Civil Engineering Graphics* to us at New Jersey Institute of Technology, Department of Mechanical Engineering, 323 High Street, Newark, New Jersey 07102.

Robert S. Ketzner

Assistant Professor of
Mechanical Engineering

Robert M. Rights

Assistant Professor of
Mechanical Engineering

ACKNOWLEDGMENT

Grateful acknowledgement is made to Dr. Frederick G. Lehman, Chairman of Department of Civil and Environmental Engineering, New Jersey Institute of Technology for advice and suggestions on the text; to Francis J. Burns, Professor Emeritus of Engineering Graphics and Robert G. Salamon, Professor of Mechanical Engineering for granting permission to use material from their Engineering Graphics classnotes and Technical Sketching manual; and to Robert V. Phillips, Professor of General Engineering and Richard S. Rusnak, Assistant Professor of General Engineering, both of the University of Wisconsin, for their advice, suggestions, and permission to use material from their lecture notes; and to Fitzhugh L. Morris, AIA Architect for his architectural assistance.

The work of Virginia Amend in proofreading and typesetting this manuscript is greatly esteemed.

The authors also wish to acknowledge and thank the several companies who supplied photographic illustrations, charts and tables, and technical information for this text.

American Institute of Steel Construction
Charles Bruning Company
Craftsman Book Company
C. E. Enterprises, Inc.
(Consulting Engineers)
Eugene Dietzgen Company
Federal Housing Administration
Frederic R. Harris, Inc.
(Consulting Engineers)
Keuffel and Esser Company
McGraw-Hill Book Company
Paulus & Sokolowski
(Consulting Engineers)
Pease Home Portfolio
Joseph T. Ryerson & Son, Inc.
T & M Associates, Inc.
(Consulting and Municipal Engineers)
United States Savings & Loan League

Newark, New Jersey   Robert S. Ketzner
January, 1975   Robert M. Rights

CONTENTS

AAABCDEFGHIJKLMNOPQRRSTUVWXYZ 1234567890
aabcdeffghijklmnopqrstuvwxyzß ſ ff ft fl fi ffi ffl

ABCDEFGHIJKLMNOPQRSTUVWXYZ
abcdefghijklmnopqrstuvwxyz 1234567890

AAABCDEFGHIJKLMMNNOPQRSTUVWVWWWXYZÆŒA
FARGHIKALALNTRRASSTTHUIÆŒØ 1234567890
abcdefghijklmnopqrsttuvwvwwwxyzff fl ffi ffl æ œ

ABCDEFGHIJKLMNOPQRSTUVWXYZ
1234567890

ABCDEFGHIJKLMNOPQRSTUVWXYZ
1234567890

AABCDEFGHIJKLMMNOPQRSTUVWXYZÆŒØ 1234567890
abcdefghijklmmnopqrstuvwxyzæœø

abcdefghijklmnopqrstuvwxyzæœ
1234567890

ABCDEFGHIJKLMNOPQRSTUVWXYZÆŒØ 1234567890
abcdefghijklmnopqrstuvwxyzæœø

ABCDEFGHIJKLMNOPQRSTUVWXYZ 1234567890
abcdefghijklmnopqrstuvwxyzæœø

ABCDEFGHIJKLMNOPQRSTUVWXYZ 1234567890
abcdefghijklmnopqrstuvwxyz

ABCDEFGHIJKLMNOPQRSTUVWXYZ
1234567890

ABCDEFGHIJKLMNOPQRSTUVWXYZÆŒ
1234567890

ABCDEFGHIJKLMNOPQRSTUVWXYZ
1234567890

ABCDEFGHI KLMNOPQRST VWXYZ
1234567890

LETTERING FOR ENGINEERS

Lettering. Lettering is an essential requirement in engineering work of all kinds. This is especially true of drawings, where legibility is needed for rapid and accurate understanding. Regardless of how expertly the line work may have been executed, its appearance and usefulness are naturally damaged by sub-standard lettering. Well executed letters and figures will greatly improve the appearance of any drawing. The main function of letters and figures is to give complete information as to **size, location, material, kinds of finish, accuracy, methods of assembling, number required, various or special notes and titles.** Legible letters, executed with speed, have been established as standard practice for **technical drawings, maps, graphic charts,** and other **professional engineering records. Charles W. Reinhardt** has received credit for having simplified the forms of lettering that is used today by engineers.

Other forms of letters that are used by engineers, architects, designers and artists include **Old Roman, Modern Roman, Gothic, Old English and "Commercial Gothic"** *(Fig. 1).*

Single-stroke letters are composed of uniform width lines or stems as formed by the pencil. The term **Single-Stroke Commercial Gothic** is often applied to such letters. Single-stroke letters are standard for most engineering purposes and will be treated in detail.

Two styles of **single-stroke commercial Gothic** letters are in general use by the design engineer: the vertical style in which all letters are capitals and lower-case, and the inclined style which may be all capitals or lower-case.

The purpose of this unit is to teach the shape of the different letters and numerals and also, the sequence and directions of the strokes used to form them. Horizontal guide lines are always used to control a uniform height for the letters. For the **Vertical style** of lettering, vertical guide lines are used. The vertical stroke of the letters should be parallel with the vertical guide lines.

The civil engineer uses engineering graphics as a graphical language which uses **lines, symbols, dimensions** and **notations** to describe accurately an object. The lines and symbols are drawn with professional drawing instruments and tools, the dimensions, notes, titles, bills of materials and technical specifications are lettered on the working drawing freehand. Lettering will be used instead of writing because it is more legible. For most types of drawings, single-stroke Commercial Gothic letters will be used. These letters are formed by straight and curved strokes of uniform width. With practice, they can be executed with ease and rapidity.

Remember, good lettering adds much to the

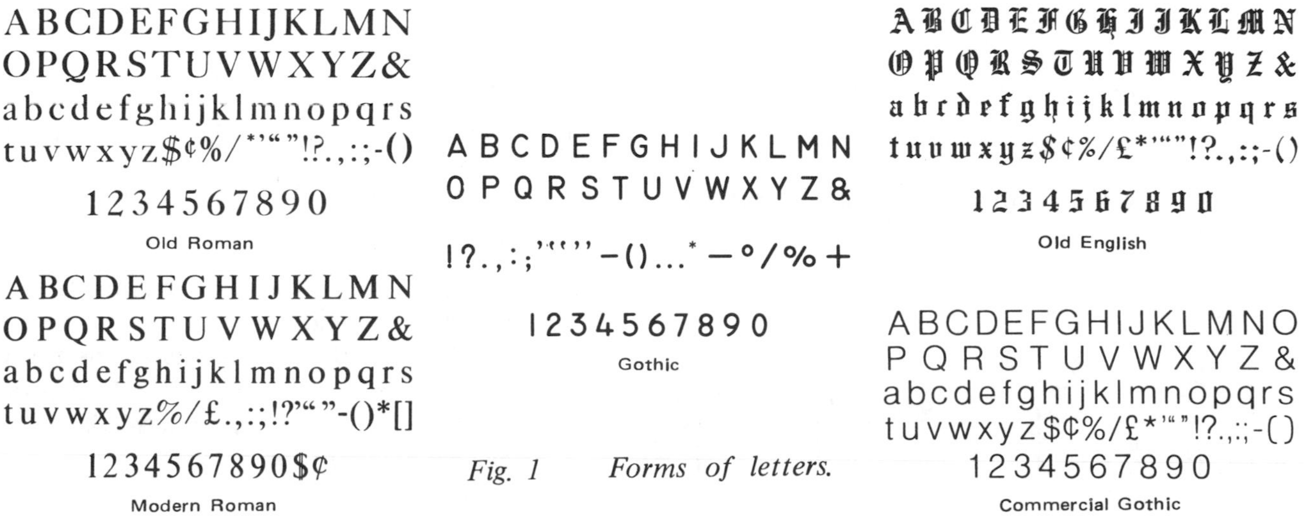

ABCDEFGHIJKLMN
OPQRSTUVWXYZ&
abcdefghijklmnopqrs
tuvwxyz$¢%/*'""?!.,:;-()
1234567890
Old Roman

ABCDEFGHIJKLMN
OPQRSTUVWXYZ&
abcdefghijklmnopqrs
tuvwxyz%/£.,:;!?""-()*[]
1234567890$¢
Modern Roman

ABCDEFGHIJKLMN
OPQRSTUVWXYZ&
!?.,:;'"''-()...* —°/%+
1234567890
Gothic

Fig. 1   Forms of letters.

𝕬𝕭𝕮𝕯𝕰𝕱𝕲𝕳𝕴𝕵𝕶𝕷𝕸𝕹
𝕺𝕻𝕼𝕽𝕾𝕿𝖀𝖁𝖂𝖃𝖄𝖅&
abcdefghijklmnopqrs
tuvwxyz$¢%/£*'""!?.,:;-()
1234567890
Old English

ABCDEFGHIJKLMNO
PQRSTUVWXYZ&
abcdefghijklmnopqrs
tuvwxyz$¢%/£*'""!?.,:;-()
1234567890
Commercial Gothic

attractive appearance of a drawing. Careless or poor lettering may spoil an otherwise excellent drawing. **Skill and speed in lettering can only be acquired through painstaking practice.**

VERTICAL CAPITAL LETTERING

Vertical Capitals. Single stroke vertical capitals may be divided into groups for studying. The letters may have an assumed height of six units and may be arranged on the basis of width. Use five units as a normal width. Letters are sometimes made either narrower or wider in order to appear well when put together in words. The difference in shapes and in number and position of the various lines, make it necessary to understand the characteristics of each letter and the effect of each letter upon the ones with which it is used.

Normal width letters include B, C, D, E, F, G, H, J, K, L, N, P, R, S, U, and Z. **Less than normal** width letters include the I. **Greater than normal** width letters include A, M, O, Q, T, V, W, X and Y. The letter W is eight units wide, being the widest letter of the alphabet. The letters A, M, O, Q, T, V, X and Y are "square" letters as they are six units wide. The width of the M is often increased by a ½ unit.

The effects of **proportion** and **stability** of area occupied must be considered when making the letters. The bar for the B, E, and H is placed above the middle so that the letters don't look top heavy in appearance. The top line of the E is made a little shorter than the bottom line and the upper portion of the S is made smaller than the lower portion. The bar of the P and the R are placed at the middle. The K, X and Z are smaller in width at the top than at the bottom.

VERTICAL CAPITAL LETTERS

E F H I L T

Letters formed with vertical and horizontal strokes.

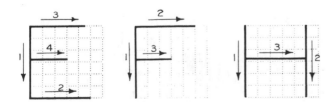

E -- The third stroke is shorter than the second stroke. The fourth stroke should be slightly above the middle and 3 units long. *(5 units wide)*

F -- The third stroke should be slightly above the middle and about 3 units long. *(5 units wide)*

H -- The third stroke should be slightly above the middle. *(5 units wide)*

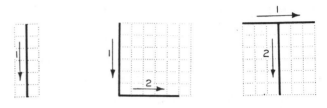

I -- The letter I is a single vertical line made with a down stroke.

L -- The L may be made with two strokes, or in one stroke if the height is small. When making this letter, guard against the tendency of the horizontal line to slope upward or downward and don't hesitate at the end of the stroke. *(5 units wide)*

T -- Learn to locate the center of the horizontal stroke quickly and don't hesitate between the two strokes of the T. *(6 units wide)*

K M N X Z

Letters formed with vertical, horizontal and oblique strokes.

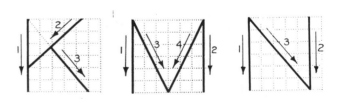

K -- This letter is not full width at the top. The second stroke ends 2 units up from the bottom. The third stroke starts at the top of the first stroke. Some start the third stroke at the middle of the second stroke if the height is small. *(5 units wide)*

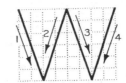

M -- The two outside strokes are usually made first. The incline strokes should meet at the center of the width and on the bottom guide line. Some engineers make this letter slightly wider if the height is smaller than normal. *(6 units wide)*

N -- The two vertical strokes are usually made first. This permits a more accurate estimate of the width of the letter. The inside line joins the top and bottom of the two parallel lines. *(5 units wide)*

W -- Make the first "V" of this letter one-half the total width of the letter, which is 8 units wide. Strokes 3 and 4 should be drawn parallel to strokes 1 and 2. *(8 units wide)*

Y -- Strokes 1 and 2 should meet in the middle of the height and make equal angles with stroke 3. *(6 units wide)*

 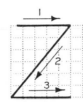

X -- This letter is not full width at the top, therefore, the two strokes meet at a point above the center. *(6 units wide)*

Z -- The first stroke is 4½ units long and is centered over the third stroke. The third stroke should be made immediately after the other or in one motion if the height is small. Some prefer to make the inclined stroke last. *(5 units wide)*

A V W Y

Letters formed with oblique strokes.

A -- This letter points to the center of the top guide line and has its third stroke located about one-third the height. *(6 units wide)*

V -- The two strokes meet at the center of the width on the bottom guide line. *(6 units wide)*

C G O Q S

Letters formed with curved strokes.

C -- Based on the *O.* A two stroke letter. *(5 units wide)*

G -- Based on the *O.* Bar of stroke 3 is at the middle of height, and the vertical part or stroke 4 extends downward about 2 units. *(5 units wide)*

O -- Start at the top of the letter, continue down to the left and around to the right. Stroke 2 will be a short stroke. *(6 units wide)*

Q -- Same as the *O* with a kern added. *(6 units wide)*

S -- May be formed from an ellipse. Make the upper part smaller than the lower part so that the letter will not look top heavy. *(5 units wide)*

B D J P R U

Letters formed with combined straight and curved strokes.

B -- Stroke 2 and 3 at right angles to stroke 1. They are straight lines, while stroke 4 is straight and curved. Stroke 5 is a circle tangent to the horizontal strokes. Stroke 3 is above the middle and the upper portion is less than 5 units wide. *(5 units wide)*

D -- Strokes 2 and 3 must be straight and start at right angles to stroke 1. *(5 units wide)*

J -- Stroke 1 must be straight and make a smooth joint with stroke 2. *(5 units wide)*

P -- Strokes 2 and 3 must start at right angles to stroke 1. Stroke 2 is in the middle. Curved portion is based on an oval and is tangent to the horizontal strokes. *(5 units wide)*

R -- Stroke 2 and 3 start at right angles to stroke 1. Stroke 2 is a straight line while stroke 3 is straight and curved. Stroke 4 if extended would meet 1 unit above stroke 3. *(5 units wide)*

U -- Strokes 1 and 2 are made parallel and stroke

3 makes a smooth joint that is tangent to both vertical lines. *(5 units wide)*

VERTICAL NUMERALS

All of the numbers are 5 units wide except 1.

 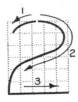

1 -- The number 1 is a single vertical line made with a downward stroke.

2 -- Stroke 1 and 2 pass through the center. The top part is not as wide as stroke 3 but is centered over the base.

3 -- The top half of the 3 is smaller than its base and it is centered over its base.

4 -- Stroke 2 of the number 4 makes approximately 45° with the vertical stroke 1. Stroke 3 is approximately ¼ the height of the number.

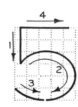 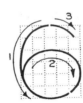 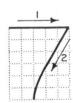

5 -- Stroke 4 is not as wide as the 5 but it is centered over the bottom part. The bottom portion of the 5 extends two-thirds of the height.

6 -- The body extends upward two-thirds of the height and stroke 3 doesn't extend as far to the right as the body itself.

7 -- Stroke 2 starts down toward a space 1 unit to the right of the left hand corner and then curves to a down direction that is perpendicular to stroke 1 and ends 2 units from the left.

8 -- The top half of the 8 is slightly smaller than the bottom half. This keeps the 8 from looking top heavy.

9 -- The body of the 9 is two-thirds the height of the number and stroke 3 doesn't extend as far to the left as the body itself.

0 -- The 0 is made in two strokes and is not as wide as an O.

VERTICAL LOWER CASE LETTERING

Small or lower-case letters are easily read because they have similar shapes. Most often they are two-thirds the height of capital letters. A line extending above the body of the letter is called an **ascender** and a line extending below the body is called a **descender**.

ORDER OF STROKE FOR VERTICAL LOWER CASE

The **vertical lower case letters** are made up mostly of circles and straight lines. The letters **a, b, d, e, g, h, k, n, o, p, q, s, u, v, x, y,** and **z** are 4 units wide. The letter **c** is 3 1/2 units wide. The letter **f** is 3 units wide. The letter **j, r,** and **t** are 2 units wide. The letter **i** and **l** are 1 unit wide. The letter **m** and **w** are 6 units wide.

The letter **c** is the same as the capital C except for height. The letter **e** has a middle stroke that is slightly above the center. A portion of the letter **f** and the **g** are formed by the circle. The letter **g** is shown with 4 strokes. The letter **h** and **n** are the same except for the length of the first stroke. A semi-circle forms part of the **h** and **n**. The dot of the **i** is 1/2 up the height of the **ascender**. The **j** is an inverted **f** with a dot instead of a cross bar and a circle

helps make up the **j**. The stroke 1 of the **k** is full height as a capital K. The **l** is a straight line that is capital height. The letter **m** is one and one-half times as wide as it is high with two semi-circles. The upper part of the **n** is a semi-circle. The letter **o** is a circle. The **p** and **q** are straight line **descenders** connected to circles. The upper part of the **r** is part of a circle and is very similar to an incomplete **n**. The letter **s** is like a capital S except smaller. The letter **t** may be full height. The letter **u** is a semi-circle, and is an inverted **n**. The letters **v, w** and **x** are the same shape as the capitals except smaller. The letter **y** is similar to the V except it has a **descender**. The letter **z** is the same shape as the capital Z except for being smaller.

VERTICAL LOWER CASE LETTERS

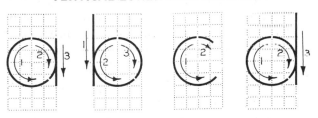

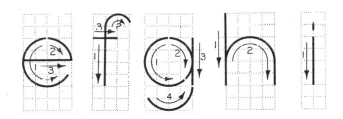

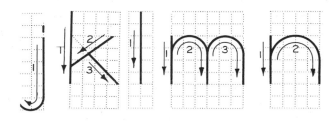

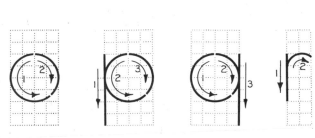

5

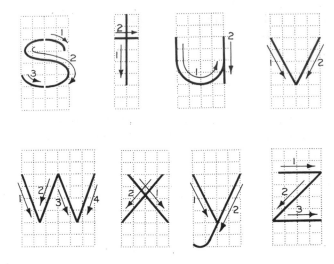

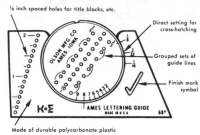

guide line ratios: 3/5 : 2/5, 2/3 : 1/3, and 1 : 1. **Guide lines** are made by turning the disc until the desired letter height is indicated on the index, then inserting the pencil into the pre-determined holes and sliding the device along the straight-edge. Sides are at 68° angle for drawing guide lines for inclined letters and 90° for vertical letters *(Fig. 2)*.

Fig. 2   Ames letter instrument.

The **Ames lettering instrument** is a convenient time-saving instrument for drawing ruling horizontal and inclined guide lines. It is placed against a straight-edge blade of the **T-square** and a hard lead pencil is inserted into the desired group of selected holes which determine the height of the letters. A slight degree of pressure against the downward side of the hole will maintain sliding contact against the blade of the T-square. Uniformly spaced guide lines of any size up to 1½" high are easily achieved with this adjustable device. It consists of a clear acrylic plastic frame and a rotatable disc with indexed rim. Holes in the disc provide for five lettering

INCLINED CAPITAL LETTERS

For the inclined style of lettering, sloping guide lines are used. The letters should be compared with the sloping guide lines so that the inclination of all the letters will be uniform.

The angle for inclined guide lines is 68° or a proportion of 2 units of run to 5 units of rise. The shapes of the inclined letters can easily be learned by substituting a rhombus grid square.

INCLINED CAPITAL LETTERS

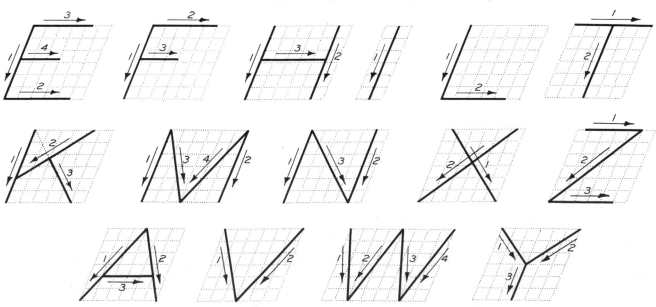

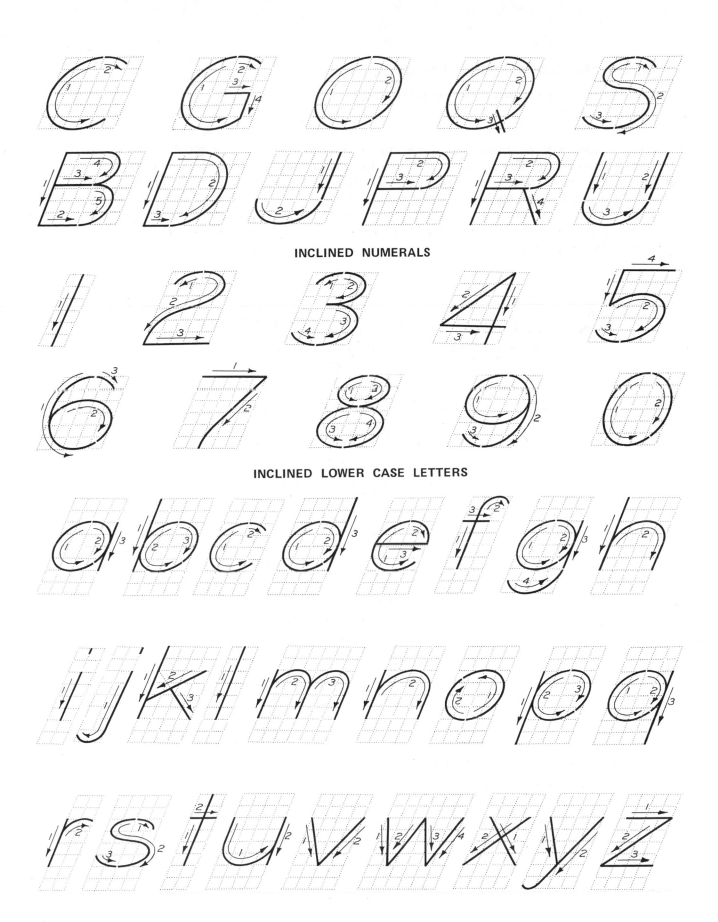

INCLINED NUMERALS

INCLINED LOWER CASE LETTERS

7

Lettering

The most important requirement for lettering as used on drawings is legibility. The second is ease and rapidity of execution. These two requirements are met in the single-stroke commercial gothic letter, now in almost universal use throughout the technical world. Preference seems to be divided between the vertical and the inclined styles. Approved specimens * of vertical and inclined letters are shown on this and the following pages and are in accordance with the American Standards Association's *American Drafting Standards Manual.*

VERTICAL LETTERS

TYPE 1

ABCDEFGHIJKLMNOP
QRSTUVWXYZ&
1234567890 $\frac{1}{2}$ $\frac{3}{4}$ $\frac{5}{8}$
TITLES & DRAWING NUMBERS

TYPE 2

FOR SUB-TITLES OR MAIN TITLES
ON SMALL DRAWINGS

TYPE 3 ABCDEFGHIJKLMNOPQRSTUVWXYZ&
1234567890 $\frac{1}{2}$ $\frac{3}{4}$ $\frac{5}{8}$ $\frac{9}{32}$
FOR HEADINGS AND PROMINENT NOTES

TYPE 4 ABCDEFGHIJKLMNOPQRSTUVWXYZ&
1234567890 $\frac{1}{2}$ $\frac{3}{4}$ $\frac{5}{8}$ $\frac{23}{64}$
FOR BILLS OF MATERIAL, DIMENSIONS & GENERAL NOTES

TYPE 5

OPTIONAL TYPE SAME AS TYPE 4 BUT USING TYPE 3 FOR FIRST
LETTER OF PRINCIPAL WORDS. MAY BE USED FOR SUB-TITLES
AND NOTES ON THE BODY OF DRAWINGS.

TYPE 6 abcdefghijklmnopqrstuvwxyz

* ASA Y14.2—1957

TYPE 1

ABCDEFGHIJKLMNOP
QRSTUVWXYZ&
1234567890 $\frac{1}{2}$ $\frac{3}{4}$ $\frac{5}{8}$ $\frac{7}{16}$
TO BE USED FOR MAIN TITLES
& DRAWING NUMBERS

TYPE 2

ABCDEFGHIJKLMNOPQR
STUVWXYZ&
1234567890 $\frac{13}{64}$ $\frac{5}{8}$ $\frac{1}{2}$
TO BE USED FOR SUB-TITLES

TYPE 3

ABCDEFGHIJKLMNOPQRSTUVWXYZ&
1234567890 $\frac{1}{2}$ $\frac{3}{4}$ $\frac{5}{8}$ $\frac{7}{16}$
FOR HEADINGS AND PROMINENT NOTES

TYPE 4

ABCDEFGHIJKLMNOPQRSTUVWXYZ&
1234567890 $\frac{1}{2}$ $\frac{1}{4}$ $\frac{3}{8}$ $\frac{5}{16}$ $\frac{7}{32}$ $\frac{1}{8}$
FOR BILLS OF MATERIAL, DIMENSIONS & GENERAL NOTES

TYPE 5

OPTIONAL TYPE SAME AS TYPE 4 BUT USING TYPE 3 FOR FIRST
LETTER OF PRINCIPAL WORDS. MAY BE USED FOR SUB-TITLES &
NOTES ON THE BODY OF DRAWINGS.

TYPE 6

abcdefghijklmnopqrstuvwxyz
Type 6 may be used in place of
Type 4 with capitals of Type 3,
for Bills of Material and Notes
on Body of Drawing.

Roman Numerals. The Roman letters were used as numerals until the 10th century A.D. In the Roman notation, the value of a symbol following another of the same or greater value is added to that of the numeral *(III = 3 or XV = 15)*; the value of a symbol preceding one of greater value is subtracted from the numeral *(IX = 9)*; and the value of a symbol standing between two of greater value is subtracted from that of the second, the remainder being added to that of the first *(XIX = 19)*. Roman numerals are commonly written in capitals, though they may be written in lower-case letters. A bar over a letter indicates multiplication by 1,000 *($\overline{V}$ = 5,000)*.

NUMERATION

Arabic	Roman	Arabic	Roman
0	...	20	XX
1	I	30	XXX
2	II	40	XL or XXXX
3	III	50	L
4	IV or IIII	60	LX
5	V	70	LXX
6	VI	80	LXXX or XXC
7	VII	90	XC or LXXXX
8	VIII or IIX	100	C
9	IX or VIIII	200	CC
10	X	300	CCC
11	XI	400	CD or CCCC
12	XII	500	D
13	XIII or XIIV	600	DC
14	XIV or XIIII	700	DCC
15	XV	800	DCCC
16	XVI	900	CM or DCCCC
17	XVII	1,000	M
18	XVIII or XIIX	2,000	MM
19	XIX or XVIIII	5,000	$\overline{V}$

TITLE BLOCK DESIGN

Every sheet of a complete set of working drawings, either architectural or the various fields of engineering, requires, identification of some kind, usually in the form of a **title block.** They are most often placed in the lower right-hand corner of the sheet. Each firm has its own design, some are rather simple while others are very detailed giving more information. Several examples are shown in *(Fig. 1)*.

Drawings of all kinds require titles. Since there are many different kinds of drawings with various purposes there must be a variety of title blocks. *Sketches, graphical reports, graphical diagrams* and *charts* all require titles. They should be definite, legible and require a minimum of time to fill in by the draftsman.

Tracings are very important to the engineer and architect; therefore, a carefully designed, well kept filing system must be maintained for filing the tracings *(originals)*. They are usually filed in flat, horizontal drawers. The commission number or job number must be found. This is best accomplished by filing drawings by the year along with the **job number** for that year. This job number, drawing number, usually serves as a filing number. It may be composed of letters, numbers or letters and numbers. Sometimes this number is repeated upside down in the upper left hand corner of the tracing, so that the drawing may be found should it ever be filed backwards in the file cabinet.

There are several ways that an engineering firm may save time. (1) Standard size drafting papers, 8½" x 11", 11"x17", 17"x22", 22"x34" and 34"x44" which are preprinted with borders and title blocks. (2) Rubber stamping the title blocks. They can be stamped on each sheet either before or after completing the design. (3) Appliques of preprinted title blocks of transparent plastic that will adhere to tracing paper. There are basically two types, one being a top application and the other one is a reverse *(applied to the*

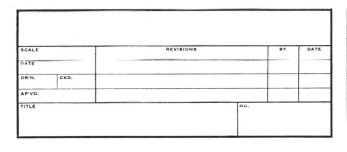

Fig. 1 Architectural and Engineering Title Block Details.

underneath side of tracing). Most architectural firms use the reverse type pressure sensitive title block appliques unless microfilming is involved.

The important items should be given attention. This can be done by the use of large letters, boldface letters, extended letters, or combination of these styles.

I Title Design
  A. **Types of Titles**
    1. Title block
      a. Where the title is confined by lines within certain limits
    2. Free title
      a. Where the title is placed on the open portion of the sheet
  B. **Information in title blocks and free titles**
    1. The name and location of what appears on the drawing
    2. The name and location of the engineering firm   preparing the drawing
    3. Sheet number and number of sheets. *(2 of 5)*
    4. Project or commission number
    5. Initials of draftsman and checker
    6. Revision information and date
    7. Signature and date of approval
    8. Date drawing was released for printing
    9. Scale of drawings, including all details
II Methods of Lettering and Centering
  A. **For Title Blocks**
    1. On a piece of sketch paper letter each line of the title as you expect to finish it, arranging the general position and lettering size of each line
    2. Determine letter heights for various lines

    3. Space guide lines vertically by scale measurement
    4. Draw a vertical center line through the rectangular title block and center the lettering horizontally with the use of tracing paper
    5. Vary lettering height according to importance---3/32'' *minimum*
  B. **For free titles**
    1. On a piece of sketch paper letter each line of the title as you expect to finish it, arranging the general position and lettering size of each line
    2. Determine the letter heights for various lines
    3. Space the various lines of the title vertically with scale
      a. Leave at least 2/3 of letter height between related lines of title, and more between the various sections of the title
    4. Draw a vertical center line through the middle of the selected position of the title, and center each line about the center line with the use of tracing paper
      a. Limit the width of the title to the length of the longest line
  C. **Methods of emphasizing title lines**
    1. By the size of the lettering
    2. By the width of the lettering
    3. Height of lettering decreases as the title proceeds downward.
III   Title arrangements *(Fig. 2).*

A.   For title blocks

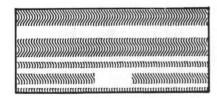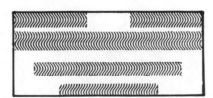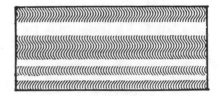

B. For free titles

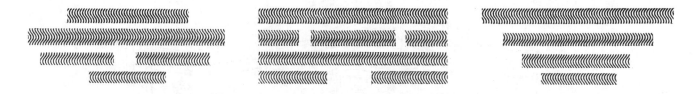

Fig. 2   Arrangement and spacing of lettering in title blocks.

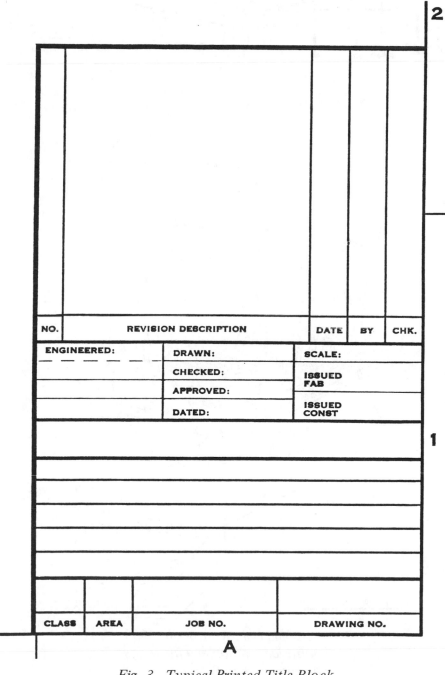

Fig. 3   Typical Printed Title Block.

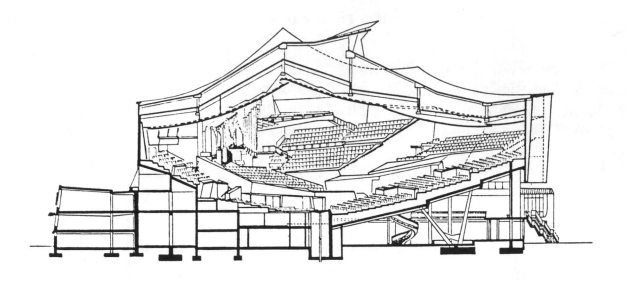

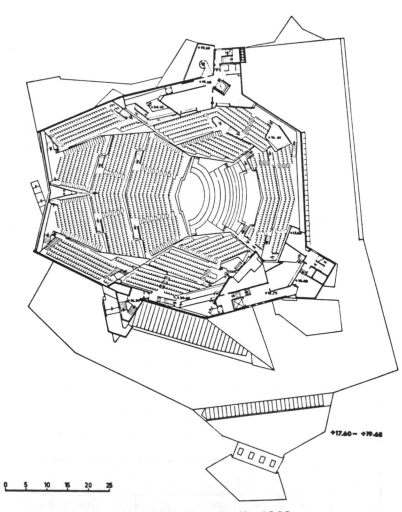

0 5 10 15 20 25

Philharmonic Hall, West Berlin 1963
(auditorium section and plan)
Architect: Hans Scharoun

SECTIONAL VIEWS AND ELEVATIONS

3

The **multi-view projections** reveal only the outside surfaces of an object: the top or plan *(horizontal)*, the front or rear *(frontal)*, and the right and left sides *(profile)*. Details which are on the inside or are underneath can be shown only as invisible lines. Using numerous invisible lines will cause the drawing to become cluttered, making it difficult to read. Sections are drawn to simplify drawings and to show the important details clearly without the use of invisible lines.

The section is obtained by passing a **cutting plane** through the object or building. All of the object or building in front of the cutting plane is removed. This exposes the inside part and the materials which the cutting plane passed through, as well as the remainder of the object or building on the far side or behind the cutting plane. *(Fig.*

1). This imaginary cutting plane is placed perpendicular to one of the three principal planes *(horizontal, frontal, and profile)* and is seen as an edge in one of the multi-views. The sectional cutting plane is indicated in its edgeview by a heavy dash-two-dot line, with arrows pointing in the direction in which the observer is looking. The projection of each section is labeled with the same letters as are shown on the edge view of the cutting plane.

When the cutting plane is in a vertical position the section obtained is called a **vertical section**. There are two principal vertical sections, *(Fig. 2)* the **transverse** and the **longitudinal** . The transverse section *(cross section)* is taken across the width of the object or building. Its correct multi-view position is to the right of the front elevation when the arrows on the section line point to the left. When the arrows on the section line point to the right, the transverse section is placed to the left of the front elevation. The transverse section, when in its correct multi-view position, can be used for the purpose

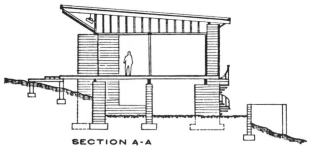

SECTION A-A

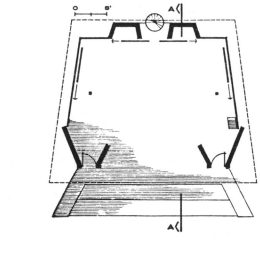

Fig. 1   Cutting plane A-A showing both a Plan and Elevation Section.

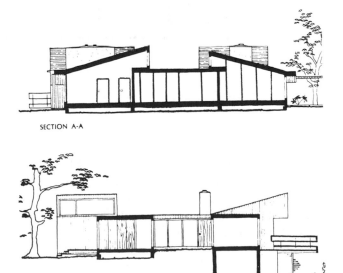

SECTION A-A

Fig. 2   Transverse and longitudinal section.

of constructing other views in the same way as the side elevation is used.

The **longitudinal section** is taken lengthwise *(Fig. 3)* through the object or building. The cutting plane line can be drawn through the entire plan if needed but may be drawn across the two outside lines only with the arrows on the section line pointing to the rear. This arrangement avoids the long heavy cutting plane line from running across the entire drawing. The longitudinal section when in its correct multiview position, can be used for constructing other views in the same way as the front elevation is used.

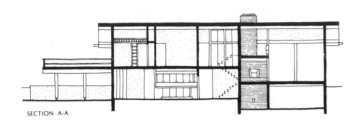

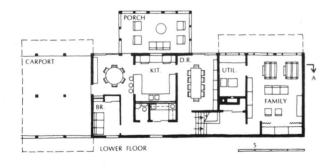

Fig. 3 Longitudinal Section showing structural walls and a horizontal section detailing the floor plan.

The **horizontal section** is obtained by passing a horizontal cutting plane through the object or building *(Fig. 3)* and imagining that all parts above the cutting plane have been removed. The floor plan is actually a horizontal section placed high enough to locate the window openings. It is not customary to show this cutting plane line. The foundation plan and the framing plan are other examples of horizontal sections. The position of the horizontal section when used in relation to the other multi-views is the same as for

the floor plan. It may be used for locating points in the other multi-views in the same way that the floor plan is used.

The **offset section** makes use of a series of cutting planes placed at right angles to one another. With the offset section, *(Fig. 4)* it is possible to include various parts of the object or building that normally would require extra sectional views. The offset section may be located in either the transverse *(right or left elevation)* or longitudinal *(front elevation)* position.

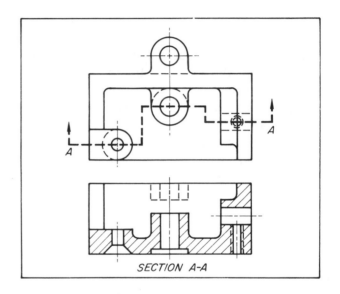

Fig. 4 Offset longitudinal section.

The **revolved sections** are formed by revolving a part of the object *(Fig. 5)* in one of the multi-views. This section explains the shape of the part and eliminates an extra view. If the revolved section is not drawn at a large enough scale to make it practical it may be drawn removed. This **removed section** *(Fig. 6)* may then be drawn at a larger scale to show greater detail.

Sections are conventionally used to show detailed information about stairs, fireplaces, wall construction, windows, foundations, beam connections, doorjambs, concrete reinforcement, etc. Details which have the smallest parts or members are most often drawn to the largest scale for ease of reading and understanding.

Fasteners like bolts, rivets, screws, rods, pins, keys and shafts that fall in the plane of the

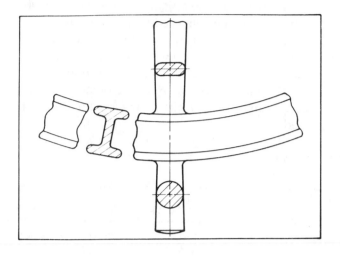

Fig. 5 Revolved section of casting.

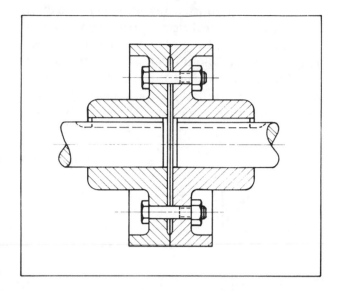

Fig. 7 Bolts, rivets, screws, rods, pins, keys and shafts are not sectioned.

cutting plane are not sectioned. This practice is adopted by both the architectural and engineer ing professions (Fig. 7).

When structural steel or thin members such as gaskets and plates are shown in section, they may be drawn in solid black if the scale of the drawing is small. Under this condition; however, adjacent pieces should have a space between them.

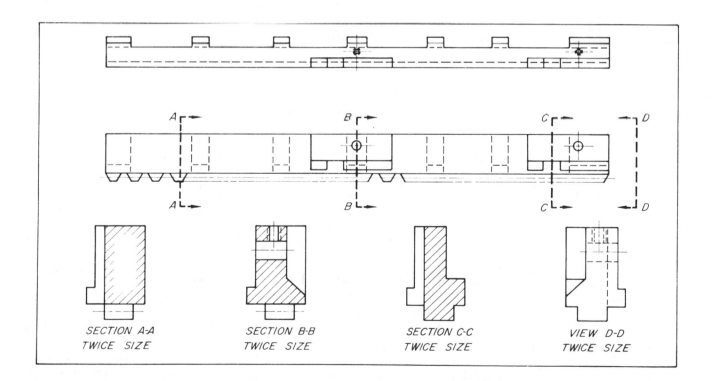

SECTION A-A
TWICE SIZE

SECTION B-B
TWICE SIZE

SECTION C-C
TWICE SIZE

VIEW D-D
TWICE SIZE

Fig. 6 Removed section showing enlarged details.

On a set of construction drawings, we often see the word **Typical** used in naming of sections on drawings---for example, **A Typical Wall Section, A Typical Column Detail**, or **Typical Detail thru Stairs**. This means that the section applies to other similar situations throughout the building and that there is no need to repeat the drawing or detail.

The parts of the object or building through which the cutting plane actually passes are represented by **architectural symbols**. In construction drawing, each known building material is represented by a characteristic symbol. *(See material symbol chart Fig. 8 & 9).* When a section of each material is cut, the corresponding symbol is used.

ARCHITECTURAL MATERIAL SYMBOLS CHART

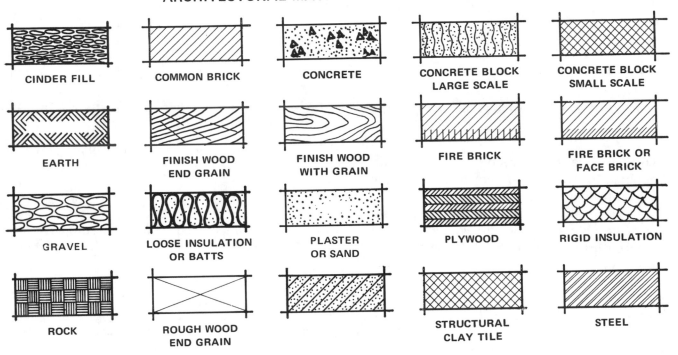

Fig. 8 Architectural symbols in plan and section.

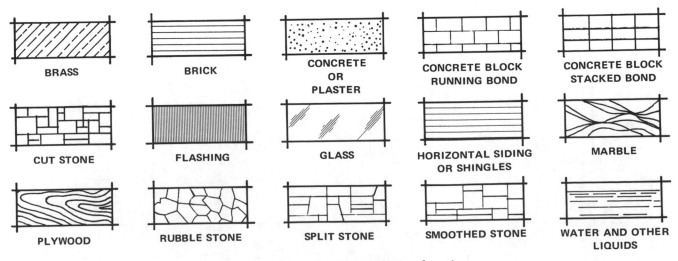

Fig. 9 Architectural symbols in elevation.

The subject of foundations includes the supporting walls below the ground level, and the piers which carry the girders. The excavation must be carried down to solid earth, free from loose or filled-in ground which later might permit unequal settlement which may cause serious cracks throughout the walls of the structure.

The footings are the lowest part of the foundations and it is that part which distributes the weight of the building or structure onto the ground at the bottom of the excavation. The purpose of the footing is to transmit this weight over a larger area in order that the pressure per sq. ft. coming on the ground or **foundation bed** will be smaller and therefore prevent settling of the ground. Where the soil is uniform in nature the pressure per sq. ft. transmitted by the footing should be the same and in no case should this pressure exceed the amount allowed for the kind of soil uncovered at the excavation. These allowances of safe loads are given in the following table:

SAFE LOADS ON FOUNDATION BEDS
SOIL BEARING CAPACITIES

Kind of Foundation Bed	Safe Load (Tons per square foot)
Soft Clay & broken shale	1
Wet Sand	2
Firm Clay	2
Sand & Clay, layers or mixed	2
Fine Dry Sand & Loose Sand Gravel Mixtures	3
Hard Dry Clay	3
Coarse Sand	4
Gravel	6
Soft Rock	8
Hard Pan	10
Medium Rock	25
Hard Rock	40

The bottom of the foundation wall or footing must always be below the **frost line,** which varies in different sections of the country.

Foundation Walls. By definition, foundation walls are those walls below the grade line of the building that support the superstructure. Similar walls around areas are termed retaining walls and are not properly a part of the foundation. The thickness of foundations, as well as other walls for different structures, is usually established by local ordinance in cities; but if no ordinance exists, then a brick foundation wall of 12 inches for two-story buildings *(or one of 8 inches for one-story buildings)* conforms to good building standards.

Only a foundation that is placed on bed rock will not settle, all other foundations will settle. The purpose of designing footings and foundations is to keep settlement to a minimum in order that the building will not be unsafe. By taking soil samples, often called **core samples,** and having them tested in the laboratory, the bearing capacity of the soil can be calculated. Once the engineer has this information, he can properly design the footings for the loads on those soil conditions.

This will help to eliminate uneven settlement which may cause a foundation to be out of plumb or not level. With great differences in settlement, the structure may be declared unsafe. The structural safety of the building may be involved.

Foundation Types. Foundations are divided into two basic types, the **spread foundations** and

pile foundations. The spread foundation distributes the building loads over a large area of soil to obtain adequate bearing capacity. The pile foundation transmits the building loads through weak soil to deeper layers of soil that have adequate bearing capacity.

Spread foundations are made up of the following load transmitting elements: columns, piers, pilasters or walls, which rest on an enlarged base called a **footing**. The footings spread the load directly to the supporting soil. **Grade beams** are also load transmitting elements which may rest on footings or piles.

The foundation supports the building's **substructure,** that portion of the building underground, and the superstructure, that portion of the building above the ground. The footings, while resting on the soil, receive the loads from **foundations walls, pilasters** or **columns** and must place the loading directly to the soil without going beyond the maximum bearing capacity of the soil *(Fig. 1).*

Footings. Several types of footings are illustrated in *(Fig. 3–8).* They are almost always made of concrete and are classified according to the way in which they are constructed, loaded and shaped. **Plain** footings are designed for light loads and are unreinforced. **Reinforced** footings have steel rods planted inside the footing to strengthen it in tension and in shear *(Fig. 2).* Reinforcing rods are placed perpendicular to the wall when loads are to be spread over wide areas, and they

are placed parallel to the wall when they must span weak spots such as excavations for service or sewer connections. Any of the footings can be either plain or reinforced.

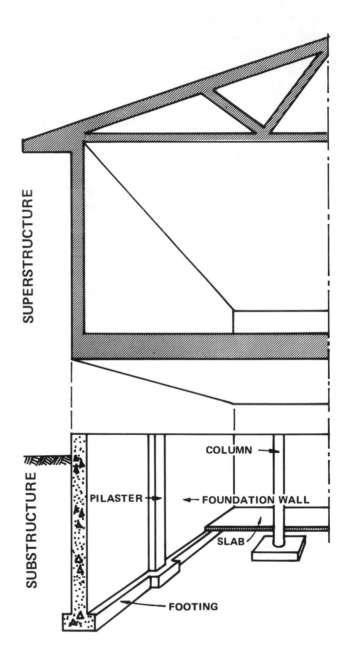

Fig. 1 *The substructure of a building, its foundation, consists of load transmitting elements such as columns, footings, foundation walls, pilasters, slabs and other elements such as grade beams and piles.*

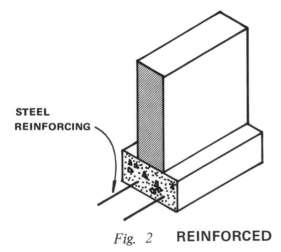

STEEL REINFORCING

Fig. 2 **REINFORCED**

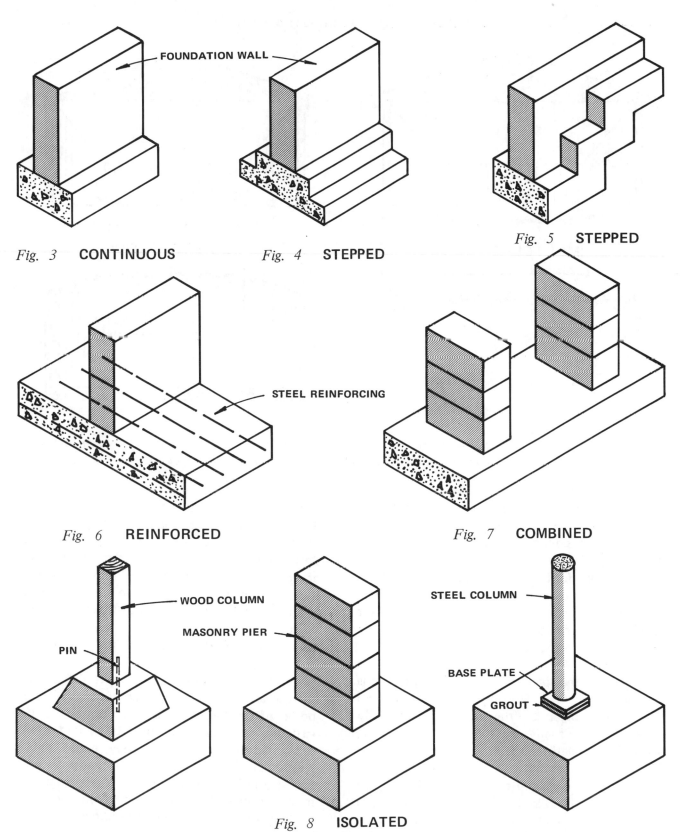

Fig. 3 **CONTINUOUS**

Fig. 4 **STEPPED**

Fig. 5 **STEPPED**

FOUNDATION WALL

STEEL REINFORCING

Fig. 6 **REINFORCED**

Fig. 7 **COMBINED**

WOOD COLUMN

MASONRY PIER

PIN

STEEL COLUMN

BASE PLATE

GROUT

Fig. 8 **ISOLATED**

Fig. 3—8 Various types of footings spread building loads over soil area. Any of the types shown may be reinforced.

21

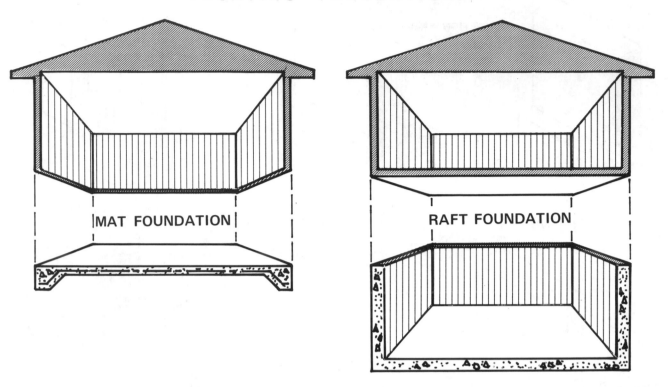

Fig. 9   Mat and raft foundations are called "floating foundations." They are heavily reinforced so that the entire foundation acts as a unit to support loads, and are used on relatively weak soils.

Continuous footings support foundation walls *(Fig. 3)*. When a single footing supports two or more columns, it is called a **combined footing** *(Fig. 7)*.

Stepped footings change levels in stages to conform to a sloping grade *(Fig. 4)*. This system will save excavation and material. Many times it will be determined by an *on site inspection* by the architect or the engineer.

Isolated footings are individual footings that receive the loads of free-standing columns or piers *(Fig. 8)*. Masonry piers are held in place by mortar to the footing; steel lally columns are usually anchored to the footing with a base plate and bolts projected from the footing, or ramset into the footings; and wooden columns are usually pinned to the footing by a stud bolt inserted into a drilled hole in the column. It may also be placed into a shoe or clip angle and nailed or bolted from the side.

Mat and Raft Foundations. These are used where the soil is of low bearing capacity, when the other types of foundations would be unsafe. Both the mat and the raft foundations are made of concrete which is heavily reinforced with steel. This makes the complete foundation act as a unit. They are often called **floating foundations.**

A **mat foundation** is a slab that is thickened at the edge and supports the load and transmits as one structural unit over the entire slab and soil surface area. A **raft foundation** *(Fig. 9)* is composed of reinforced walls and floor and is constructed by excavating until the weight of the soil removed is approximately equal to the weight of the foundation and the superstructure. By doing this settlement is kept to a minimum because the building load on the soil is equal to the weight of the soil removed.

Foundation Walls. As structural elements that transfer loads, foundation walls form an integral part of spread foundations. They must support vertical loads, from the superstructure; they must overcome lateral loads from side wall ground pressure and the superstructure; provide an anchorage for the superstructure against uplift and lateral wind forces. *(See Fig. 10).*

Foundation walls must also be durable, be waterproof, provide a barrier against fire, and control air and heat flow. If the foundation surrounds a habitable space, the wall must have a suitable appearance and accommodate window openings, doors and other possible openings.

Columns, Piers and Pilasters. Each of these elements act as a compression member and transmit loads to footings. Columns and piers are free standing while pilasters are built into the wall in order to stiffen the wall. This serves to add lateral support to a wall.

Grade Beams are located approximately at grade level, receive the building loads and transfer them

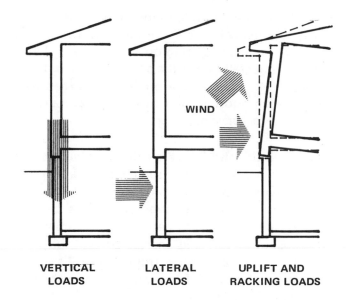

| VERTICAL LOADS | LATERAL LOADS | UPLIFT AND RACKING LOADS |

Fig. 10 Foundation walls must: (1) resist vertical loads from the weight of the building and its occupants; (2) resist lateral loads from the soil, water and other superimposed loads; and (3) anchor the building to the foundation.

GRADE BEAMS

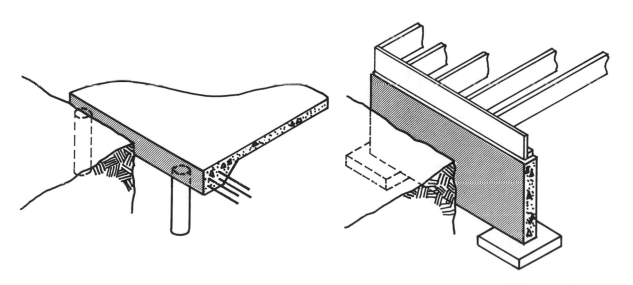

GRADE BEAM SUPPORTED ON PILES   **GRADE BEAM SUPPORTED ON FOOTINGS**

Fig. 11 Grade beams take several forms: (a) they may be poured integrally with slab-on-ground; or (b) they may transmit vertical loads to other foundation elements such as footings.

to either spread or pile foundation. Grade beams may take many forms. The example shown in *(Fig. 11)*, include a reinforced concrete beam placed integrally with the concrete slab and supported on piles, and a precast reinforced wall carried on footings and supported laterally by concrete or masonry piers.

Pile Foundations. Piles are column-like units that transmit loads past poor soil conditions to lower soil having better bearing capacity *(Fig. 12)*. Piles serve the same function as footings, because they transmit loads to better soil stratum which is capable of carrying and supporting the load. Piles receive the loads from the walls, from isolated columns or from grade beams as shown in *(Figs. 8 & 11)*.

There are generally speaking two types of piles: *point bearing* types which carry the loads to lower and stronger soil through their points, and the *friction* type which develops the required bearing capacity through surface friction between the pile and the ground. Piles may be made of concrete, steel or wood *(Fig. 13)*.

Fig. 13 Pile driver placing 45 foot wooden piles for highway bridge abutment.

PILE FOUNDATIONS

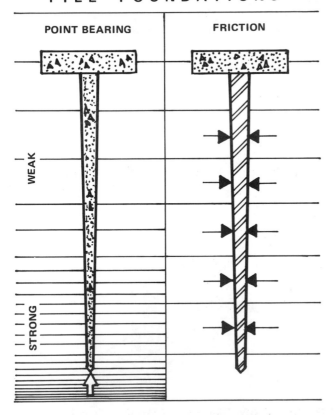

Fig. 12 Point bearing piles rest on strong soils; friction piles depend on friction between the pile and the soil.

GENERAL DESIGN AND CONSTRUCTION

Foundation Sizes

Loads that are carried by foundation walls can be divided into: (1) *dead loads*, made up of the weight of the foundation and the superstructure; and (2) *live loads*, made up of loads from snow, furniture and people. These live loads may be subdivided into *horizontal* or *vertical* loads, loads that are *static* or non-moving as opposed to *dynamic* or moving loads, loads which are *concentrated* at a point on the foundation or a load that is distributed *uniform* along a surface. Dead loads can be found by summing up the weight of all the materials used in the construction. Live loads are variable and may include the following: earth pressure on foundation walls and loads due to blast, earthquake and impact forces.

Footings are required for all masonry foundations regardless of the soil bearing capacity.

Footing sizes for normal residential footings follow a general rule-of-the-thumb size for normal soil as follows: the width of the footing should equal twice the wall thickness. If the wall thickness is **w**, the footing width would be **2w** and its depth would be **w**. Footings should not be less than 6" thick and without reinforcing rods, should not be less than 1-1/2 times the footing projection *(See Fig. 14)*. Footings should always be located at a depth that exceeds the frost line for that location and climate. This is measured from the finish grade line. Foundations should also extend below any fill material so that they will rest on undisturbed earth.

Footing Material. Footings are usually made of concrete cast in place with a minimum compressive strength of 2000 psi at 28 days.

Reinforced Footings. When the soil is of low bearing capacity the footings should be reinforced with steel. When the footing extends more than 1-1/2 times the footing depth, it should be reinforced transversely with steel.

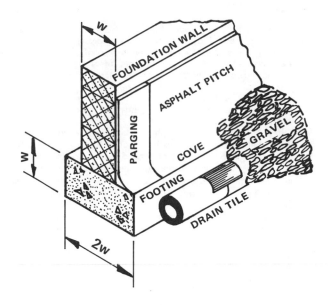

Fig. 14 Continuous foundation wall and footing showing wall thickness and footing width.

Stepped footings are required on lots which have sloping grades.

GLOSSARY

Actual Dimension The actual measured dimension of a masonry unit.

Anchor A piece or assemblage, usually metal, used to attach parts (e.g., plates, joists, trusses or other masonry) to masonry or masonry materials.

ASTM American Society for Testing Materials.

Bearing Wall A wall that supports a vertical load in addition to it own weight.

Bond Beam A horizontal reinforced masonry or reinforced concrete beam designed to strengthen a masonry wall. In concrete masonry it may be used to reduce the probability of cracks developing in the wall.

Bond Course The course consisting of units which overlap more than one wythe of masonry.

Bond: Structural Bond--Tying wythes of a masonry wall together by lapping units one over another or by connecting them with metal ties.

Chase A groove or continuous recess built in a masonry wall to accommodate pipes, ducts or conduits.

Column Vertical compression member whose width is less than four times its thickness, and whose height exceeds three times its least lateral dimension.

Composite Wall A masonry wall composed of solid and hollow masonry units.

Compressive Strength The maximum compressive load (in lbs. per sq. in.) that a masonry unit will support divided by the gross cross-sectional area of the unit in sq. in. (Where compressive strength is based on the net cross sectional area it should be specifically stated.)

Concrete Block
    Decorative block--Various types of concrete masonry units with beveled face shell recesses which provide a special architectural appearance in wall construction (i.e., Shadowall block).
    Faced block--Concrete masonry units having a special ceramic, glazed, plastic, polished or ground face.
    "Q Block"--Concrete masonry units certified as meeting the requirements of a quality control program administered by the National Concrete Masonry Association.
    Slump Block--Concrete masonry units produced so they "slump" or sag before they harden, for use in masonry wall construction.
    Split-face Block--Solid or hollow concrete masonry units that are machine fractured (split) lengthwise after hardening to produce a rough, varying surface texture.

Course One of the continuous horizontal layers of masonry units, bonded with mortar. One course is equal to the thickness of the masonry unit plus the thickness of one mortar joint.

Dead Load The weight of all permanent and stationary construction or equipment included in a building. (See live load).

Efflorescence Deposit of soluble salts, usually white in color, appearing upon the exposed surface of masonry.

Exterior Wall Any outside wall or vertical enclosure of a building other than a party wall.

Faced Wall A wall in which facing and backing are of different materials and are bonded together to exert common action under load.

Fire Division Wall Any wall which subdivides a building so as to resist the spread of fire. It is not necessarily continuous through all stories to and above the roof.

Fireproofing Any material or combination of materials built to protect structural members so as to increase their fire resistance.

Fire Wall Any wall which subdivides a building to resist the spread of fire and which extends continuously from the foundation through the roof.

Flashing A thin, impervious sheet material, placed in mortar joints and across air spaces in masonry to collect water that may penetrate the wall and to direct it to the exterior.

Flashing Sheet metal or other suitable material built into the wall for the purpose of (1) collecting any water that may penetrate the wall, and (2) to divert such moisture to the exterior.

Foundation Wall A load-bearing wall below the floor nearest to exterior grade serving as a support for a wall, pier, column, floor or other structural part of a building.

Furring A method of finishing the interior face of a masonry wall to provide space for insulation, prevent moisture transmittance, or to provide a level surface for finishing.

Header A masonry unit which overlaps two or more adjacent wythes of masonry to provide structural bond. Also called bonder.

Header Course A continuous bonding course of header brick.

Head Joint: The vertical mortar joint between ends of masonry units.

Joint Reinforcement Steel wire, bar or fabricated reinforcement which is placed in horizontal mortar joints.

Lateral support (of walls) Means whereby walls are braced either horizontal, by columns, pilasters or cross walls, or vertically by floor and root constructions.

Lintel A structural member to carry the load over an opening in a wall.

Live Load The total of all moving and variable loads that may be placed upon or in a building (See dead load).

Masonry Bonded Hollow Wall A hollow wall in which the facing and backing are bonded together with solid masonry units.

Masonry Cement Portland cement and other materials pre-mixed and packaged, to which sand and water are added to make mortar.

Mortar A plastic mixture of one or more cementitious materials, sand and water.

Moisture Content (concrete masonry units) The amount of water contained in a unit, expressed as a percentage of the total absorption (i.e., concrete masonry unit at 40% moisture content contains 40% of the water it could absorb.)

Nominal Dimension The dimension greater than the actual masonry dimension by the thickness of a mortar joint, but not more than 1/2''.

Noncombustible Any material which will neither ignite nor actively support combustion in air at a temperature of 1200°F when exposed to fire.

Non-load-bearing wall A wall which supports no vertical load other than its own weight.

Partition An interior wall, one story or less in height.

Party Wall A wall used for joint service by adjoining buildings.

Pier An isolated column of masonry.

Pilaster A thickened wall section or column built as an integral part of a wall.

Plain Masonry Masonry without reinforcement, or reinforced only for shrinkage or temperature changes.

Reinforced Masonry Masonry containing embedded steel so that the two materials act together in resisting forces.

Retaining Wall Any wall subjected to lateral pressure other than wind pressure, or a wall built to support a bank of earth.

Solid Masonry Unit Masonry units having a core area less than 25% of the total cross-sectional area of the unit.

Solid Masonry Wall A wall built of solid or hollow masonry units laid contiguously, with joints between units completely filled with mortar.

Spandrel Wall That part of a panel curtain wall above the head of a window in one story and below the sill of the window in the story above.

Stack Any structure or part thereof which contains a flue or flues for the discharge of gases.

Story That portion of a building included between the upper surface of any floor and the upper surface of the floor next above, except that the topmost story should be that portion of a building included between the upper surface of the topmost floor and the ceiling or roof above. Where a finished floor level directly above a basement or cellar is more than 6 feet above grade such basement or cellar is considered a story.

Stretcher Masonry unit laid with its length horizontal and parallel with face of the masonry.

Weep Holes Openings placed in mortar joints of facing materials at the level of flashing, to divert to the exterior any moisture collected on the flashing.

Wythe A continuous vertical section of masonry one masonry unit in thickness. Also called withe or tier.

INTRODUCTION TO STRUCTURAL STEEL 5

The shop where structural steel is fabricated into members that are later erected in the field to form the completed structure does often produce the structural steel which is used to make these members. This steel is produced at **rolling mills** and shipped to the fabricating shop in a variety of standard shapes and forms. A knowledge of the more important characteristics of structural steel will assist the student to a better appreciation of the reasons for the standard practices which are a part of the **structural draftsman's** everyday work. A clear understanding of the various forms and shapes in which material is available is essential, before he can prepare detail drawings of the work to be performed in the shop *(Fig. 1)*.

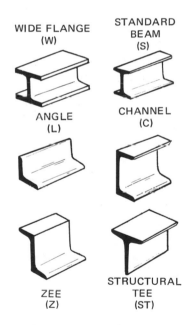

WIDE FLANGE (W)

STANDARD BEAM (S)

ANGLE (L)

CHANNEL (C)

ZEE (Z)

STRUCTURAL TEE (ST)

Fig. 1 Standard structural shapes.

Steel structures are made up of "rolled shapes" fastened together with rivets, bolts, or welds. The function of structural steel drawings is to show how these shapes are to be fabricated in the shop and then erected to form the various members of bridges, buildings, etc. Dimensions for detailing these and other less common shapes

are shown in the (AISC) American Institute of Steel Construction handbook, and the handbooks of the individual steel companies.

NECESSARY DRAWINGS

Structural steel work necessitates the making of a variety of plans and a typical list of such follows: Designers and draftsmen who work on each type need varying minimum amounts of training and experience. Plans that deal with **original design** require designers with a vast range of experiences, **details** require a man who has knowledge and experience in structural drafting but may not have great knowledge of strength of materials or structural design, and **tracing** may be done by persons who are able to draw nicely but who need not understand the purpose of the work.

General Plan and Elevation Plan No. 1. Includes such materials as ground elevations, existing structures which are to remain unchanged, clearances which must be maintained, high and low water marks, property lines and locations of the structure on the property. In short, all the possible data which is to be used in the design. It is sometimes called the **plot plan** or **layout drawing.**

Shear and Moment Diagrams Plan No. 2. These are used in the design by the designer and not included in the final prints that are sent to the client.

Steel Arrangement Drawing Plan No. 3. The general layout of the structure and the location of each piece of steel is shown. When the structure is large each individual piece must be detailed, hence very few dimensions appear on the drawing. Here we find only such controlling dimensions as those for column spacing, beam spacing, etc. When a structure is quite small, as a simple truss, this drawing may be dimensioned completely and annotated and the detail drawings omitted. In either case each piece of steel must be given a number or letter to be used in listing the piece in a bill of materials. This plan is sometimes called the **erection drawing** *(Fig. 2).*

Detail Drawings Plan No. 4. These are used to show the dimensions of each individual piece of steel. Each hole must be shown and located. If other operations such as crimping or beveling are to be performed, it is necessary to specify each one completely on a detail drawing.

False-Work Plan-Plan No. 5. These plans are usually made for large jobs. This is done to save materials that are used in the false work construction by enabling it to be so constructed that it can be knocked down and reassembled on other jobs or else to facilitate the building of complicated forms.

Bills of Materials Plan No. 6. It is a part of the detailer's work to make a complete bill of material principally to help the shipping clerk. It should include the piece number and the weight of each member *(Fig. 2).*

Rivet List Plan No. 7. It is essential that a rivet list be made because it will show the number of and the dimensions and weight of all rivets, bolts, spikes, etc., used in the erection.

Index Sheet Plan No. 8. To show all drawings prepared for the job together with the latest revision letter or number of each. Besides this index it usually is also advisable to show reference drawings on all work. Thus the foundation plans should refer to the steel arrangement drawing and the plot plan and detail sheets should show the sheet of the steel arrangement drawing to which they refer.

In general, the work of designing a structure is done by the engineering department and the sketches showing the diagrammatic layout of the structure and the selected sizes of members are sent to the drafting room.

The detailer makes a detailed drawing based upon these sketches and upon the data concerning the sizes of the members. When necessary an erection drawing is also made. Occasionally, structures are designed in the drawing room when, for instance, this may be done by copying a similar structure that has been designed and/or built by the company.

DETAILING STRUCTURAL STEEL

Using data given to him on an arrangement drawing, the detailer's first step is to draw the "Working Lines." These represent, approximately, those lines along which the loads are assumed to act and are the lines used by the designer for his computations. Their lengths are usually figured to the nearest thousandth of a foot and when dimensioned are usually given to the nearest sixteenth of a foot. Having done this, the steel is then drawn around these lines. In theory the load in a member is transmitted along its center of gravity but in riveted structures this is practically impossible as the stresses are transmitted through the rivets and the clearances required for the riveting determine the lines along which the rivets may be placed.

This is called a **gage line** and for most structural shapes the locations of such lines have been standardized and appear in the steel handbooks. Using the gage lines, already drawn, as working lines the desired steel shapes are readily drawn to scale around them. In such drawings the steel may be, and often is, drawn to a larger scale than that used for the lengths of the working lines, the intersections of these working *(or gage)* lines are called **working points** or panel points and it is from these that dimensions are figured *(Figs. 3 & 4).*

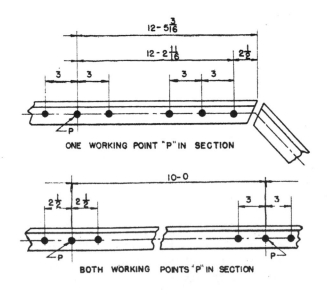

Fig. 3 . Working points.

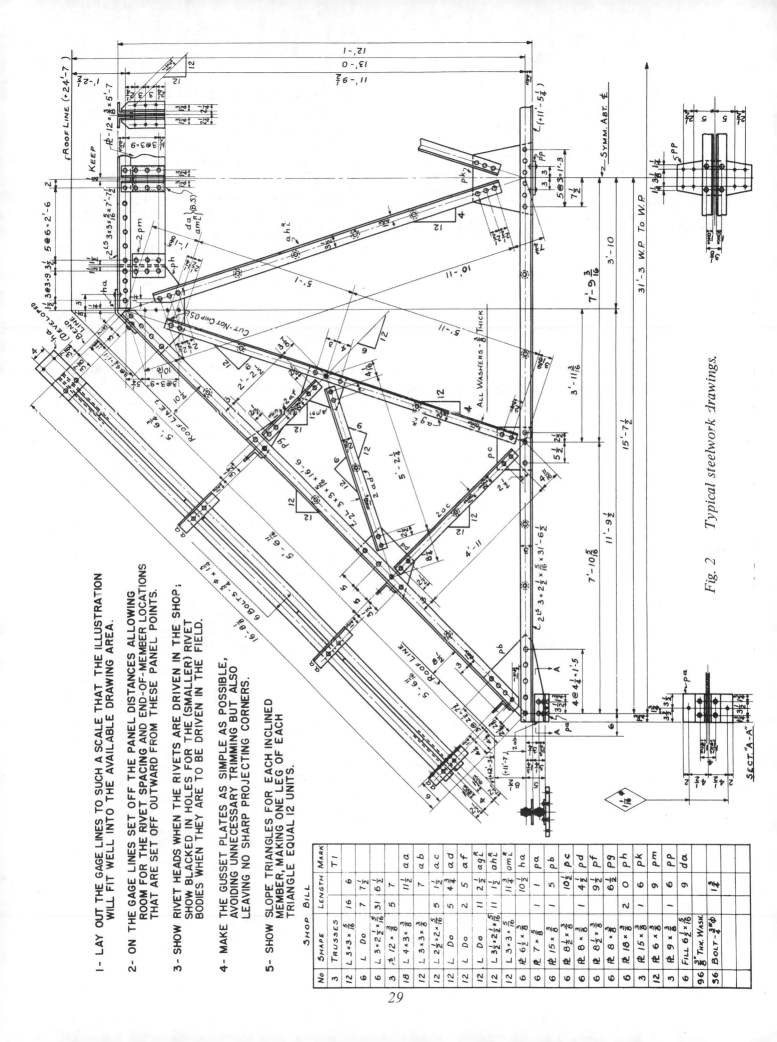

1- LAY OUT THE GAGE LINES TO SUCH A SCALE THAT THE ILLUSTRATION WILL FIT WELL INTO THE AVAILABLE DRAWING AREA.

2- ON THE GAGE LINES SET OFF THE PANEL DISTANCES ALLOWING ROOM FOR THE RIVET SPACING AND END-OF-MEMBER LOCATIONS THAT ARE SET OFF OUTWARD FROM THESE PANEL POINTS.

3- SHOW RIVET HEADS WHEN THE RIVETS ARE DRIVEN IN THE SHOP; SHOW BLACKED IN HOLES FOR THE (SMALLER) RIVET BODIES WHEN THEY ARE TO BE DRIVEN IN THE FIELD.

4- MAKE THE GUSSET PLATES AS SIMPLE AS POSSIBLE, AVOIDING UNNECESSARY TRIMMING BUT ALSO LEAVING NO SHARP PROJECTING CORNERS.

5- SHOW SLOPE TRIANGLES FOR EACH INCLINED MEMBER, MAKING ONE LEG OF EACH TRIANGLE EQUAL 12 UNITS.

Fig. 2   Typical steelwork drawings.

29

SHOP BILL

No	SHAPE	LENGTH	MARK
3	TRUSSES		T I
12	L 3×3×5/16	16	
6	L Do	7	7½
6	L 3×2½×5/16	31	6½
3	Pℓ 12×3/8	5	
18	L 4×3×3/8		11½ aa
12	L 3×3×3/8		7 ab
12	L 2½×2×5/16	5	1½ ac
12	L Do	5	4¾ ad
12	L Do	2	5 af
12	L Do	11	2½ agR
6	L 3½×2½×5/16	11	1½ ahL
12	L 3×3×3/16		11¾ amL
6	Pℓ 6½×3/8		10½ ha
6	Pℓ 7×5/8	1	pa
6	Pℓ 15×3/8	1	pb
6	Pℓ 8½×3/8	1	10½ pc
6	Pℓ 8×3/8		4½ pd
6	Pℓ 8½×3/8		9½ pf
6	Pℓ 8×3/8		6½ pg
6	Pℓ 18×3/8	2	0 ph
6	Pℓ 15×5/8	1	6 pk
12	Pℓ 6×5/8		9 pm
3	Fill 6½×5/16	1	9 pp
6	Pℓ 9×3/8		9 da
96	3" THK. WASH.		
56	BOLT-¾"Φ		1¾

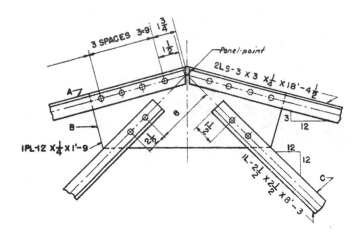

Fig. 4   Typical joint layout.

Once the steel outlines have been drawn, "cut-off" lines limiting the lengths of the members are added so as to insure sufficient clearance between pieces. This matter of clearance is of great importance. Steel handbooks usually carry tables headed *"Standard Variations in Cutting and Shearing"* or *"Rolling and Cutting Tolerances."* In detailing, an allowance is made for these variations since an extra mill charge is made when precise cutting is specified *(Fig. 4)*.

With the ends of the steel members deter-

mined it becomes possible to draw in the rivets and here it is the clearance that dominate the other considerations.

The gage lines along which rivets are placed are determined by available clearances and so, too, are the locations of field rivets with respect to shop rivets. Preferred spacing is given by the A.I.S.C. code with an absolute minimum of three times the body diameter of the rivet. The spacing of the last rivet from the end of the piece is also given by the code. In addition to these rivet spacings another factor must be considered in that rivets which are to be placed in the field must be so located that the riveting gun and the bucking up tool have access to them.

It should be seen, also, that rivet spacing affect the placement of clip angles for roof purlins and the mounting and bearing details which are drawn next. Typical details are shown on *(Fig. 5)*. Notice that the rivet spacing is not always a minimum where a slightly larger one doesn't increase the size of the gusset plate required. In the design of mounting details for trusses, the expansion and contraction of steel must be considered. At one end of the truss the mounting angles have a 1¼" hole in them for anchor bolts. At the other end of the truss the mounting angles have a slot 1¼" wide

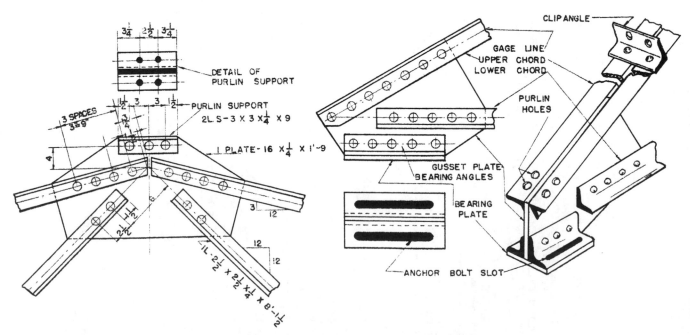

Fig. 5   Clip angle and mounting plate details.

30

by 4" long centered on the gage line. This slot permits this end of the truss to slide, when the truss changes its length by expanding or contracting.

Many connection details have been standardized and they can be found in a steel handbook. They have been carefully designed by engineers of the steel companies and their use means a decided saving in time, punching operations and amounts of material.

The last steel to be drawn is the gusset plates that connect members at a joint. Since the rivets have already been drawn in, the edges of the gusset plate can be determined by the required edge clearance. Unnecessary cuts in gusset plates are avoided but care should be taken not to leave projecting sharp corners that might injure workmen. Notice that rivets on through members are usually placed in such a position that the gusset plate is kept as small as possible.

DETAILING PRACTICE
STRUCTURAL STEEL

Separate drawings made to a sufficiently large scale to carry complete information are called **shop detail drawing.** When possible, the drawing of all members is shown in the same relative position that they will occupy in the completed structure: vertical, horizontal, or inclined. Long vertical or inclined members may be drawn in a horizontal position, a vertical member always having its lower end at the left, and an inclined member drawn in the direction it would fall.

In steel construction a member is composed of either a single rolled shape or a combination of two or more rolled shapes. The scale of shop drawings ranges from 1/4" = 1'-0" to 1" = 1'-0". Often, for long members, the cross section is drawn to a larger scale than the length. Sometimes it is even advantageous to pay no attention to scaled length, but to draw the member as though there were breaks in the length so that rivets or bolt spacings at the ends can be drawn to the same scale as the cross section.

Dimensions are always placed above the dimension line, and the dimension lines are not broken but continuous. Length dimensions are expressed in feet and inches. **All inch symbols are omitted** unless there is the possibility of misunderstanding, thus *(1 bolt should be 1" bolt)* to distinguish between the size and number, and dimensions should be hyphenated thus: **6'-9, 5'-0 3/8, 4'-8.** Plate widths and sections depths of rolled shapes are given in inches. Dimensions are given to commercial sizes of materials.

Rolled shapes are specified by abbreviated notes, as described and shown on page 34, *(Structural Steel Shapes).* **Erection marks** are necessary in order to identify the members which are indicated on the drawing by capital letters and numbers in the subtitle. The **erection diagram** then carries these marking numbers which identify the position of the member *(Fig. 8).*

Assembly marks are used when the same shape is used in more than one place on a member. The member is completely specified once followed by the assembly mark, a lower-case letter in brackets. Then the complete specification is not repeated; only the assembly mark is given.

Distance to center lines of another connecting member is given, by placing the distance, preceded by a minus sign at the end of the length dimension. These distances to center are a great aid in checking the details with an assembly or layout drawing.

Rivets and bolts are dimensioned in the view that shows them as circles. Dimension pertaining to a row of rivets or bolts are given in a straight line. *(See Table 17, page 244)* for usual gages of angles. The size of rivets, bolts and holes is given in a general note. **Shop rivets and bolts** are indicated by an *open circle,* the size of the fastener head. Holes for **field rivets and bolts** are indicated by *blacked in circles* the diameter of the hole *(Fig. 7).*

Clearance between various members of a structure are necessary so that there will be no interferences, because of manufacturing inaccuracies. More clearance should be allowed for **field erection** than for **shop fabrication.** Field clearance should be approximately *1/2 inch,* and **shop clearance** should be about *1/4 inch.*

Bolt and Rivet Spacing

A. **Bolt and rivet gage lines and gage distances.**

   1. Gage lines are lines along which bolts and rivets are placed.

     a. Usually run parallel to the long axis of angles, beams and channels. *(Fig. 6).*

   2. **Gage distances** - commonly called simply "gage".

     a. Distance between two gage lines if more than one row of bolts or rivets. *(Fig. 6).*

     b. Distance from known edge of a structural shape to a row of rivets or bolts.

     c. Auxiliary gage distance (g_1) - distance needed to clear corner radii on structural shapes plus edge distance for mating part. *(Fig. 6).*

B. **Pitch** - distance between bolts and rivets along a gage line *(Fig. 6).*

   1. Minimum pitch is 3 x diameter of the bolt or rivet.

C. **Edge distances** - distance from edge of a structural shape to center of bolt or rivet hole. *(Fig. 6).*

   1. Minimum edge distances *(for 3/4" bolts or rivets and larger).*

     a. For rolled edges - *1 1/4 x diameter of the bolt or rivet.*

     b. For sheared edges - *1 1/2 x diameter of the bolt or rivet.*

GENERAL RULES FOR DETAILING

1. Make the part to be detailed with very thin black lines. Should it be necessary to show adjoining parts of the structure, these parts should be shown by lines which are just dark enough to print.

2. In structural work the dimension lines are unbroken and the figures are placed above the dimension lines. See *(Fig. 2).* All distances which are twelve inches or greater are expressed in feet and inches. No decimals are used. Some companies; however, make all dimensions in inches up to eighteen inches and others up to twenty-four inches.

3. Dimensions should be placed as near the part to which they refer as possible. At intersections of working lines, there is bound to be some overlapping of the body and dimension lines, therefore, great care must be taken so that the dimensions can be easily read and understood.

4. When several dimensions are alike and adjacent, as in the case when several rivets are adjacent to each other, the dimensions may be given by indicating the number of spaces times the distance on centers of the rivets which equals the whole distance. Thus, if there are five rivets at a joint, spaced 2½" on centers the dimension may be written as (4 spcs., at 2½" = 10") *(Fig. 2).*

5. Shop rivets are shown as open circles and field rivets as black dots. When several shop rivets occur at a joint, frequently only the first and the last rivets are drawn in; but where field rivets occur, all rivets must be drawn in to prevent any possibility of error *(Fig. 7).*

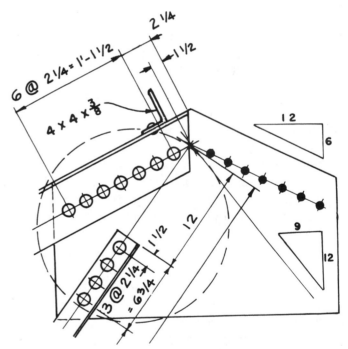

Fig. 7   Shop and field rivets.

DIMENSIONING

When all the steel has been accurately drawn to scale the dimensioning may be started. It should be noted that in structural drafting the detailer is not given a layout drawing from which he might scale dimensions but is given instead the

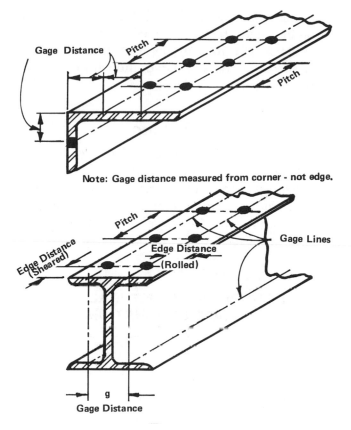

Note: Gage distance measured from corner - not edge.

For standard "g" and "g₁" see A.I.S.C. manual

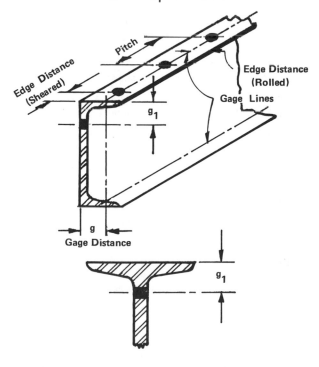

Fig. 6   Gage Lines and Gage Distances for Angles, Beams and Channels

skeleton, or steel arrangement, drawing upon which he then constructs a layout. It is from his own layout that steel dimensions are scaled or determined.

For clarity, and where possible, dimension lines are to be kept a minimum of ½'' away from any parallel lines. As each steel member usually requires at least several of these there usually is some overlapping; hence, pains must be taken to maintain clarity. Usually the nearest dimension line will contain the short distances indicated while the farthest will have the fewest breaks, with the overall dimension placed last. This tends to avoid intersections of extension lines with dimension lines.

Before adding the dimension lines a consideration of the use to which they are to be put is of great value. For truss members this means that the dimensions needed are distances between working points *(if these lie on the piece)*, distances from the working points to rivet holes, and the end distances.

For the gusset plates the needed dimensions are the distances from the working point to the first rivet. These can't be laid out on one line because they interfere. For this reason a truss member will have at least three lines of dimensions. Nearest to the member will be a line of dimensions containing the end distances and distances between all rivets. The second dimension line will contain the distances to the first rivets and a distance between them is drawn. Finally, a distance between working points is often given. No distances are omitted except those from the rivets to the edge of the gusset plates.

When members meet at right angles, dimensions can be determined by direct addition and subtraction. When they meet at an angle the dimensions must often be scaled. When the scale of the drawing is small, it may be necessary to draw an enlarged detail of the joint on scrap paper in order to scale dimensions accurately.

The angle of the slope of sloping members is given by drawing a small triangle against a member, with the long leg of the triangle equal to 12 units and the other proportionate to the nearest sixteenth of an inch *(Fig. 17)*.

NOTES

In addition to the fully dimensioned drawing a set of notes should be given and should include such items as:

RIVET HOLES

Rivet holes are either punched directly to full size or sub-punched and then reamed. Either method is more economical than drilling.

When holes are sub-punched and reamed, the first operation is to form a hole some 3/16" less in diameter than that of the rivet body; the reaming enlarges this to 1/16" greater diameter than that of the rivet.

This method insures removal of all possible distorted or damaged metal from around the hole.

Straight punched holes and drilled holes are made 1/16" larger directly. By making the rivet hole greater in diameter than the rivet an ample allowance is made in the event the pieces don't line up.

TWO-ANGLE MEMBERS

When two-angle members are made up it is customary to place the long legs back-to-back, separated by the thickness of the gusset plate.

STITCH RIVETS

Since the gusset plate is between the two-angle members it is necessary to keep the legs of the angles uniformly separated throughout their length. This is done by placing washers having a thickness equal to that of the gusset between the members and holding these washers in place with so-called "stitch" rivets. In tension members these are placed 3'-6" apart; in compression members 2'-0" apart and are drawn in place and noted but are not dimensioned.

PAINTING

Before shipping any steel it is necessary that it be given a shop coat for which red lead is commonly used.

BILL OF MATERIALS

In structural drawing it is customary to list all materials used in the construction. All angles, plates, rivets, bolts, washers, etc., must be included. It is also customary to add approximately 10% to the quantities of rivets, bolts, washers, and nuts required; though the angles or beams are noted to size.

MARKING

To expedite assembly and erection, the detailer assigns a distinguishing mark to each individual piece. Identical pieces are given the same mark: pieces that are alike except for being right- or left-handed are given like marks with the letter "R" or "L" added.

HOT-ROLLED STRUCTURAL STEEL SHAPE DESIGNATIONS

Designations	Type of Shape
W 24 × 76 W 14 × 26	W shape
S 24 × 100	S shape
M 8 × 18.5 M 10 × 9 M 8 × 34.3	M shape
C 12 × 20.7	American Standard Channel
MC 12 × 45 MC 12 × 10.6	Miscellaneous Channel
HP 14 × 73	HP shape
L 6 × 6 × ¾ L 6 × 4 × ⅝	Equal Leg Angle Unequal Leg Angle
WT 12 × 38 WT 7 × 13	Structural Tee cut from W shape
ST 12 × 50	Structural Tee cut from S shape
MT 4 × 9.25 MT 5 × 4.5 MT 4 × 17.15	Structural Tee cut from M shape
PL ½ × 18	Plate
Bar 1 φ Bar 1¼ φ Bar 2½ × ½	Square Bar Round Bar Flat Bar
Pipe 4 Std. Pipe 4 X - Strong Pipe 4 XX - Strong	Pipe
TS 4 × 4 × .375 TS 5 × 3 × .375 TS 3 OD × .250	Structural Tubing: Square Structural Tubing: Rectangular Structural Tubing: Circular

PLATES are ordered as the smallest rectangle which will contain the plate desired. Thus (1 pl-18" X ½" X 12"). Note that plates come in even widths only, that is, in 1" steps of increment.

ANGLES are ordered in the order of size of long leg, short leg, thickness, and length. Thus (1L-3½" X 3" X ¼" X 6'-9").

TEES are ordered by flange, stem thickness, and length. Thus (WT15 x 50 x 10'-8").

ZEES are ordered by height, thickness, weight per foot, and length. Thus (Z4 x 10.3 x 7'-10").

CHANNELS are ordered by depth, weight per foot and length. Thus (C15 x 40 x 18'-6").

SIMPLE SQUARE FRAMED BEAMS

Framed Beam Connections. A common requirement in structural work is that the connection must be able to carry all the load that the beam can carry. Using the beam B3 from the erection diagram shown *(Fig. 8)*, select a framed beam connection which will have as much strength as the **W14**. Consulting Table 16, page 243 of the appendix A - **W14** has a three *(3)* row framed beam connection listed. The design calls for 3/4" diameter rivets which is the fastener diameter. Table 1-A3 list loading in kips *(a kip is 1000 pounds)*. Using A 325-N rivets, we have a maximum total shear of 39.8 kips for a 3 row framed beam connection. The allowable uniform load for a laterally supported beam **W14X30** for a 20 ft. span is 33 kips *(33,000 pounds)*. Since one-half of this uniform load would be picked up by the supporting beam at each end of the **W14X30**, the maximum beam reaction, for which sufficiently strong connections must be provided would be one-half of 33 kips or 16.5 kips. Since the maximum reaction for which the connection for this particular **W14X30** beam need be designed is but 16.5 kips, and the amount the 3 row connection will support is 39.8 kips, the 3 row connection is safe. The framed beam connectors are located by finding the 'c' distance for the support beams

W24X76 and **W21X82** *(See Table 10 p. 229)*. The **'c'** distance equals 5/16" for both beams so the back to back distance of the framed beam connectors will be a minus 5/8" from 20 feet or 19'-11 3/8".

Beam Size. The center to center distance of the supporting beams is 20 feet *(See framing plan Fig. 8)*. Find one-half the web thickness for each supporting beam *(see reprint from steel manual)*. The table shows this to be 1/4", to this add 1/2" *field clearance* to each side. This equals 3/4" or a total of 1 1/2". Subtract the total 1 1/2" from the center to center distance of 20 feet. The beam length is 19'-10 1/2".

Coping Clearance. The framing plan calls for the top of steel to be (-5 1/2") except where noted. The **W14X30** must be notched at the top at one end to keep it from bumping into the flange of the supporting beam. Such a notch is called a *cope, block* or *cut*. Since the **W14** and one of the supporting beams are flush at the top, the minimum depth of the cut should equal the 'k' distance *(See Table 10 p. 229)* of the supporting member so as to clear its web fillet. The depth of cut equals 1 9/16" for the **W21x82** supporting beam. The length of cut, as measured from the end of the beam, will allow clearance for the flange of the supporting member. This dimension equals the 'a' distance *(See Table 10 p. 229)*. The supporting beam has a 4 1/4" length of cut so the length of the cope for the beam detail will be 4 1/4".

COLUMN DETAILS

Much of the work to fabricate the framing for multi-story buildings is usually called for on the **column details**. These details frequently become quite complicated and require careful planning to insure that they will be entirely legible when completed. The designer should first lay out the details of the columns by making freehand sketches. On these sketches all the required information, including the essential dimensions, is collected as a means of visualizing the finished appearance of the shop drawing. The amount of room that will be needed at various points along each face view to avoid crowded, messy and hard-to-read details may be worked out in advance.

In order to furnish the fabricator with the precise and complete information needed to produce the columns required in a structure, the designer usually prepares in addition to properly dimensioned plans of the required framing at several levels, a **column schedule** similar to that shown on *(Fig. 9)*. The required size and make-up of the columns, between various levels of framing are shown on the column schedule. As the total load carried by a column increases, through the accumulation of the loads contributed by each level of beam framing, the size of the column must be increased, progressing from the top of the structure to its foundations. Not only does the designer indicate the required size in each case, but he also specifies the elevation at which these sizes must change, that is at which the column must be spliced. He shows this by dimensioning from a reference line.

Column billet plates are required because the masonry foundations are incapable of taking the column load at anything like the intensity of pressure, or stress that the load produces in the column itself. The size and thickness of the billet plate needed to distribute the concentrated load from a column to its masonry foundation is shown in the column schedule *(Fig. 9)*.

The designer must indicate the size and location of any **anchor bolts** which are to be furnished by the fabricator, but set in place by the contractor whose responsibility it is to complete the foundations in advance of the steel erection. To insure proper coordination of the work between the foundation contractor and the fabricator, and to insure that the intent of his design is properly carried out in the fabrication of the steel, the designer usually shows typical column base details on his drawings. Small base plates are often permanently attached to the bottom of the column in the fabricating shop. Larger plates are almost always shipped loose, to be set accurately to grade and leveled

by the erector, prior to commencement of erection of the main framing. Anchor bolt holes in base plates are made 5/16" larger than the diameter of the bolts, to allow for inaccuracies in the setting of these bolts. The bottom end of the column shaft and ends of the columns which are spliced, are required to be milled, to provide a true over-all contact bearing, because it is by means of such bearing that the stress in one length of column is transferred to the next length below, and to the base at the bottom of the column. We will use column No. 13, *(See Fig. 10)* of beam detail, for example of column detailing. Shop drawings of a column may be shown in an upright position, with the bottom of the shaft at the bottom of the drawing or in a horizontal position with the bottom of the shaft to the left of the drawing. The practice of giving each of the four faces of a column a letter, which is shown on the shop details, is very generally followed. It is particularly helpful to the shopman in laying out his work, and reduces the probability of shop errors *(See Fig. 10)*.

As viewed looking down on the top of a column, the lettering progresses alphabetically in a *counterclockwise direction* around the shaft. **Face 'A'** is always a flange in the case of H-type columns. When face A is used to show the work on both flanges, this view is labeled A *(using solid lines)* and also **C** *(using dotted lines)*.

Transverse sections taken through a column are always shown looking toward the bottom of the column *(towards the left of the drawing when the column is detailed in a horizontal position.)*

See (Fig. 10), for column No. 13 detailing. For ready reference, the first line of dimension at the top of the shop drawing gives the distance between established levels of framing and the column spacing *(12' -0")*. The reference lines *(center line symbol)* representing these established levels are identified on the drawing by name and elevation and are extended downward across the various views. Below this line of dimensions, the milled length of the column shaft is given, and noted **"Mill Line to Mill Line"** *(13'-5 1/2')*.

Next, the location of the top and bottom of

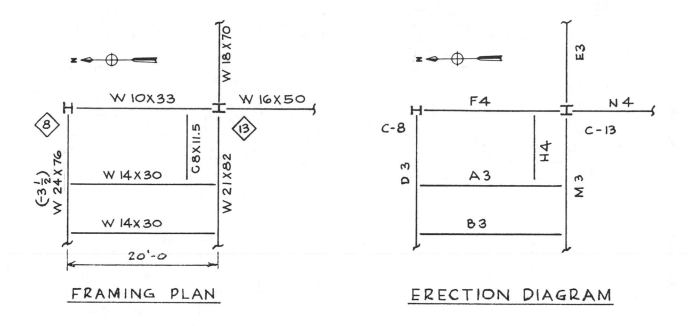

FRAMING PLAN   ERECTION DIAGRAM

NOTE

TOP OF STEEL $(-5\frac{1}{2})$ BELOW
FIN. FIRST FLOOR $(\pm 0'-0)$
EXCEPT WHERE NOTED OTHERWISE.
USE $\frac{3}{4}$ RIVETS, $\frac{13}{16}$ HOLES.
FIELD CLEARANCE TO BE $\frac{1}{2}$ INCH.

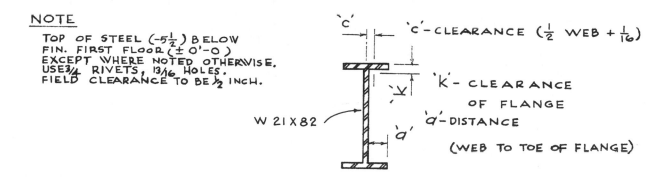

$'c'$ - CLEARANCE $(\frac{1}{2}$ WEB $+ \frac{1}{16})$

$'k'$ - CLEARANCE
   OF FLANGE

$'a'$ - DISTANCE

(WEB TO TOE OF FLANGE)

W 21 X 82

NOTE

$\frac{3}{4}$ RIVETS, $\frac{13}{16}$ HOLES
SHOP PAINT - ONE
COAT REDLEAD
AND OIL.

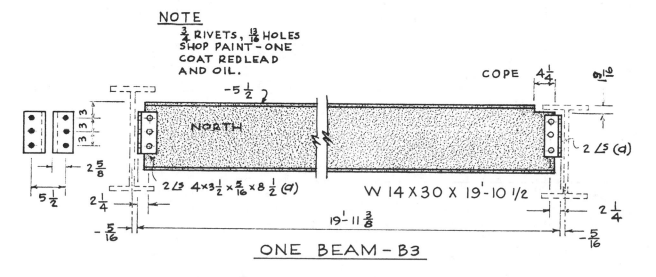

ONE BEAM - B3

Fig. 8 Framing and erection plans of B3.

STEEL COLUMN AND FOOTING SCHEDULE

COLUMN NO.	Sections (bulkhead / floors)	Base plate (plan)	FLANGE POSITION	BILLET PLATE	CONCRETE FOOTING
1-A	8 W 24 / 8 W 35	20 x 20	I	14 x ⅞ x 1'-2	4'-6"x4'-6"x1'-4
1-B	10 W 54	34 x 18 (2'-1¼)	I	32 x 3½ x 1'-0	6'-0"x6'-0"x1'-4
1-C	10 W 49	26 x 18	I	24 x 2½ x 1'-0	5'-4"x4'-5"x1'-6
1-E	8 W 31	24 x 16	I	19 x 2 x 1'-0	4'-8"x4'-8"x1'-4
1-I	8 W 24 / 8 W 24	20 x 20	I	12 x 1 x 0'-10	3'-6"x3'-6"x1'-4
3-A	8 W 24 / 8 W 31	18 x 17	H	14 x 1 x 1'-0	4'-4"x4'-4"x1'-4
4-B	8 W 35	—	I	14 x ⅞ x 1'-1	3'-8"x3'-8"x1'-4
4-D	8 W 24	—	I	12 x 1 x 0'-10	3'-0"x3'-0"x1'-4
2-E	10 W 45 / 10 W 54	—	I	19 x 2 x 1'-7	5'-6"x5'-6"x1'-7
2-I	8 W 24 / 8 W 31	20 x 20	I	16 x 2 x 1'-4	5'-4"x4'-8"x1'-6
5-A	10 W 54	36 x 18	H	33 x 4 x 1'-0	6'-3"x6'-3"x1'-9
5-B	12 W 92 / 12 W 120 (1'-6, 7½)	—	H	29 x 3 x 2½ x 5	8'-4"x8'-4"x2½x2
5-D	12 W 85 / 12 W 99	—	H	28 x 3 x 2½ x 4	7'-9"x7'-9"x2½x4
5-F	8 W 24 / 12 W 99	—	I	25 x 2½ x 2½ x 1	7'-4"x7'-4"x2'-0
6-B	8 W 31	—	I	15 x 1⅞ x 1'-2	4'-0"x4'-0"x1'-4
6-D	8 W 31	—	I	15 x 1⅞ x 1'-2	4'-0"x4'-0"x1'-4
8-A	10 W 49	20 x 20	I	16 x 2 x 1'-4	5'-0"x5'-0"x1'-6
8-B	10 W 66	36 x 18	I	33 x 4 x 1'-0	6'-0"x6'-0"x1'-6
8-D	10 W 60	36 x 18	I	32 x 4 x 1'-0	7'-0"x6'-0"x1'-7
8-H	8 W 40	20 x 20	H	14 x 1⅞ x 1'-2	4'-6"x4'-6"x1'-4
7-G	8 W 24 / 8 W 31	—	H	14 x 1⅞ x 1'-1	4'-6"x4'-6"x1'-4

Level references:
- TOP OF BULKHEAD EL. +35'-5" (9'-6")
- TOP OF ROOF SLAB EL. +25'-11" (12'-10")
- FIN. SECOND FLR. EL. +13'-1" (13'-1")
- FIN. FIRST FLR. EL. ±0'-0" (11'-8")
- FIN. CELLAR FLR. EL. -11'-8" (1'-10")
- FIN. BOILER RM. EL. -13'-6"

NOTE: FIRST DIMENSION OF BILLET PLATE PARALLEL TO COLUMN FLANGES.
1" ANCHOR BOLTS PLACED 9" CENTER TO CENTER.

Fig. 9 Steel Column and Footing Schedule.

38

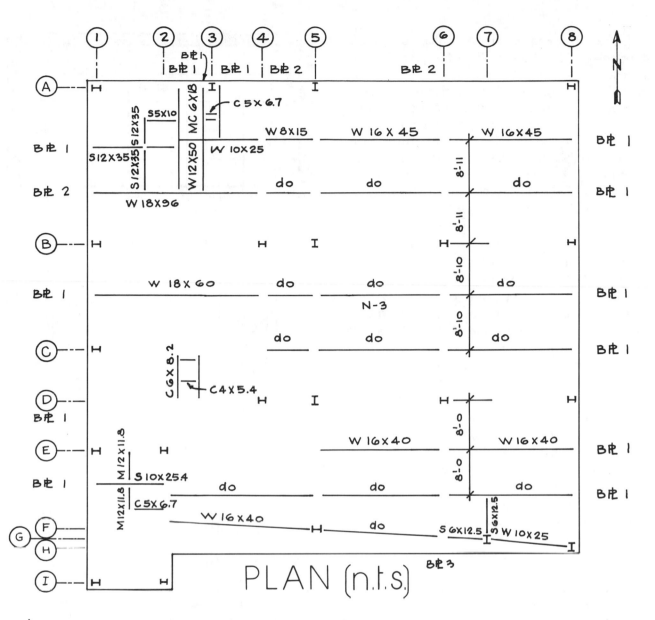

PLAN (n.t.s.)

STEEL FRAMING SCHEDULE					
NORTH TO SOUTH MEMBERS			WEST TO EAST MEMBERS		
SIZE	FROM	TO	SIZE	FROM	TO
W 21X96	N. WALL	4 B	W 18X60	1 B	4 B
W 24X64	4 B	4 D	W 18X60	1 C	W 24X84
W 24X76	2 E	2 I	W 18X60	W. WALL	4 D
W 24X76	5 A	5 B	W 12X27	1 E	2 E
W 24X76	5 B	5 D	M 8X18.5	4 B	5 B
W 24X76	5 D	5 F	M 8X18.5	4 D	5 D
W 24X94	N. WALL	6 B	W 16X50	2 E	W 24X76
W 24X94	6 B	6 D	W 16X45	5 B	6 B
W 24X84	6 D	S WALL	W 16X45	5 D	6 D
			W 16X45	6 B	8 B
			W 16X45	6 D	8 D

each beam framing to face A is given by dimensions referred to the established level of framing of which the beam is a member. *(-5 1/2")*. Instead of a dimension giving the distance between the top and bottom of the beam a description of the beam itself is substituted, except that the actual *(rather than the nominal)* depth of the beam is used in the description. In like manner, the top and bottom position of beams framing to each column face is shown on the view of that face before proceeding with the dimensions locating the hole which must be made in the column for the connections of these beams. An extension dimension with an arrow, labeled **"Mill"**, points to the extension line at the ends of all column shafts which are to be milled. Dimensions locating open holes are generally shown above the view being dimensioned. To locate such a group, an extension dimension is given showing the distance from the bottom **Mill Line** to the lowest open hole in the group. Then the **pitch distance** is shown along the **gage line.**

If a seated beam connector is to be **shop riveted** or **bolted** to the column, an extension dimension is given, showing the distance from the bottom **Mill Line** to the top of the **seat angle.** In the case of top and seat angles, the holes in the outstanding legs are located in transverse sections taken looking towards the bottom of the column. These fittings are omitted entirely from the views in which they would appear in profile.

Open holes and rivets need not be shown on the edge view of the column flanges, on the edge view of the outstanding leg of top and seat angles, or on the edge of spliced plates.

As far as possible the punching or drilling of **column webs** and **flanges** is kept on the standard **gage lines,** and these gage lines are located and shown by dimensions *(Fig. 6).*

COMMON METHODS OF FRAMING

Beam and Girder Framing. Bridge decks, floors, and roof of buildings are usually supported on a rectangular grid of steel members. Different names are given to the individual parts of the grid, depending on the type of structure and the part of the structure supported on the grid. The

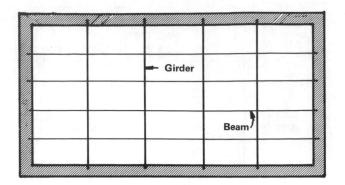

Fig. 11 Beam and girder framing.

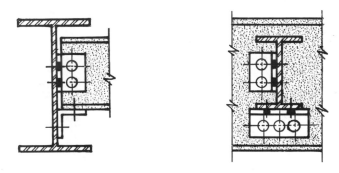

Fig. 12 Beam to girder connection.

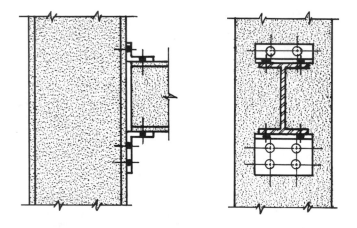

Fig. 13 Beam to column connection.

members spanning between main support walls are called **girders,** and those they support are called **beams** *(Fig. 11).*

In bridge construction, the smaller structural members that are parallel to the direction of traffic are called **stringers** and the transverse members are called **floor beams.** In roof construction, the grid components are usually refer-

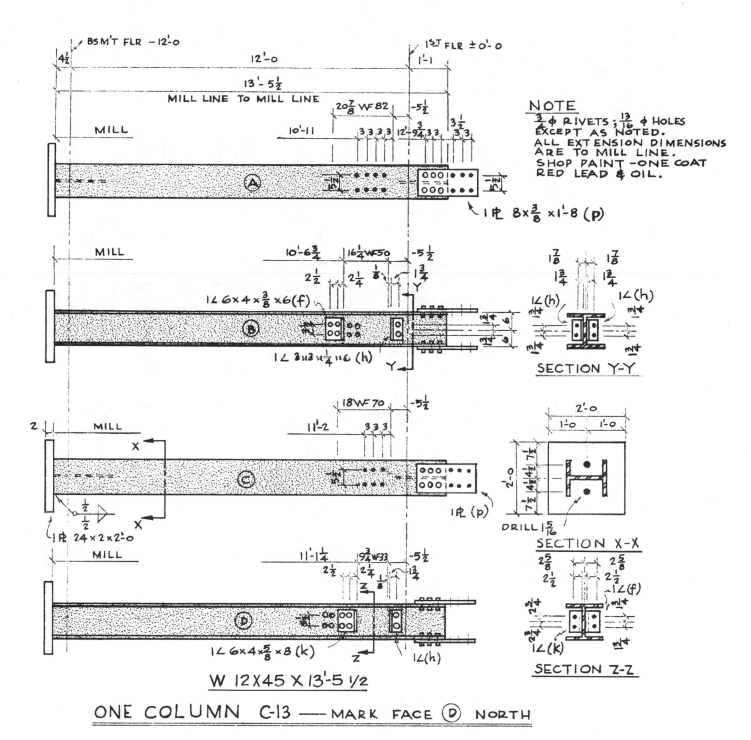

Fig. 10 Shop details of column C-13.

red to as **purlins** and **rafters**. In floor construction, these members are called **joists** and **girders**.

Beam and girder framing is used for short spans and where shallow members are used due to the lack of headroom clearance.

Trusses. Where headroom is not a factor and long spans are desired, trusses are used. A **truss** is a coplanar system of structural members joined at their ends to form a rigid framework. These members, when formed into a triangle, represent

41

the simplest type of truss. Some of the more common types of roof and bridge trusses are illustrated in *(Fig. 14)*. In these trusses, the top members are called the **upper chord**; the bottom members the **lower chord;** and the diagonals **web** members.

Trusses act like long deep girders with cut-out webs. Roof trusses must carry their own weight plus the weight of roof framing and built-up roofing, wind loads, snow loads, suspended ceilings and possible mechanical equipment stored overhead. It must also support a live load to take care of construction, maintenance and repair loading. Bridge trusses must support their own weight and that of the deck framing plus a live load imposed by traffic *(automobiles, trains, trucks, etc.)*, and possible impact caused by the live loads. **Deck trusses** carry the live load on the top chord, and **through trusses** on the bottom chord.

Framing with roof trusses is similar to beam and girder framing, with the trusses substituted for the girders. Since truss spans usually are long and roof decks are made of light material, the roof must be braced against both lateral and longitudinal forces with additional horizontal and vertical trusses.

In bridges, two parallel trusses are usually used *(Fig. 15)*. They must be properly braced because a bridge structure is exposed to both lateral forces due to wind pressure and vibrations caused by the impact of moving loads. These stresses are resisted by lateral trusses placed in between the chords of the main vertical trusses, and portal and sway bracing placed between each pair of end posts and verticals.

Rigid frames. When using beam and girder framing, trussed bracing is not necessary if equilibruim is maintained by joint restraint at the connection of girders to columns. When girders are so connected to columns that both members must rotate through the same angle, the structure is called a **rigid frame.** Rigid frames are very often used for highway bridges because of their pleasing appearance and because they can span 50 feet or more with less depth than required for simply supported girders or trusses. The bot-

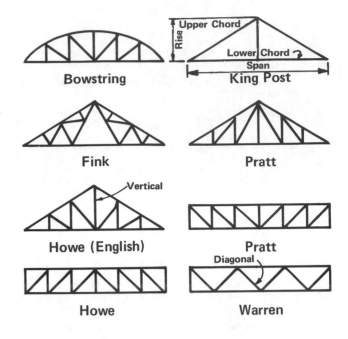

ROOF TRUSSES

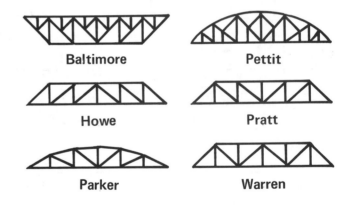

BRIDGE TRUSSES

Fig. 14 Common types of roof and bridge trusses.

toms of rigid frame girders are given a smooth curve and at the same time provide ample haunches to resist the bending moments at the columns. The verticals are tapered from a wide section at the top to a minimum width at the bottom *(Fig. 16)*.

42

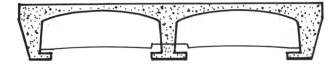

Fig. 16 *Rigid frame girders are used for highway spans.*

GLOSSARY

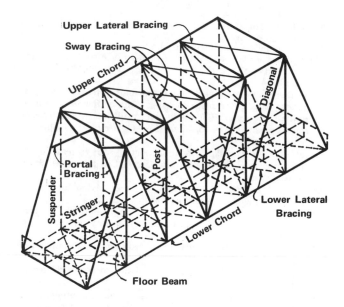

Fig. 15 *Bridges are formed by two parallel trusses.*

Batten Plate A small plate used near the ends of built-up members to hold two parts of any member in their proper position.

Bay The space between two consecutive sets of columns or beams and trusses.

Beam A horizontal member forming a part of the floor support, roof support, or frame of a structure.

Bent A vertical framework, usually columns and beams that support other members. A truss and two columns make up a bent.

Built-up Section A compound section composed of shapes or shapes and plates, to increase sectional area and strength.

Cantilever A beam, girder, or truss that projects beyond the supports.

Chord The upper members of a roof or bridge truss are called the "upper chord." The lower members, the "lower chord."

Clearance Space or distance between connecting members to facilitate erection.

Clip Angle A small angle used to fasten light connections. They may be attached to top chord of trusses or to columns and beams.

Column A vertical member subject to compression. In buildings, columns form a part of the frame and support the dead and live loads.

Connection Small pieces of steel shapes used to attach various members to each other. A gusset plate, etc.

Coping The punching out of small pieces of steel at the ends of beams, channels, etc., frequently used to remove material which would otherwise interfere with framing.

Cutting Removal of metal from structural steel. Its subdivisions are generally used, that is, one speaks of shearing, punching, etc., while the term cutting is generally reserved for the process which uses flame.

Falsework This is the name given to temporary structures used to support the permanent material during construction.

Finished Mill Products Steel shapes which can be used directly in construction.

    Bar Hot rolled or cold-drawn round, square, hexagonal and multifaceted long shapes, generally larger than wire in cross section. Also hot- or cold-rolled rectangular flat shapes (flats) generally narrower than sheets and strip.

    Blackplate Cold-rolled flat carbon steel products thinner than sheets and wider than strip, generally used for coating with zinc, tin or terne metal.

    Boil Cold-rolled flat product less than 24" wide and less than 0.005" thick.

    Pipe See Tubular Products.

    Plates Hot-rolled flat products generally thicker than sheets and wider than strip.

    Sheets Hot or cold-rolled flat products generally thinner than plate and wider than strip.

    Strip Hot- or cold-rolled flat products generally narrower than sheets and thinner than plates.

    Structurals Hot-rolled steel shapes of special design (such as H-beams, I-beams, channels, angles and tees) used in construction.

    Terneplate Blackplate which has been coated with terne metal (lead-tin alloy).

    Tinplate Blackplate which has been coated with tin.

    Tubular Products Hollow products of round, oval, square, rectangular and multifaceted cross sections. In construction, round products are generally referred to as pipe; square or rectangular products with thinner wall sections as tube or tubing.

    Wire Cold finished products of round square or multifaceted cross section, generally smaller than bars; round wire is cold drawn, 0.005" to less than 1" in diameter; flat wire is cold rolled, generally narrower than bar.

Flange The top and bottom projection or outstanding parts of a beam, channel or girder.

Gage Lines The line along which rivet holes are punched in structural members.

Girder A member designed to carry bending stress, usually it supports other members.

Gusset Plate A plate which connects two structural members back to back.

Hot Forming Forming of hot plastic metal into desired shapes, with little change in the mechanical properties of the metal.

Ingot Cast pig iron or steel shape made by pouring hot metal into molds.

Lattice Bar Short diagonal bars that are used to connect several parts of a structural member.

Lintel A structural member that is used to carry the wall over a masonry opening such as a window, door or arch.

Malleability The ability to be shaped without fracture either by hot or cold working.

Panel The divisions in the chord of a truss.

Pitch Distance between centers of rivets. For a roof truss, pitch is the ratio of the rise to span (24'-0" span, 8'-0" rise = 1/3 pitch).

Plates Bearing plates are used under the ends of trusses, beams or girders, etc. Cover plate or flange plate or flange plate used to increase section. Filler plate used to fill between surfaces of shapes when riveted together. Gusset plate used at joint of a truss, etc.

Purlin A purlin is a light beam supporting roof rafters. Purlins run from truss to truss and are fastened to the upper chord of each truss.

Separator A casting, piece of pipe or other device for holding structural members a desired distance apart.

Shearing The process of cutting members by applying a heavy blade, a shear, under pressure. It is similar in action to a paper cutter.

Span Distance between center line of bearing of end supports of a beam or truss.

Splice Longitudinal joint usually consisting of plates riveted to web and flanges of shape.

Steel Iron-carbon alloy, containing residual and sometimes alloying elements, characterized by its strength and toughness; distinguished from iron by its ability to be shaped by hot and/or cold working as initially cast.

Alloy Steel Steel in which the residual elements exceed limits prescribed for carbon steel, or alloying elements are added within specified ranges.

Carbon Steel Steel in which the residual elements are controlled but alloying elements are not usually added.

Heat Resisting Steel Low chromium steel (chromium 4% to 12%) which retains its essential mechanical properties at temperatures up to 1100°F.

High Strength Low Alloy Steel Steel with less than 1% of any alloying element, manufactured to high standards for strength ductility, and partial chemical specifications.

Mild Steel Carbon steel with carbon content between 0.15% and 0.25%.

Stainless Steel Steel containing 12% to 20% chromium, with excellent corrosion resistance, strength and chemical inertness at high and low temperatures.

Stiffener An angle that is fastened to a plate in order to prevent buckling.

Tie A member subject to tension.

Truss A steel structure whose members take only tension or compression forces.

Web That portion of a wide flange, or channel between flanges.

Welding Creating a metallurgical bond between metals with heat and sometimes with the use of pressure and filler metal.

Arc Welding Welding methods employing an electric arc as the source of heat.

Gas Welding Welding methods employing a fuel gas (acetylene, hydrogen) and oyxgen as the source of heat.

Shielded Welding Processes using gases or fusible granular materials to shield the weld area from damaging effects of oxygen and nitrogen in the air.

Shielded Metal Arc Welding (also known as manual metal arc, and stick electrode welding). Arc welding in which a flux coated metal electrode is consumed to form a pool of filler metal and a gas shield around the weld area.

Inert Gas Shielded Arc Welding Arc welding in which shielding is provided by an inert gas envelope (such as argon, helium, a combination of both or carbon dioxide) from an external supply. Filler metal is supplied by either a consumable metal electrode, as in inert gas shielded metal arc welding (MIG), or by a separate filler rod used with a non-consumable tungsten electrode, as in inert gas shielded tungsten arc welding (TIG).

Submerged Arc Welding Arc welding in which the weld area is shielded by fusible granular material which melts to protect the weld area. Filler metal is obtained either from a consumable electrode of separate filler rod.

Working Lines The portion of the gage line between two working points is called a working line.

Wrought Iron Relatively pure iron, mechanically mixed with a small amount of iron-silicate slag; characterized by good corrosion resistance, weldability, toughness and high ductility.

Wrought Products Products formed by rolling, drawing, extruding and forging.

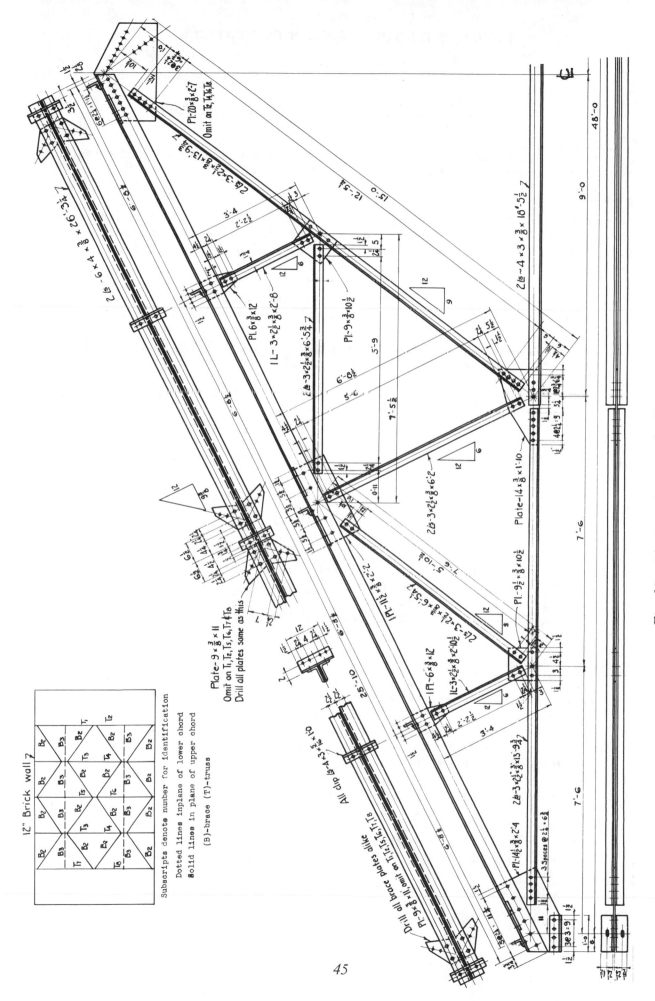

Fig. 17 Working drawing of a Fink Truss.

45

TYPICAL STRUCTURAL STEEL SPECIFICATIONS

STRUCTURAL STEEL & MISCELLANEOUS METALS

1. ### GENERAL CONDITIONS
   All work in this section shall be performed in accordance with the require-ments of the Contract Documents.

2. ### SCOPE
   The work under this section shall include all labor, materials, appliances and services necessary to complete all structural steel and miscellaneous iron and related work required by the drawings and/or as described in this specification, generally as follows:

   a. All steel beams, columns, open web joists, bearing and levelling plates, lintels, anchor bolts for steel and miscellaneous iron work.

   b. Temporary supports, guys and bracing required to erect structural steel frame and maintain the frame in alignment during construction.

   c. Erection of all steel and loose lintels exceeding 200 pounds in weight.

   d. Shop painting of all work and field touch-up.

   e. Preparation of steel erection, anchor bolt and bearing plate setting plans and detailed shop drawings.

   f. All other labor and materials as may be reasonably inferred as required to make the work of this section complete.

3. ### WORK NOT IN THIS SECTION
   a. Furnishing of anchor bolts for wood construction.
   b. Grouting of all levelling and bearing plates.
   c. Setting of all anchor bolts.
   d. Setting of all loose lintels weighing 200 pounds or less.
   e. Field coat of paint.

4. ### GENERAL REQUIREMENTS
   a. This Contractor shall check all drawings and shall be entirely respon-sible for the completeness of the work. The Contractor shall be responsible for all errors of fabrication and for the correct fitting of all members detailed on the shop drawings. The Contractor shall verify all measurements in the field affecting his work before delivery of his material.

   b. This Contractor shall provide anchors, etc. cut, punch and drill steel as required for the work of other trades. He shall cooperate with the other contractors regarding all parts of his work which are in any manner related to the work of others and he shall arrange and execute his work in such a manner that the work of other contractors will not be delayed.

c. The Contractor shall deliver all the structural steel as required in the proper sequence to keep pace with the general work on the project. This Contractor shall be held responsible for all damage to the work of other contractors caused by the installation of his work, and any other work or materials damaged because of carelessness, negligence or lack of precaution on the part of this Contractor. He shall be held liable for same at his expense.

5. SHOP DRAWINGS
This Contractor shall furnish four prints of erection and detail drawings for approval by the Architect. Shop drawings are to be prepared by a detailer experienced in this type. All shop drawings much be thoroughly checked before being submitted. They shall show all sizes, dimensions and details necessary for the proper fabrication and erection of all work under this contract. Do not fabricate until drawings are approved by the Architect and Engineer. Approval of shop drawings will be for size, arrangement and strength only. Errors in dimensions will be the responsibility of this Contractor.

6. MATERIALS AND WORKMANSHIP
a. All material shall be new, clean and straight. All work to be done in a neat, workmanlike manner and to be complete in every respect.

b. All work and materials shall comply in every respect with the latest edition of:

(1) A.I.S.C. Specifications.
(2) Standard A.S.T.M. Specifications.
(3) Standard A.W.S. Code for Arc & Gas Welding in Building Construction.
(4) Specifications for Assembly of Structural Joints Using High Strength Steel Bolts approved by Research Council on Riveted and Bolted Joints.
(5) Steel Joist Institute Standard Specifications.

c. All welding must be performed by welders who have been certified by an approved Testing Laboratory within the previous two year period. Proof of such certification to be submitted to the Architect before work is performed.

d. All structural Steel shall conform to the following:

(1) Beams, Columns, Lintels, Connections and Base plates - A.S.T.M. Specifications A 36.
(2) Open Web Steel Joists - A.S.T.M. Specifications A36, A242, A441 and A375 designed and manufactured in accordance with Standard Specifications of Steel Joists Institute latest revision.

S 1-2

7. FABRICATION

a. Finished members shall be true to line and free from twists, bends and open joints between component parts. If straightening or flattening is required, it shall be done in a manner that will not injure the material.

b. Columns shall be milled at bearing ends to a true surface, at right angles to the axis, to insure uniform bearing. All milled surfaces shall be protected from corrosion as soon as milled, by a suitable approved coating.

c. Column base and cap plates shall be of sizes indicated on the drawings, with straight and true top and bottom surfaces. Base plates may be straightened by pressing to obtain satisfactory contract bearing.

d. Holes for bolts shall be drilled or punched 1/16" larger than the nominal diameter of the bolts. Burning to enlarge unfair holes is not permitted. Holes that must be enlarged shall be reamed. Bolts shall fit holes snugly and nuts shall be drawn up tight and shall have full grip on bolts.

8. ERECTION

a. All structural steel shall be erected by the Contractor as rapidly as the progress of the general work will permit.

b. All structural steel and iron shall be set accurately to the lines and levels established on the drawings.

c. Framework shall be plumb and level. Individual pieces shall be considered plumb and level where the error does not exceed 1 to 500 for the total length of the member. For columns, the error from plumb shall not exceed 1 to 1000 for the total height of the column. Bolt up during erection to provide for dead load, wind, and erection stresses. Provide temporary bracing and shoring as required to maintain steel safely in alignment until tying-in work of other trades is completed. Shop or drawing errors may be corrected in the field only if approved by Architect or Engineer.

9. CONNECTIONS

a. All field and shop connections shall be designed to support live and dead loading and horizontal wind loads.

b. All field connections to be bolted or welded.

(1) Girder to Column connections and Beam to Column connection shall be made using High Strength Bolts with hardened Steel Washers.

(2) Steel Joists to beam connections shall be field welded. Bolts may be used for fitting-up purposes only.

S 1-3

(3) All other connections may be made using standard Square-Head Bolts with standard Washers and Square nuts.

(4) Field welding may be used in lieu of bolting only with the approval of the Architect or Engineer.

c. Shop connections to be welded.

10. PAINTING

a. All shop paint for structural steel shapes in this contract shall be an approved brand of red lead and linseed oil, approximately 16 pounds per gallon.

b. All surfaces inaccessible after assembly, shall be given two (2) coats of above paint before assembly. Use two different colors.

c. Before shop painting, all surfaces must be thoroughly cleaned of scale and dirt. All steel in this contract shall be painted one good coat of the shop paint, brand as herein before specified, after fabrication but before leaving the shop. All paint must be applied to dry surfaces.

d. Bolts, welds, steel abrasions, rust, scale, and other defects in shop paint shall be touched up in the field by this Contractor immediately prior to application of field coats by the Painting Contractor.

11. INSPECTION AND TESTS

a. The architect and Engineer, or their authorized Inspectors, shall have the privilege of inspecting the work in the shop or field during the period of fabrication or erection.

b. The Contractor shall furnish to the Architect a copy of the mill test reports from the prime producer for all structural steel.

12. ALLOWANCE
This Contractor shall allow (2) tons of miscellaneous structural shape to be used as directed. Unused portion of this allowance to be credited to the Owner at prevailing rates. This item is in addition to shapes specifically called for elsewhere.

13. SUBSTITUTIONS
The Architect reserves the right to require the Contractor to substitute shapes of other makes than those indicated on the construction drawings when it is apparent that the shapes specified cannot be furnished within the time required for the progress of construction. The Contractor shall make the said substitutions without additional compensation.

14. DEBRIS
This Contractor shall be responsible for removing all debris due to his contract from the premises.

STEEL DECK

1. **GENERAL**
All work of this Section shall be performed in accordance with the requirements of the Contract Documents.

2. **SCOPE**
Contractor shall furnish all equipment, labor and material for the complete installation of steel decking & slab forms on all supported floor areas indicated on the plans and as specified herein.

3. **STANDARD SPECIFICATION: LATEST EDITION**
   a. Specification for the Design of Light Gage Cold Formed Steel Structural Members – American Iron & Steel Institute.

   b. Specification of Metal Roof Deck Technical Institute, including load table approval.

4. **MATERIAL**
   a. **Steel Floor Slab Form Deck**
      (1) Steel floor slab form deck shall be uncoated corrugated steel capable of supporting a construction load of 20 p.s.f. plus the weight of concrete floor slab during pouring.
      (2) Steel decking shall be 1-1/2" 22 GA. Type B factory coated with paint primer.
      (3) All necessary clips and washers required for welded attachment of the steel form deck to structural steel supports shall be furnished.

   b. Welding electrodes for field welding of deck shall conform to ASTM-A233 Series E70.

5. **SHOP DRAWINGS**
   a. Contractor shall prepare shop drawings consisting of erection diagrams and assembly attachment details.

   b. The Contractor shall submit the completed and checked shop drawings for approval to the Architect. The Architect reserves the right to modify these details if, in his opinion, such modification is deemed to be necessary and fabrication shall be in accordance with such revised or modified details. Drawings "not approved" or "approved as noted" shall be resubmitted to the Architect for approval.

   c. Approval of the shop drawings shall in no way relieve the Contractor of his responsibility for their completeness and accuracy.

   d. No fabrication shall commence prior to approval of the shop drawings except that the Contractor may proceed with fabrication on the basis of "Approved as Noted" drawings provided that the noted corrections are made.

e. Shop drawings shall show location, type and size of all field welding.

f. The number and distribution of shop drawings submitted for approval shall be as specified in the General Conditions.

6. <u>INSTALLATION</u>
    a. Deck shall be welded directly to the steel supports. All welding shall be in complete accordance with approved shop drawings and manufacturer's recommendations.

    b. Where necessary to permit satisfactory attachment, welding washers shall be used.

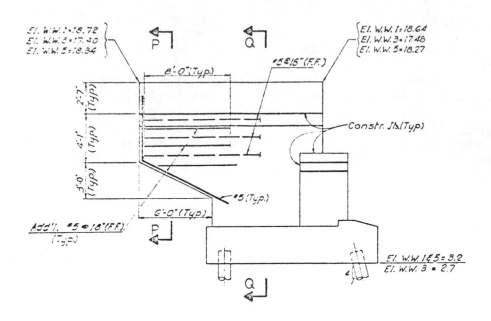

El. W.W.1 = 18.72
El. W.W.3 = 17.40
El. W.W.5 = 18.34

El. W.W.1 = 18.64
El. W.W.3 = 17.48
El. W.W.5 = 18.27

8'-0"(Typ.)

#5@18"(F.F.)

2'-7" (Typ.)

4'-1" (Typ.)

3'-0" (Typ.)

Constr. Jt.(Typ.)

#5 (Typ.)

Add'l. #5 @ 18"(F.F.)
(Typ.)

6'-0" (Typ.)

El. W.W. 1 & 5 = 3.2
El. W.W. 3 = 2.7

P   Q

WINGWALLS 1, 3 & 5
Scale: ¼" = 1'-0"

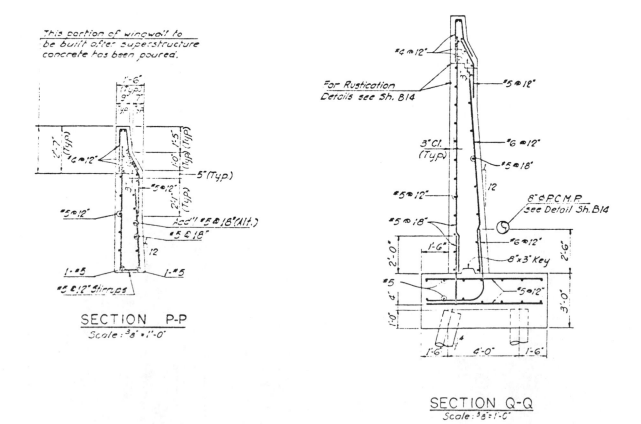

This portion of wingwall to
be built after superstructure
concrete has been poured.

1'-6" (Typ.)

2'-7" (Typ.)

#6 @ 12"

1'-0"   1'-5" (Typ.)

5" (Typ.)

#5 @ 12"

#5 @ 12"

2'-1" (Typ.)

Add'l #5 @ 18" (Alt.)

#5 @ 18"

12

1-#5   1-#5

#5 @ 12" Stirrups

SECTION P-P
Scale: ⅜" = 1'-0"

#4 @ 12"

For Rustication
Details see Sh. B14

#5 @ 12"

3" Cl.
(Typ.)

#6 @ 12"

#5 @ 18"

#5 @ 12"

12

8" Ø P.C.M.P.
See Detail Sh. B14

#5 @ 18"

1'-6"

#6 @ 12"

2'-0"

8"x3" Key

2'-6"

#5

#5 @ 12"

4"

1'-0"

3'-0"

1'-6"   4'-0"   1'-6"

SECTION Q-Q
Scale: ⅜" = 1'-0"

REINFORCED CONCRETE

Concrete is a masonry material composed of cement, aggregate that is clean and strong; usually crushed stone or gravel, fine aggregate *(sand)* that is clean, sharp and nonuniform in size. This will make for strong structures. Such aggregate is relatively costly; however, many times a more economical aggregate will be used in the pouring of sidewalks, driveways, etc.

Concrete is very weak in tension, especially in the diagonal directions. To overcome this weakness, steel bars are added within the concrete to absorb the tension load. These rods are round or square in cross section and they have projections produced along their lengths in the steel mills by the use of special rolls so as to increase their resistance to " **stripping.**" This resistance is known as "**bond.**" To further increase their anchorage in the concrete, they are usually bent back on the ends in order to form hooks such as those shown in some of the following details *(Figs. 1 & 13)*. Such bars are used for simple tension absorption. Those that absorb the lateral tension along the lower edges plus the diagonal shear tension are bent up at the ends along a 45⁰ line which is approximately the path that shear tension failure usually follow. In addition, since there are seldom enough of these latter in the structure, therefore it may be necessary to add a series of U-shaped pieces near the ends of the concrete span in order to cut across the shear lines and absorb strain. These are called **stirrups** and may be seen in *(Figs. 4, 5 & 9)*.

There are two additional types of bars used in reinforced concrete. They are known as **temperature steel** and **tie steel**. The function of both are rather apparent from their names. **Temperature steel** carries no structural load but is placed at intervals just inside the exposed face of the masonry structure to absorb the stresses induced by the changes of temperature, as concrete expands and contracts just as other materials, and thus aids in preventing unsightly cracks from forming on the surface. In addition,

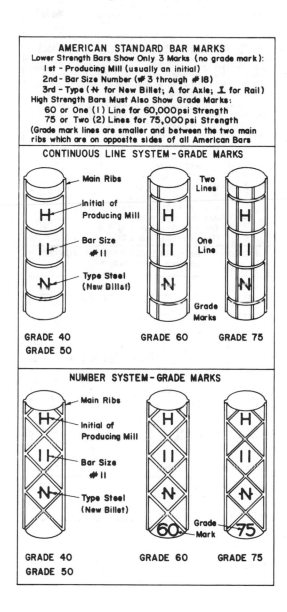

Fig. 1 U.S. Standard Bars - Identification Marks.

should such cracks form and water freeze in them, the resulting expansion of the ice below minus four degrees centigrade would crack out sections of the structure and eventually destroy it. This temperature steel isn't usually deformed but is simply encased in the concrete as plain lengths of rod. The **tie steel** functions only to

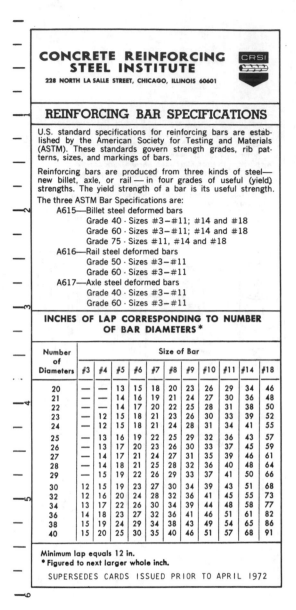

CONCRETE REINFORCING STEEL INSTITUTE

228 NORTH LA SALLE STREET, CHICAGO, ILLINOIS 60601

REINFORCING BAR SPECIFICATIONS

U.S. standard specifications for reinforcing bars are established by the American Society for Testing and Materials (ASTM). These standards govern strength grades, rib patterns, sizes, and markings of bars.

Reinforcing bars are produced from three kinds of steel—new billet, axle, or rail — in four grades of useful (yield) strengths. The yield strength of a bar is its useful strength.

The three ASTM Bar Specifications are:

A615—Billet steel deformed bars
Grade 40 · Sizes #3—#11; #14 and #18
Grade 60 · Sizes #3—#11; #14 and #18
Grade 75 · Sizes #11, #14 and #18

A616—Rail steel deformed bars
Grade 50 · Sizes #3—#11
Grade 60 · Sizes #3—#11

A617—Axle steel deformed bars
Grade 40 · Sizes #3—#11
Grade 60 · Sizes #3—#11

INCHES OF LAP CORRESPONDING TO NUMBER OF BAR DIAMETERS*

Number of Diameters	Size of Bar										
	#3	#4	#5	#6	#7	#8	#9	#10	#11	#14	#18
20	—	—	13	15	18	20	23	26	29	34	46
21	—	—	14	16	19	21	24	27	30	36	48
22	—	—	14	17	20	22	25	28	31	38	50
23	—	12	15	18	21	23	26	30	33	39	52
24	—	12	15	18	21	24	28	31	34	41	55
25	—	13	16	19	22	25	29	32	36	43	57
26	—	13	17	20	23	26	30	33	37	45	59
27	—	14	17	21	24	27	31	35	39	46	61
28	—	14	18	21	25	28	32	36	40	48	64
29	—	15	19	22	26	29	33	37	41	50	66
30	12	15	19	23	27	30	34	39	43	51	68
32	12	16	20	24	28	32	36	41	45	55	73
34	13	17	22	26	30	34	39	44	48	58	77
36	14	18	23	27	32	36	41	46	51	61	82
38	15	19	24	29	34	38	43	49	54	65	86
40	15	20	25	30	35	40	46	51	57	68	91

Minimum lap equals 12 in.
* Figured to next larger whole inch.

SUPERSEDES CARDS ISSUED PRIOR TO APRIL 1972

Fig. 2   Reinforcing bar specifications.

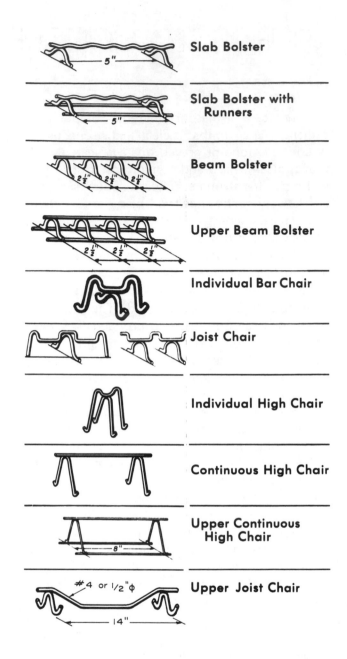

Slab Bolster

Slab Bolster with Runners

Beam Bolster

Upper Beam Bolster

Individual Bar Chair

Joist Chair

Individual High Chair

Continuous High Chair

Upper Continuous High Chair

Upper Joist Chair

Fig. 3   Various types of bar supports.

hold the main steel in place and the whole steel being tied or clipped together with special devices so as to form a steel lattice. When the concrete is poured the tie steel is encased along with the other but serves no further useful purpose (*Fig. 6*).

When drawing **reinforced concrete details,** the steel pieces should be drawn separately and thoroughly with an illustration for each type bar and with the proper identification made for

each. The detail need not be drawn to scale and may be composed of a single heavy line. In most cases one detail may serve for more than one bar if proper identification is given. The steel in the main detail drawings of the structure should be shown in their lateral positions by heavy dash lines which need not be drawn to scale as to thickness but which should be drawn to scale for their position and length. In the cross sec-

STANDARD BENDING TOLERANCES
For bar sizes #3 through #11

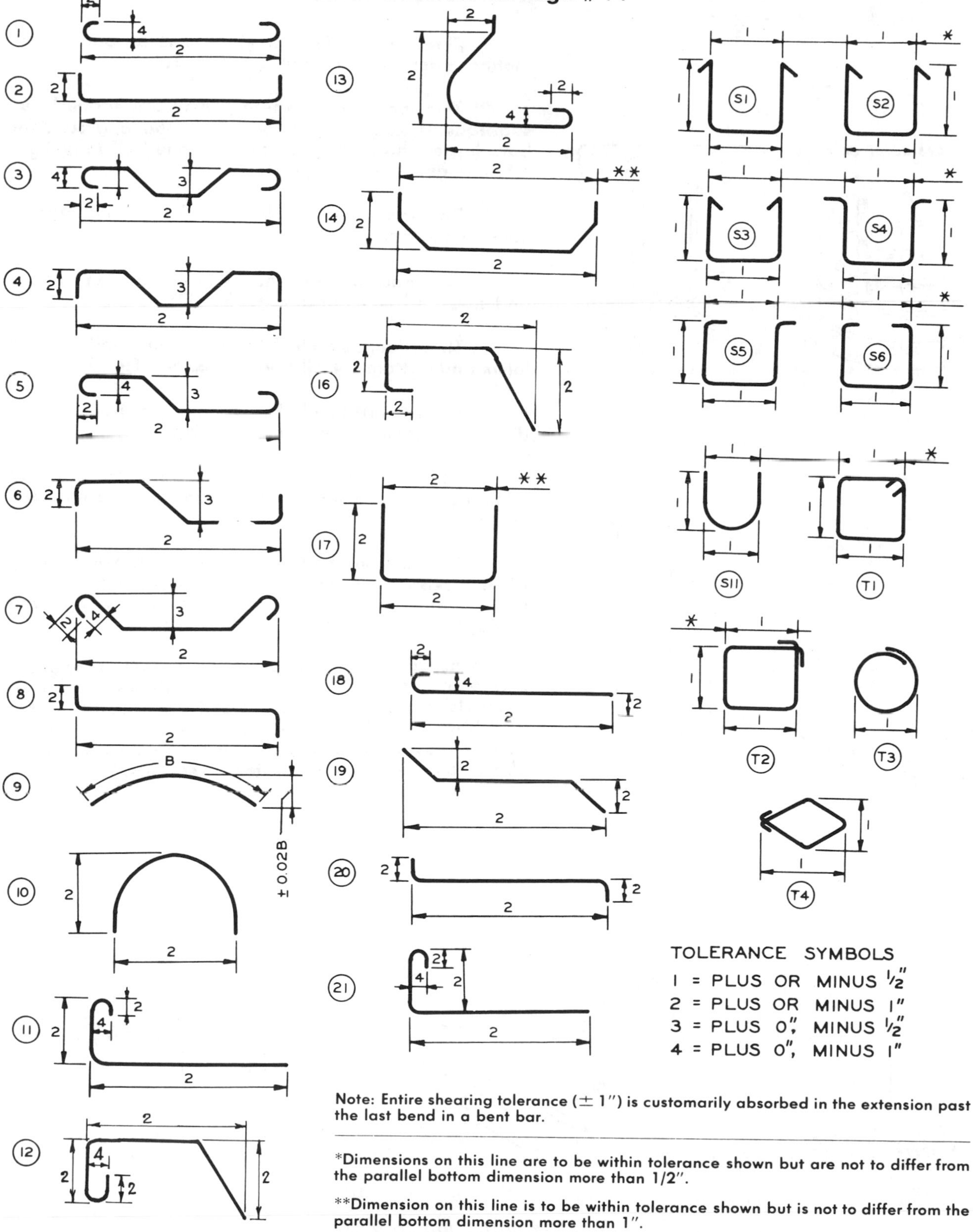

TOLERANCE SYMBOLS

1 = PLUS OR MINUS ½"
2 = PLUS OR MINUS 1"
3 = PLUS 0", MINUS ½"
4 = PLUS 0", MINUS 1"

Note: Entire shearing tolerance (± 1") is customarily absorbed in the extension past the last bend in a bent bar.

*Dimensions on this line are to be within tolerance shown but are not to differ from the parallel bottom dimension more than 1/2".

**Dimension on this line is to be within tolerance shown but is not to differ from the parallel bottom dimension more than 1".

Fig. 4   Standard bending tolerances for bar sizes No. 3 thru No. 11.

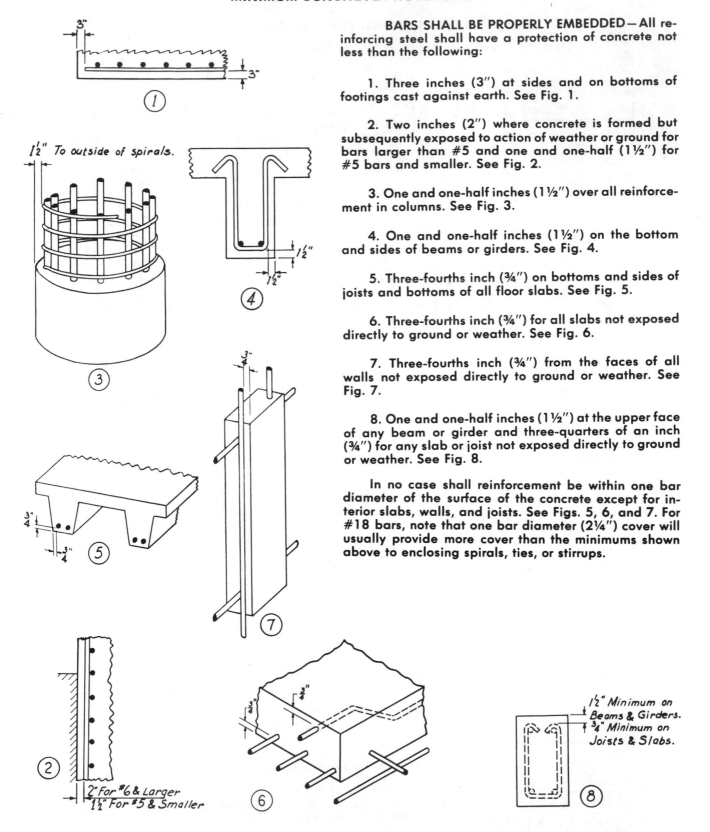

BARS SHALL BE PROPERLY EMBEDDED — All reinforcing steel shall have a protection of concrete not less than the following:

1. Three inches (3") at sides and on bottoms of footings cast against earth. See Fig. 1.

2. Two inches (2") where concrete is formed but subsequently exposed to action of weather or ground for bars larger than #5 and one and one-half (1½") for #5 bars and smaller. See Fig. 2.

3. One and one-half inches (1½") over all reinforcement in columns. See Fig. 3.

4. One and one-half inches (1½") on the bottom and sides of beams or girders. See Fig. 4.

5. Three-fourths inch (¾") on bottoms and sides of joists and bottoms of all floor slabs. See Fig. 5.

6. Three-fourths inch (¾") for all slabs not exposed directly to ground or weather. See Fig. 6.

7. Three-fourths inch (¾") from the faces of all walls not exposed directly to ground or weather. See Fig. 7.

8. One and one-half inches (1½") at the upper face of any beam or girder and three-quarters of an inch (¾") for any slab or joist not exposed directly to ground or weather. See Fig. 8.

In no case shall reinforcement be within one bar diameter of the surface of the concrete except for interior slabs, walls, and joists. See Figs. 5, 6, and 7. For #18 bars, note that one bar diameter (2¼") cover will usually provide more cover than the minimums shown above to enclosing spirals, ties, or stirrups.

Fig. 5   *Concrete protection around bars.*

tion detail however, the same steel as far as possible must be drawn completely to scale.

Since the steel is usually placed in the tension side, a beam supported on both ends would require its steel in the lower portion with the bars placed as low and as close together as possible within the following limits. Steel requires at least 3/4" of covering for slabs and 1½" for beams so that the concrete may be firmly tamped down between the rods and that way avoid air pockets. Between parallel bars the *minimum spacing is 2½ X diameter for round rods* and *3 X the side for square rods.* The clear spacing between bars must never be under that indicated or *1¼ X the size of the coarsest aggregate (Fig. 5).*

When the reinforcing is uniform and continuous only a small portion needs to be shown in section and only a small area of that needs to be shown by the concrete symbol. The reason being that concrete is a non-homogeneous material it should not be cross hatched as we show cast iron or steel, etc., and the symbol adopted is somewhat pictorial in that it attempts to show small pieces of aggregate with stippling between and around to represent the cement particles and fine aggregate*(Chapter 3,Figs. 8&9)*.

For slabs it is easier and more economical to use prepared mesh instead of weaving in with rods.

It is standard practice to shade in the areas that are cross sectioned as this produces a cleaner detail. The back side of the tracing is colored in with a fairly opaque color, yellow is an excellent selection, as this will produce a good contrasting blueprint. The difference in opacity of the various parts of the tracing produce differing shades on the final blueprint and will emphasize the sections without destroying the detail.

The **bill of materials** is most important and should be thoroughly checked to show all steel, fittings, pipe, tile drains, mesh, cubic yards of concrete, mix, etc. Dimensioning should be so complete that the drawing could be turned over to an office clerk to make up the order.

Certain questions inevitably arise and the foregoing information was added in order to

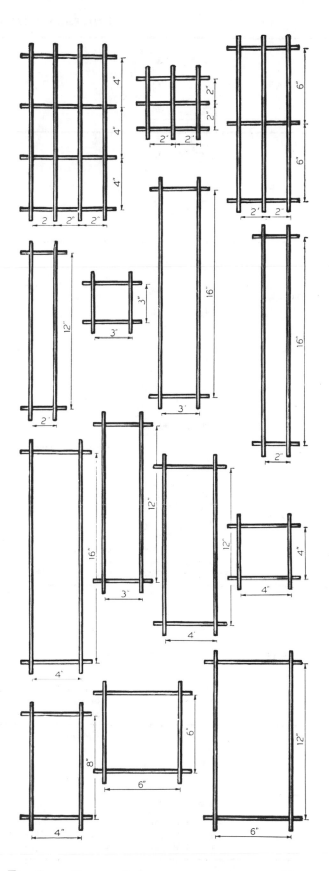

Fig. 6   *Some of the many spacing combinations possible with welded wire fabric.*

57

UNIVERSAL STANDARD COLUMN TIES*

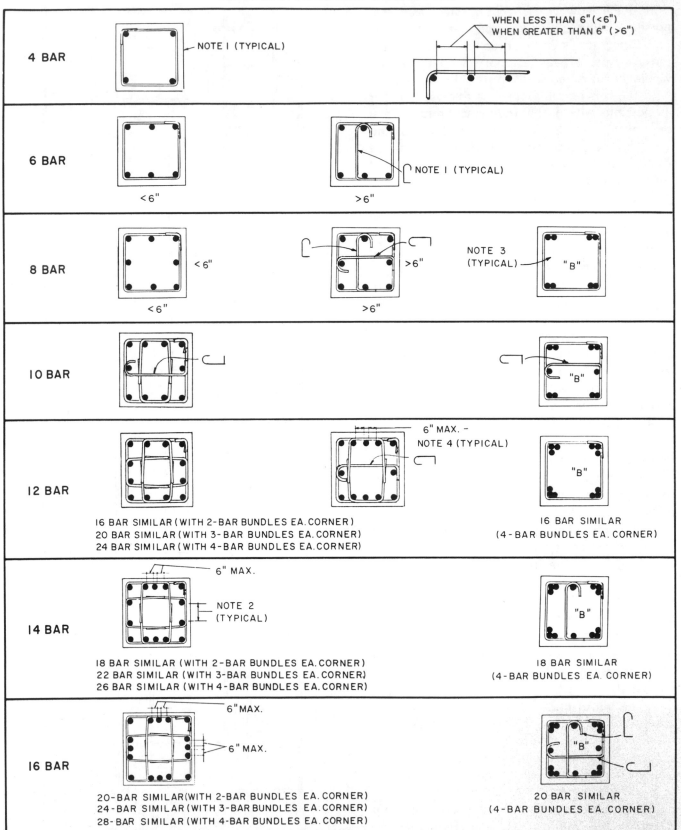

Fig. 7   Universal Standard Column Ties

answer the more common questions. In addition the following is a help to the students:

STANDARD PRACTICES

Steel ends approximately 2" from the end of the span ends, that is, is embedded at least 2".

The number of rows of steel should be as few as possible in accordance with the specified number of bars and the minimum spacing stated.

The number of bars is determined by proper design calculations.

The bars are not to be bent to match the camber.

The beam depth is measured at the minimum depth section. Camber is an added thickness.

The railings need not be of pipe. It may be made of concrete, at the discretion of the instructor.

When hooked bars are to be used they are bent up on a radius of four times their diameter, or a minimum of 2½" and are usually bent through 180° *(Fig. 14)*.

In footings the bars are usually carried through two diameters beyond the bends.

CONCRETE "T" BRIDGES

Short span "T" shaped bridges are used over streams on golf courses, in public parks and in gardens. Longer "T" bridges are prefabricated for use as highway bridge beams, sometimes prestressed, generally trucked and hoisted into

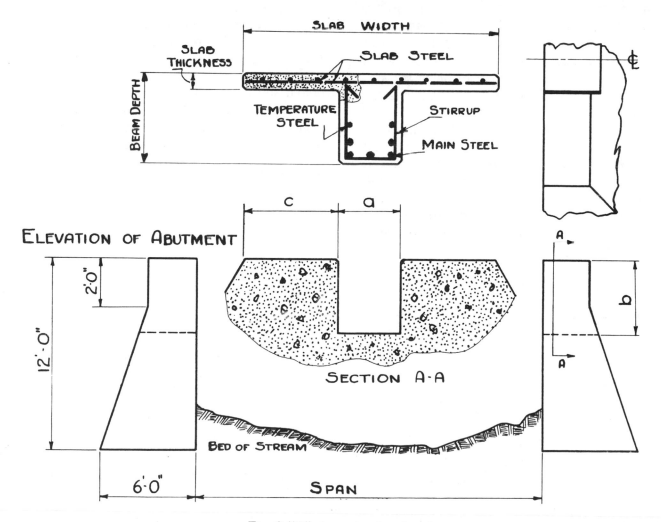

Fig. 8 "T" shape bridge details.

59

place. The "T" stem in some cases is tapered to save weight and to aid in removal from the form (See fig. 8).

The description of the project is as follows: it is desired to replace a small bridge over a brook. When the original was washed out the abutments were not damaged, and need not be detailed, except that the outlines in immediate contact with the bridge should be indicated by dotted lines. The "T" beams will fit in the abutments at both ends. The top of the slab is crowned to discharge rain water. Crown is an additive and is 1/4 inch per foot, running the width of the slab, from the center. If detailed the slope may be exaggerated. The beams are to rest directly in the end abutments and the depth indicated is the measurement from the bottom of the beam to the top of the slab at the center of the beam. Camber, if used, would be 0.60 inches of rise per foot unit of run. Camber is generally aesthetic, and is seen in the length of beam, the extra height being added at the ends and bottom to give a slight arch effect to the underside of the bridge.

Reinforcing bars will run horizontally, spacing and size to be determined from design calculations. The slab reinforcement is to be centered vertically. All edges of the concrete beam will be beveled to prevent sharp corners which fracture easily. Inside corners are to be filleted. Bevels and fillets are approximately one inch. The entire beam is poured as one unit, and a pipe railing, commercial banister or concrete railing is used as required by code. The finished drawing will show: cross sections, longitudinal sections, steel details, bill of materials, railing details, and additional notes as required.

While the preceding bridge is basically a handbook design, the bridges of the Swiss engineer Robert Maillart (1872-1940) are cited for their innovative design and aesthetics. He eliminated all non-functional concrete, making his bridges light and airy. One of his later works, a parabolic vault building spans 16 meters, is 12 meters high, yet only 60 millimeters thick. Later architects and engineers built even thinner shells of greater spans. Had Maillart lived longer, he may have designed incredible bridges.

Today's architect and engineers are designing hyperbolic parabolloid shells (See fig. 9). formed by using two skew lines, AC and BD as the edges of the surface, and another line AB moving parallel to the surface ABEF and touching AC and BD. The hyperbolic paraboloid shells curve is three dimensional and the surfaces are warped. They are more rigid than a plane surface, yet can be formed with straight timber and straight re-bars. In some designs the roof is supported only on two corners of the hyperbolic paraboloid, while other designs use a continuing set of shells to form multiple roofs (See fig. 10).

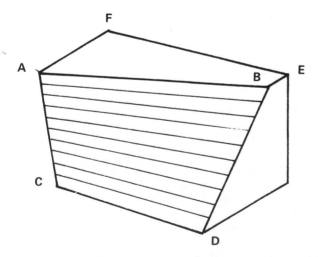

Fig. 9 Hyperbolic Parabola showing plane director

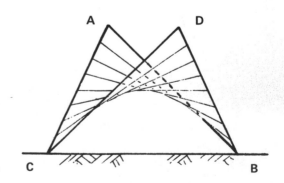

Fig. 10 Hyperbolic Parabola

CONCRETE BLOCK STRUCTURES

Ordinary buildings are often constructed with concrete masonry units, (CMU) which require no unique design and are familiar to most trades. Various materials such as slag, lava, glass, cinders, pummice and clay have been used, but the cement-sand aggregate is most often used. Blocks are available in many sizes including metric, *(See Table 36, Concrete Masonry Units, p. 271)* but the nominal sizes most often used 8x8x16 and 12x8x16 inches. Many other styles and types are available: corner (solid end), control joint (end configuration such that no bonding will occur between next block), L-blocks, lintel, sills, jambs, half pilaster and chimney blocks. Plastic and ceramic tile faced blocks, shadow (recessed) and screen (open) blocks are also available.

CASTING CONCRETE

Concrete is also available precast in statues, fountains, benches, columns, banisters, steps, architectural friezes and mouldings, planters and pools.

Concrete is also used for walls cast in place. Concrete walls are formed using commercial steel plates or wood forms. Other unusual materials such as plastic, plaster, distressed wood have been used to mold texture into the wall surface. Other surface treatments, used after the forms are removed, include: hammering, chipping, washing off the top surface to show the aggregate, rubbing, sandblasting, brooming, stamping, and others. Various decorative walls have been designed and detailed with combinations of materials and different colors to give mural and design effects.

In addition to the normal method of placing concrete by buggies and buckets, pumping is used where the erection of cranes would be hazardous in areas around wires, or impossible as in tunnels. The greater cost of pumping may be offset by the cost of cutting and rerouting power lines around the construction site. However, the pumping is limited to a few hundred feet.

Concrete can be placed underwater by means of funnels or pipes continuously loaded, open at the bottom so the concrete displaces the water in the form.

Air gunning the concrete mixture into place is common for the building of swimming pools and in placing stucco, sound-absorbent coatings or plaster on flat or curved surfaces. This requires skilled workers and the proper equipment, but is time saving and can place the mixture on surfaces not normally possible, including up-side down. Since it is driven into place it is more compacted and will fill voids around re-bars better than other techniques.

CANTILEVER TYPE RETAINING WALL

This particular design is to hold back an earth fill, i.e., the stem is strong enough to hold back the fill without requiring the aid of buttresses or counterforts. It is poured in two sections, **footing** and **stem**, keyed. The section to be drawn will be 20' of a longer wall, with pipe rail at the top and drains 6'-0" on centers and 1'-6" above ground level. There will be a coping.

Reinforcement runs two ways, that in the heel is to be at the top and that in the toe is to be in the bottom so that both may take tension. They will extend from the end to a point about 12" past the center of the stem. They will be 3" deep in the concrete and held by tie steel ½ inch in diameter, 1'-6" O. C., and inside the main steel supports *(Fig. 11)*.

The stem will be nearly vertical in the front, with ¼ inch per foot batter, the rear sloping as necessary. Stem reinforcement parallel to rear face and 2" deep in the concrete. It is hooked at the lower end and bent 90° on the upper end. It will be three lengths as indicated in the assignment since the bending moment decreases as the top is approached. The stem reinforcement is to run well down into the footing for bond. Temperature steel will run parallel to the front face, 2 inches deep in the concrete, and will be ½ inch diameter, 9 inches O. C.

Tie steel will be used front and back. It will be 3/8 inch and 1'-6" O. C. and will run horizontally inside the steel that it supports.

Place this cantilever type retaining wall problem on a 2-A sheet and show the following details: Cross-section of the wall, a longitudinal view, railing detail, steel bending details, bill of materials, necessary notes and dimensions.

Read all of the preceding material on concrete for general facts that apply to all concrete work and apply such as may seem relevant to this design *(Fig. 12)*.

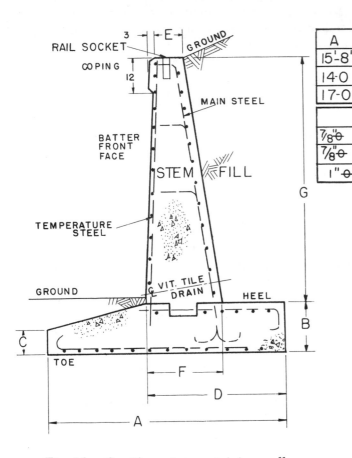

Fig. 11   Cantilever type retaining wall.

A	B	C	D	E	F	G	H	J
15'-8"	24"	18"	8'-0"	12"	24"	21'-0"	5'	5'
14-0	24	20	7-0	12	18	20-0	5	5
17-0	30	24	8-6	15	24	24-0	6	6

TOE		HEEL		STEM	
7/8"⌀	5½" O.C.	7/8"⌀	7" O.C.	1"⌀	6" O.C.
7/8"⌀	6" O.C.	7/8"⌀	8" O.C.	1"⌀	6½" O.C.
1"⌀	6" O.C.	1"⌀	8" O.C.	1"⌀	5" O.C.

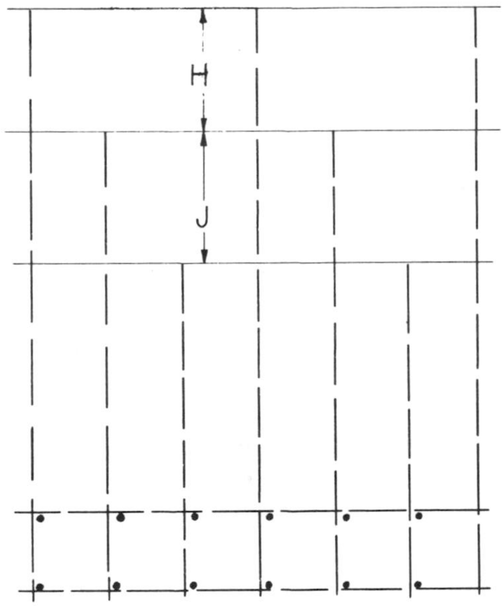

Fig. 12   *Sketch showing differences in lengths of main steel.*

GLOSSARY

Aggregate Hard, inert material mixed with portland cement and water to form concrete. Fine aggregate: pieces less than and including 1/4" in diameter; coarse aggregate: pieces larger than 1/4" in diameter.

Calcium Chloride An accelerator added to concrete to hasten setting (not to be considered an antifreeze).

Cement A binding agent capable of uniting dissimilar materials into a composite whole.

Concrete A composite material made of portland cement, water and aggregates and, perhaps, special admixtures.

Construction Joint A joint placed in concrete to permit practical placement of the work section by section.

Control Joint A joint placed in concrete to form a plane of weakness to prevent random cracks from forming due to drying shrinkage.

Cylinder Test A laboratory test for compressive stress of a field sample of concrete (6" in diameter by 12" in length).

Fill The sand, gravel or compacted earth used to bring a subgrade up to a desired level.

Form Temporary structure erected to contain concrete during placing and initial hardening.

Footing The base of a foundation or column wall used to distri-

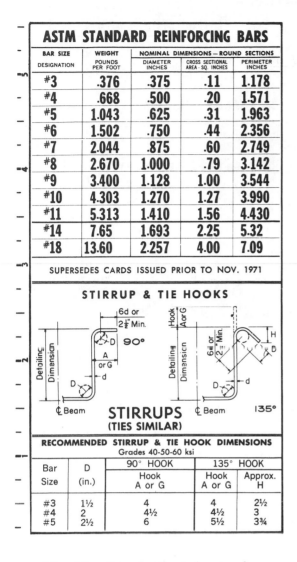

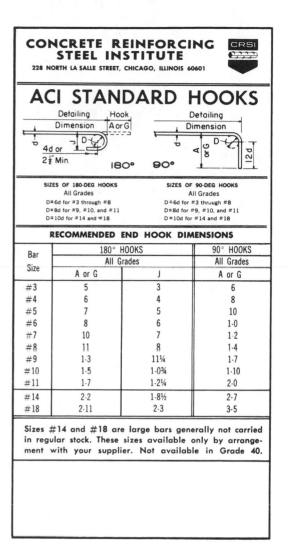

Fig. 13   Standard reinforcing bars.

Fig. 14   ACI standard hook details.

bute the load over the subgrade.

Graded Aggregate Aggregate containing uniformly graduated particle sizes from the finest fine aggregate size to the maximum size of coarse aggregate.

Graded Sand A sand containing uniformly graduated particle sized from very fine up to ¼".

"Green" Concrete Freshly placed concrete.

Grout A liquid mixture of cement, water and sand of pouring consistency.

Monolithic Concrete Concrete placed in one continuous pour without joints.

Mortar A mixture of portland cement, water and sand.

Plastic Concrete Easily molded concrete that will change its form slowly only if the mold is removed.

Portland Cement Cement made by heating clay and crushed limestone to a clinker and grinding to a pulverized state.

    Type 1 and 1A--Used in general construction when special properties of other types are not required.

    Type II and IIA--Used in general construction where moderate heat of hydration is required.

    Type III and IIIA--Used when high-early strength is required.

    Type IV--Used when low heat of hydration is required.

    Type V--Used when high sulfate resistance is required.

Precast Concrete Concrete components which are cast and cured off-site or in a factory before being placed into their position in a structure.

Prestressed Concrete Concrete subjected to compressive forces by the pre-stretching (or stressing) of reinforcing bars or cables within, which develops greater strength and stiffness.

Ready-mixed Concrete Concrete mixed at a plant or in trucks enroute to the job and delivered ready for placement.

Reinforcing Steel placed in concrete to take tensile stresses.

Slab, Structural A suspended, self-supporting, reinforced concrete floor or roof slab.

Slump A measure of the consistency of concrete mix (in inches).

Slump Test Method of measuring slump by means of filling a conical mold, removing it, then measuring the "sag" or slump of the sample.

Subgrade The fill or earth surface upon which concrete is placed.

Swale A low, flat depression to drain off storm water.

Water-cement Ratio The amount of water (gallons) used per sack of cement (94 pounds) in making concrete. It is an index of strength, durability, watertightness and workability.

<u>PLAIN AND REINFORCED CONCRETE</u>

1. <u>GENERAL</u>
   All work of this section shall be performed in accordance with the requirements of the Contract Documents.

2. <u>SCOPE</u>
   The work under this section shall include all labor, materials, appliances
   and services necessary to complete all plain and reinforced concrete and
   related work required by the drawings/and/or as described in this specification generally as follows:

   a. Includes all the labor and material for setting and grouting in accurate
       position all anchor bolts and bearing plates for the steel work. The
       anchor bolts and bearing plates will be furnished by the Steel Contractor.

   b. Preparation of erection and detail shop drawings, as required.

   c. Installation of anchors, sleeves, hangers, inserts, reglets, pockets,
       chases, etc. and cutting, grouting, patching, etc., required for work
       by other trades.

   d. Furnishing and installing all steel reinforcing rods and mesh as indicated
       or required.

   e. All other labor and materials as may be reasonably inferred as needed to
       make the work of this section complete.

3. <u>WORK NOT INCLUDED IN THIS SECTION</u>
   a. All site work concrete including walks and curbs.

4. <u>COOPERATION WITH OTHER CONTRACTORS</u>
   a. This Contractor shall cooperate with other contractors regarding all parts
       of his work which are in any manner related to the work of others. He
       shall arrange and execute his work in such manner that the work of other
       contractors will not be delayed.

   b. This Contractor shall provide for the installation of all manner of
       inserts, brick anchors and other fastening devices required for the in-
       stallation of other work. This contractor shall furnish and install all
       such devices when they are required for the installation of any framing,
       materials or equipment which is part of his contract. Otherwise this
       Contractor shall cooperate in the placing, with other contractors who
       require any fastening devices for their work and he shall maintain them
       in their proper location during the progress of his work.

   c. This Contractor will be held responsible for all damage to the work of
       other contractors caused by the installation of his work, if the damage
       is caused by lack of precaution, carelessness or negligence on the part
       of this contractor.

5. <u>RE-DESIGNS</u>
Any changes or departures from the construction and details shown on the drawings shall be made only after an approval is obtained in writing from the Architect, and countersigned by the Owner.

6. <u>SHOP DRAWINGS</u>
   a. The Contractor shall furnish to the Architect for his approval four sets of completely checked shop drawings of all reinforced concrete work and special concrete floor construction. No work shall be installed until these shop drawings have been approved by the Architect. Any drawing submitted without first being checked will not be considered. The Contractor shall submit the necessary number of prints for final approval. A complete set of shop drawings bearing the Architects approval stamp shall be kept on the job.

   b. The approval of the shop drawings shall be for general arrangement and design and does not relieve the Contractor from the responsibility for the correctness of dimensions and for compliance with the intent of the plans and specifications.

   c. All bar and mesh placing and bending details shall conform to the "A.C.T. Manual of Standard Practices of Detailing Reinforced Concrete Structures", latest edition.

7. <u>SUPERVISION - INSPECTION - TESTS</u>
   a. The Contractor shall notify the Architect and the laboratory in writing three days in advance of pouring any concrete in order that the necessary supervision of the work may be given.

   b. The Architect, Owner and their Agents shall have free access to all points where concrete materials are stored, proportioned or mixed and all materials, equipment, and methods used shall be subject to inspection, tests and approvals by the Architect and laboratories.

   c. The Contractor shall include in his bid the amount of Five Hundred Dollars ($ 500.00) to cover the costs of the services of a testing laboratory to be hired by the Architect. The Contractor will pay all fees of this laboratory upon submission of an invoice by the Architect. Any balance not paid for inspection services will be credited to the Owner. The services required of the laboratory shall be as follows:

      1. Sieve analysis of aggregates actually delivered to job.

      2. Design of concrete mixes to produce specified concrete strengths from aggregates as delivered. Approval by the Architect of all concrete mixes shall take place before any concreting may proceed.

      3. Taking and testing of specimen cylinders taken from concrete actually placed in the work.

      4. Initial inspecting and checking operations at mixing or batching plant if ready mix concrete or batch delivery of material is used.

d. The Contractor shall furnish the laboratory with sufficient material to make the required tests indicated above. Design of concrete mixtures to produce specified concrete strength shall be done by using trial mixes as outlined under Section 302 of the A.C.I. Building Code. The laboratory trial mixtures shall develop concrete of compressive strength 15% higher than the required minimum to be acceptable for use in the field.

e. The source of supply of the aggregate and cement shall not be changed during the course of the job without previous notice to the Architect and the material from any new source shall be subject to acceptance or rejection as based on tests to be made by the testing laboratory. The contractor will pay for any mix redesign. This will not be taken from the allowance.

f. During the progress of the work, for every 50 cubic yards of concrete placed, or for any one day's pour up to 100 cubic yards four tests cylinders shall be made and stored in accordance with the Standard Method of Making and Storing Compression Test Specimen of Concrete in Field A.S.T.M. C-29. Two of the specimens shall be tested after seven days and two after 28 days. The seven day strength will be assumed to have 65 per cent of the 28 day strength. Compression test shall be conducted in accordance with A.S.T.M. Specification C-39.

g. Should the strength of the test cylinders fall below the required strength the Architect may require changes in aggregate proportions for the remainder of the work and may require load tests at the Contractor's expense on the portion of the structure which fails to develop the required strength. Such load tests shall conform to the requirements (Section 202) of the A.C.I.

8. LABOR AND WORKMANSHIP
   a. Only Labor experienced and skilled in the handling of reinforced concrete work shall be employed and the work shall be in charge of experienced foremen.

   b. All workmanship shall be of good quality and all work shall be executed in accordance with good standard practice.

9. MATERIALS
   a. General: All materials shall conform to "A.C.I. Building Code for Reinforced Concrete," latest edition. All specifications mentioned herein are to be latest edition.

   b. Cement: All cement shall be Standard Portland Cement conforming to A.S.T.M. Specifications C-150, Type I; air entraining cement to A.S.T.M. Specifications C-175.

      (1) The Contractor has the option of substituting High-Early Strength Portland Cement which shall conform to A.S.T.M. specifications C-150 Type III where so desired to expedite the work. He shall modify any and all details of construction including "curing" so that he produces the strength and durability of concrete as required by these specifications.

c.   Concrete Admixtures: To increase cement dispersion and workability of the concrete mixtures shall be used and shall conform to A.S.T.M. Specifications C-233. The admixtures (or approved equals) shall be as follows: for water-tightness and hot weather placement-"PLASTIMENT"; for cold weather placement - "SIKACRETE"; for air entraining-"SIKAAER"; all as manufactured by the Sika Chemical Corporation, Passaic, N. J. Proportioning of admixtures shall conform to manufacturer's recommendations.

d.   Aggregates: Concrete aggregates shall conform to A.S.T.M. Specifications C-33. The maximum size of the coarse aggregate shall be not larger than one-fifth of the narrowest dimension between forms of the member for which the concrete is to be used; nor larger than three quarters of the minimum clear spacing between reinforcing bars; nor larger than 3/4".

e.   Water used in mixing concrete shall be clean and free from oil, acids, alkalies, organic materials or deleterious substances.

f.   Metal Reinforcements: Reinforcing Steel shall be new billet, intermediategrade, conforming to A.S.T.M. Specifications A-15; deformations, to A.S.T.M. Specifications A-305; welded wire fabric, to A.S.T.M. Specifications A-185.

g.   Floor Hardener: Concrete floors subject to heavy traffic are to remain exposed in the finished work shall be treated with an approved type floor hardener. This treatment shall consist of the "Esco" method as made by the Preservative Products Co., or as approved, in not less than 2 coats with color as selected in locations required. The application shall be made in strict accordance with the manufacturer's directions.

10. STORAGE AND SUPPLY OF MATERIALS
     a.   All materials shall be stored in proper manner, subject to the approval of the Architect to assure adequate protection against damage or injury by the elements or contamination with injurious substances. Any damaged or deteriorated materials shall be removed from the premises immediately and replaced at Contractor's expense.

     b.   An adequate supply of all materials shall be kept on hand at all times to assure uninterrupted progress of the work.

11. DETAILS OF CONSTRUCTION
     All details of construction including forms and bending, placing supporting and tying or reinforcement shall be in conformity with "A.C.I. Building Code Requirements for Reinforced Concrete," latest edition.

12. FORMS
     a.   Forms shall be clean, smooth, sufficiently tight to prevent leakage of cement, securely braced and maintained in position and properly shored and braced to support construction loads at all times during the progress of the work without deflection of an objectionable nature. Sufficient temporary openings shall be provided to permit cleaning and inspection just prior to dimensions of the members as called for on the drawings.

b.   Shores shall be placed on adequate, unyielding mud-sills.

c.   All external and internal corners of forms shall be chamfered.

d.   Forms shall be constructed to accomodate all openings, inserts, anchors, and ties in all concrete work required by other trades. Such installations shall be checked by the Trade involved as to location and completion before pouring of concrete.

e.   All footings shall be formed at the sides.

f.   Floor Lath Type forms shall be fastened to supporting members and braces as specified by manufacturer.

13. PLACING OF METAL REINFORCEMENT
   a.   All metal reinforcement shall be free from loose mill and rust scale or other coatings that reduce or destroy bond.

   b.   No concrete shall be placed before the reinforcement has been inspected and approved by the Engineer. A reinforcing bar setter shall be on the job when concrete is poured.

   c.   All reinforcement shall be securely held in place with approved metal supporting, spacing and tying devices, details of which shall be on the placement drawings.

14. CONCRETE MIXTURES
   a.   Stone concrete shall have minimum compressive strength of 3000 lbs. p.s.i. at 28 days. The slump shall not exceed 5". The minimum cement content shall be 5-1/2 bags per cubic yard. The maximum water cement ratio shall be 6-1/2 gallons per sack of cement (except for air-entrained concrete, which shall be 5-1/4 gallons per sack of cement).

   b.   Concrete mixes shall be determined by a testing laboratory.

   c.   Slump tests shall be made in accordance with A.S.T.M. Specifications C-143.

   d.   If, during the progress of the work, it is found that concrete of the required workability and strength cannot be attained with the materials furnished by the Contractor, the Architect may order such changes in proportions or materials, or both, as may be necessary to secure the desired properties. Any changes so ordered shall be made at the Contractors expense, and no extra compensation will be allowed by reason of such changes.

15. MIXING
   a.   The concrete shall be mixed until there is a uniform distribution of the materials and shall be discharged completely before the mixer is recharged.

b. For job mixed concrete the mixer shall be rotated at a speed recommended by the manufacturer and mixing shall be continued for at least one minute after all materials are in the mixer.

c. Ready-mixed concrete shall be mixed and delivered in accordance with the requirements set forth in the "Tentative Specifications for Ready Mixed Concrete (A.S.T.M. C-94)."

16. DEPOSITING

a. Before depositing concrete the excavation shall be free of water, frost, loose or softened earth; the forms shall be cleaned of all debris, ice or snow. No concrete shall be deposited in water.

b. Concrete shall be deposited as nearly as practicable in its final position to avoid segregation due to rehandling or flowing. No concrete that has partially hardened or been contaminated by foreign material shall be deposited in the work nor shall retempered concrete be used. Concrete shall not be dropped greater than 4 feet. Pouring pockets shall be provided for greater heights.

c. When concreting is once started it shall be carried on as a continuous operation until the placing of the panel or section is completed. The top surface shall be generally level. When construction joints are necessary they shall be made in accordance with paragraph marked "Construction Joints".

d. All concrete shall be thoroughly compacted by means of mechanical vibrators during the operation of placing and shall be thoroughly worked around reinforcement, embedded fixtures and into the corners of the forms. Care shall be taken not to disturb the reinforcing.

e. Where conditions make compacting difficult or where the reinforcement is congested, batches of mortar containing the same proportions of cement to sand as used in concrete shall be first deposited in the forms. The concreting shall be carried on at such a rate that the concrete is at all times plastic and flows readily into spaces between the bars.

17. CONSTRUCTION JOINTS

a. Construction joints shall be formed with keyed bulkheads located as shown on the drawings and/or as herein specified. Reinforcement shall continue through the joints and additional reinforcing placed as shown on details.

b. Concrete deposited on one side of a construction joint shall be allowed to set at least 24 hours before the adjoining concrete is poured. Before new concrete is poured against the hardened concrete, all laitance shall be removed and the surface of the hardened concrete roughened at the joint in such a manner that will not leave loose or damaged material at the surface. The joint shall then be saturated with water and covered with a coating of neat cement grout against which the new concrete shall be placed before this grout has attained its initial set.

c. Unless otherwise shown on the drawings, construction joints shall be located as follows:

    (1) <u>Foundation Walls</u>: Vertical joints shall be placed so that maximum continuous pour does not exceed approximately 60 feet in length. Horizontal construction joints shall not be permitted, except as shown on the drawings.

    (2) Floor slab on Ground; Joists shall be located so that slab can be poured in alternate panels, each panel not exceeding 1600 square feet in area, nor 40 feet in any one length.

18. <u>CURING AND PROTECTION</u>
a. Exposed surfaces of concrete work shall be kept moist for a period of at least 7 days after placement; and for high early strength concrete at least 3 days after placement; floor slabs shall be cured with a no-bituminous liquid compound (TMC #10 Colorless Curing Compound as produced by Thompson Materials Corp., Belleville, N. J. or approved equal) applied as per the manufacturer's specifications at a rate of 1 gallon/sq. yd. Application shall be made immediately following final finishing. If delay occurs allowing surface of concrete to set it shall be thoroughly moistened prior to application of material. Surface of concrete shall be kept free of traffic for the duration of the curing. All finished concrete surfaces shall be adequately protected from damage of any source. Wet cure shall be provided for slabs requiring hardener treatment.

b. In cold weather, adequate equipment shall be provided for heating the concrete materials and protecting the concrete during freezing or near freezing weather. No frozen materials or materials containing ice shall be used.

c. All concrete materials and all reinforcements, forms, fillers, and ground with which the concrete comes in contact shall be free from frost.

d. Whenever the temperature of the surrounding area is below 40 degrees F., all concrete placed in the forms shall have a temperature of between 70 degrees and 80 degrees F., and adequate means shall be provided for maintaining a temperature of 50 degrees and 70 degrees F. for not less than 72 hours after placing or for as much more time as is necessary to insure proper curing of the concrete. No dependence shall be placed on salt hay or chemicals for the prevention of freezing.

e. No concrete shall be deposited when the atmosphere temperature is below 20 degrees or it is predicted that the temperature will fall below 20 degrees within forty-eight (48) hours from the time of the pouring.

19. <u>VAPOR BARRIER</u>
Slabs on ground shall be poured over a layer of "Visqueen" vapor barrier six mils (.006) thick, lapped not less than 6".

20. <u>SLAB FINISHED</u>
    a. All interior slab surfaces to be covered with resilient tile shall be steel trowelled to a smooth finished. Surface finish shall not vary more than 1/4" when tested with a 10' straight edge. Exterior platforms and steps shall be neatly wood floated; risers shall have a steel trowelled finish.

21. <u>MISCELLANEOUS WORK</u>
    a. Install concrete pits and other construction as required to complete the project. Covers and frames specified to be furnished by other Contractors.

22. <u>CEMENT FILL AT STAIR TREADS & PLATFORMS</u>
    The treads and platforms of all pan type steel stairs shall be provided with cement fill consisting of Portland cement, sand and course aggregate in the proportions of 1:2:3 mix. Surfaces shall be screeded and steel trowelled.

23. <u>DEBRIS</u>
    This contractor shall be responsible for removing all debris due to his contract from the premises.

7

ELEMENTARY SKETCHING

Introduction. Sketching needs a certain amount of pencil skill. Anyone can learn this skill with a little explanation and some practice. Sketching, like writing, must be readable, must communicate the information you intend. A sketch of a box should give everyone who reads your sketch the unmistakable impression that it portrays a box. The test of a sketch is not how long or how short a time it took, or its technique, but the truth of the portrayal.

Paper. Initially, paper is merely a medium on which to practice. Any scratch paper will do, white or yellow, if it takes pencil lines. The paper should not be too small or too large as the size will affect your feeling of space. Let us suppose you have ordinary 8½ by 11 inch white typing paper. Fold this sheet in half so that you have a booklet of four pages approximately 4 by 11 inches. Since these are practice sketches only, do not save them; sketching mistakes are not to be saved.

Pencil. Later we will try different kinds of pencils and drawing instruments, but initially the pencil should be medium soft (*HB or 2½ secretary's pencil*), give a dark black line and not wear rapidly. Mechanical drawing pencils don't make good sketching pencils as they produce lines which are thin yet dense, while the "B" grades are extremely soft for engineering sketching. Secretarial pencils, available in grade 2½, are suitable for freehand sketching.

Many people do not know how to hold a pencil after a lifetime of writing. Do not hold the pencil too tightly or too loosely. Whitened knuckles are an indication of a tight grip which will lead to fatigue and cause poor sketching. A grip too loose will not produce a dark line.

Procedure. Position the paper on the desk turned about 60 degrees to the left. The narrow edge of the paper should be toward you (*Fig. 1*). This is the normal letter writing position of the paper.

By eye, beginning in the upper left corner

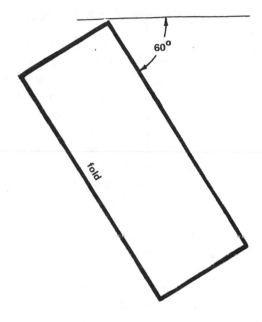

Fig. 1 Position of paper.

of the paper drop down about an inch and in from the edge about ¼ inch. Place your pencil point on the paper at this point and stop! Look at your pencil. Keep the point where it is and look at the top of the pencil (*the top of the pencil should slope away from you*). Next, by eye, locate the place at the top of the paper about 45 degrees up and to the right. (*Fig. 2*). That is your end point. Keep your eye on that point and

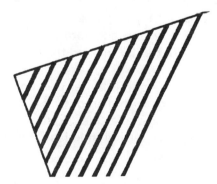

Fig. 2 Diagonal lines.

73

without hesitation draw a pencil line to that point. Examine the line you have just drawn for darkness and for ending at the point desired. Do not try to correct lines, do more lines parallel to the first line and about 1/8 inch apart. Do not pause once you have begun a line. Draw about ten lines.

Lay your pencil down and look at your lines. Some are blacker than others and just look better. Some lines go where you wanted them to go. Circle these lines. Try to duplicate these by drawing next to them. A grey line is a poor line. Try for bold black lines, not feathery lines.

Turn the paper around and use the three other corners. Practice until you can quickly make three good lines even in blackness and somewhat parallel. Rotate the pencil every stroke to use a different spot on its point, do not resharpen the pencil after every line. Normal students will fill up several sheets in practice before getting the feel of the bold sketched stroke. Practice about five minutes, reread the instructions and practice again. You should be able to do the stroke so fast that you see your hand as a blur. Experiment with varying pressures until the line is even in blackness throughout its length. Practice with different pencils also.

Sloping Lines to the Left. On a blank sheet draw the strokes you have just learned across the middle of the paper. These lines go up and to the right. Now draw lines up and to the left making the same angle with the top of the sheet. Do several short parallel lines. You may want to turn your paper so that it feels at a natural slope for you to draw. The final result will be a distorted **diamond** (*Fig. 3*). If you look at the diamond, it is a plane lying flat on your paper. You should practice this until you are sure you can draw a diamond quickly and accurately. Try to make the planes lie flatter by making the lines with less slope.

Make the diamonds bigger and smaller. Cover an entire sheet with diamonds. Sketch a checker board, 8 squares to a side. Sketch a landscape from an airplane letting the land be different size squares. (*Fig. 4*).

Fig. 3 Diamonds.

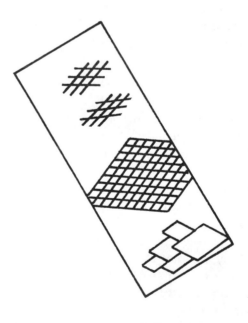

Fig. 4 Diamond variations.

Sketching Rectangles. By making two parallel sides longer than the other two parallel sides, the diamonds appear to be rectangles. Fill up a sheet with rectangles. *(Fig. 5).*

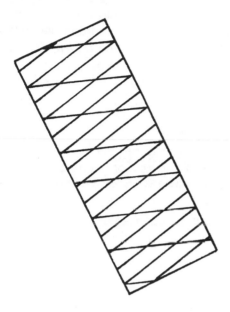

Fig. 5 Rectangles.

Draw one diamond with the lines just meeting at the corners, no line being too short or too long. Diamonds should be practiced until the lines, though not necessarily straight, appear to be parallel. Of course you are still doing jet black lines and have had to sharpen your pencil several times.

Notice what a broad line you get when you are lazy and do not sharpen your pencil often

enough. You can also sharpen your pencil and blunt the point to give you these wide strokes if you care to experiment. The pencil point, either blunted or worn down, can give you strokes that are at least one-sixteenth of an inch wide *(Fig. 6).*

In general, when sketching planes, keep the angles very slight, less than 15 degrees *(Fig. 7)* shows the plane sketched with different angles.

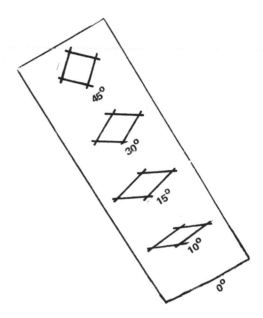

Fig. 7 Planes of different slopes.

Sketching Solids. Most man made objects are made of solids, and it is a simple step to add a few

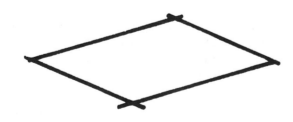

Fig. 6 Broad line sketching.

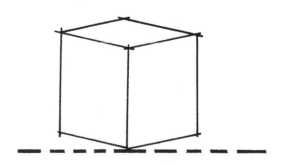

Fig. 8 Cube.

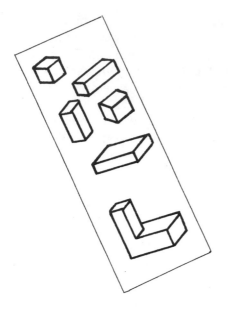

Fig. 9 Boxes.

In sketching solids, you should still draw the box as if it were made of glass, so that by light layout lines you have a complete solid and a correct geometric sketch. Do not omit the basic construction just because the lines are hidden.

Practice drawing the cube at first, both solid and glass. Add more cubes on the top and at the sides by extending the lines you have already drawn. After you have mastered drawing of the cube, you should practice several variations by cutting the cube. Cut the cube in half horizontally, *(Fig. 10)*, then vertically, trying always to keep your lines parallel and even. The cube can be made into shapes such as houses, buildings or steps either right or left. Sketch cubes with square holes from the front to the back, from the top to the bottom, keep the holes square. Get the lines evenly spaced from the sides by drawing light layout lines by eye *(Fig. 11)*.

lines to the diamond to get a box shaped figure. *(Fig. 8)*. Sketch a diamond with sides no longer than one inch. At each corner draw a vertical line down about an inch long. At the ends of these lines draw a diamond parallel to the top diamond and as nearly the same size as possible. Your figure will look like a box. Draw a lot of these with quick confident strokes *(Fig. 9)*. Boxes are the basic shape in sketching.

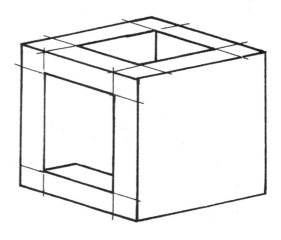

Fig. 11 Cut cube.

Sketching is only the application of these principles. The cube can be turned into a rectangular solid, and the sketch could be a footlocker, a child's block, a radio, or a desk. Try sketching some of these but keep them small and do them fast. *(Fig. 12)*. When these small sketches are satisfactory, begin working with an 8½ by 11 inch sheet and sketch two dice, both cubes about 1 inch size.

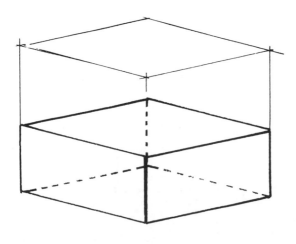

Fig. 10 Half cube.

Van

Toaster/oven

Flourescent Fixture

Chest

Refrigerator/Freezer

Fig.12 Sketches of rectangular object

Geometric Construction. The next step with the box is to use it in developing geometric shapes. Let us do the pyramid first. Draw a small box. Find the center of the top where the pyramid would touch if it fits into the box. You can do this by eye, but a more accurate method is to sketch lightly the diagonals of the top. The bottom of the pyramid is the base of the cube. Finish the sketch by drawing the edge lines of the pyramid running from the top point to each bottom corner *(Fig. 13)*.

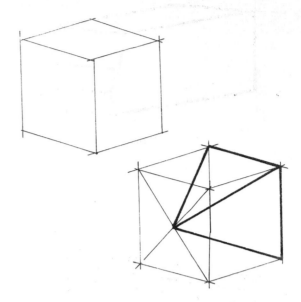

Fig. 14 Pyramid, vertical base.

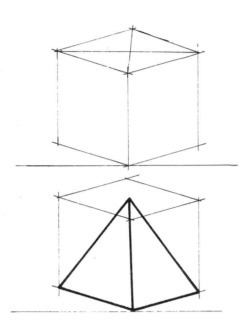

Fig. 13 Pyramid.

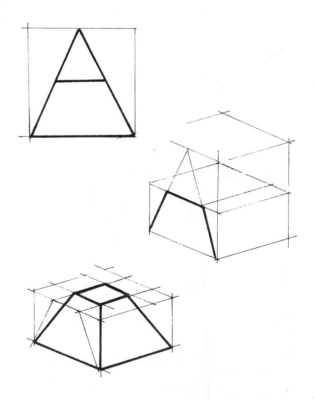

Fig. 15 Truncated pyramid.

Of course a pyramid does not always rest flat on the ground. Still keeping the cube small, draw another pyramid in the cube by putting the base standing on its edge and being the back face of the cube *(Fig. 14)*. Do not skip any of the geometric constructions.

The pyramid may also be truncated. First cut the pyramid horizontally, about half the height of the cube. The result will be a square parallel to the base, but smaller *(Fig. 15)*.

Other Geometric Constructions. Cubes can also be cut on the slant. Be sure to use the geometry of box construction. If you cut the cube from the top back line to the front lower line, the slant-ing lines of the cut are parallel. Try several of these to test your ability. Also cut the cube from corner to corner with a vertical plane. *(Fig. 16)*. Next cut the cube with a vertical plane, about 1/8 inch in from one edge to the other. Start the basic construction, lightly tick off the cut and sketch it in. Darken the lines.

Drawing slopes and vertical cuts like these is good practice for drawing many man made objects. Highway slopes, windshields of cars and hoppers all use sloping planes *(Figs. 17 & 18)*.

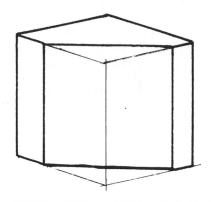

Fig. 17 Cut cube.

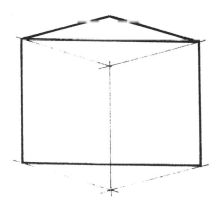

Fig. 16 Triangular prism.

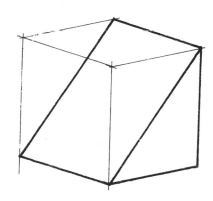

Fig. 18 Cut cube.

Still using parallel lines, try sketching oblique prisms. Choose one with a square base and sketch it. Oblique prisms have the top the same size and shape as the base and parallel to it *(Fig. 19)*.

Many other geometric constructions can be sketched using the cube. Some are right triangu-lar prisms, hexagonal prisms and even dodeca-hedrons. Geometric construction is the secret of drawing these figures.

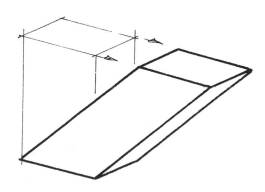

Fig. 19 Oblique prism.

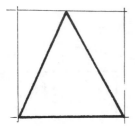

Step 1

Use other variations of the cube such as the octahedron which is two right square pyramids joined base to base *(Fig. 21)*.

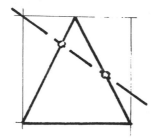

Step 2

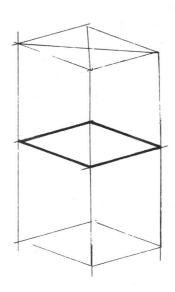

Step 1

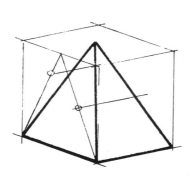

Step 3

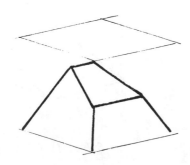

Fig. 20 Truncated prism

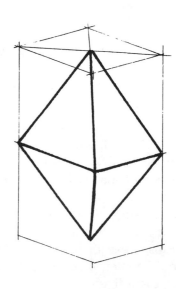

Fig. 21 Octahedron

80

Drawing Any Object of Cubes and Rectangles.
Use the combination of the cube and the rectangular box to build up shapes of different objects.

Assume an automobile is made up of rectangular boxes. In sketching refer to the instructions for sloping cuts on cubes. Sketch this geometrically, extending the hidden construction lines of the box *(Fig. 22).*

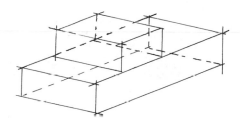

Fig. 22 Box for automobile.

Suppose you have an idea for a new shape of a car. Sketch it to see what the proportions look like. Make the basic box of the body wider, higher, etc. Designers have dozens of notebooks filled with different finished sketches developed from small working sketches such as you have just drawn. Make a semi-finished sketch of a boxed car. Let the class vote to determine the best proportioned shape. Place all the sketches on the chalk board rail and look at them all at once. Leave them there for several days. Most classes after discussion and time, will change their vote *(Fig. 23).*

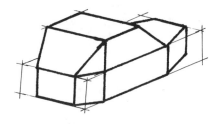

Fig. 23 Automobile.

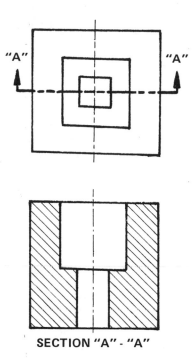

SECTION "A" - "A"

Fig. 24 Orthographic view.

A simple cube doesn't need a cutaway view, but a view of a foundation of a building or a simple machine part may need sectioning. Sketch a cube with a square hole from top to bottom, but have the hole decrease to half its original size at the mid height. Sketch this using sectioning. Section lines are drawn at the slant and evenly spaced. Make them thinner than object outlines but the same blackness *(Fig. 25).*

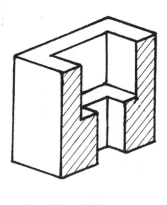

Fig. 25 Sketched section.

ADVANCED SKETCHING

8

Sketching Circles. The circle is based on the square. Sketch a square as it appears perpendicular to you. The circle if placed within the square will just touch the midpoint of the sides of the square. If you learn and use carefully this method for sketching a circle, excellent results should ensue. With continued usage, you should soon develop an eye for proper curvature proportions and the geometric framing described herewith need then only be kept in mind and not actually sketched.

Method. On two perpendicular lines tick off the desired diameter *(Fig. 1)*. Through the ticks, sketch a square and, in the square, its diagonals *(Fig. 2)*. Divide each diagonal roughly into sixths *(Fig. 3)*. The circle to be sketched will pass outside of the second tick on the diagonal of the quadrant.

When sketching start as shown, making short and almost flat seeming *(at first)* arcs. As you proceed, hold the sketch at arm's length from time to time to check your accuracy. When circles are large you should make use of a card-edge to secure enough points for reasonable control *(Fig. 4)*.

Fig. 1 Two perpendicular lines.

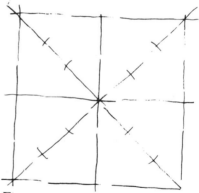

Fig. 2 Drawing the square.

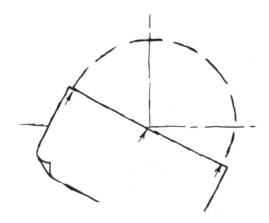

Fig. 4 Cardboard guide.

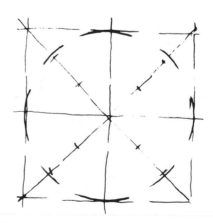

Fig. 3 Sketching circular arcs.

Fig. 5 Spheres.

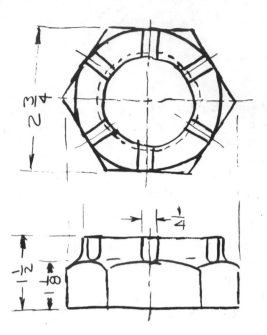

Fig. 7 Hex nut.

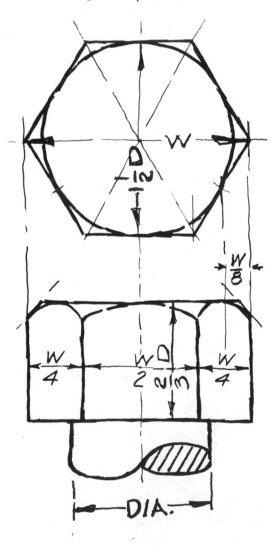

Fig. 6 Bolt head proportions.

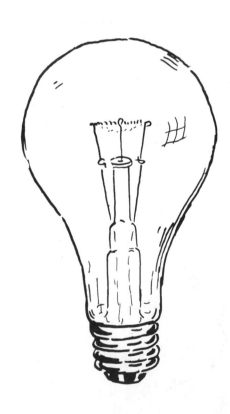

Fig. 8 Light bulb - circles, ellipse and helix.

Sketching Ellipses. Some painstaking drill is necessary before you master the sketching of really good elliptic forms, ones which will appear truly oval and have proper proportions.

The best sketching procedure is to lightly block in the enclosing rectangle and, at the major diameter ends, arcs whose diameters are such that they fill ½ the width of the enclosure *(Fig. 9)*. Through the minor axis ends sketch two relatively long flat arcs *(with no actual flat sections)*. Combined results, paired off, should produce the pleasantly elliptical form desired.

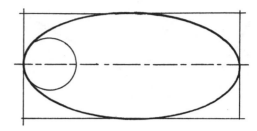

Fig. 9   Sketching ellipses.

Trammel. A well-known method for accurately plotting enough control points to enable you to handle large sized ellipses using a card-edge, as shown *(Fig. 10)*.

To use this method begin by sketching in the perpendicular center lines. Next, mark off on a card edge a set of three arrows, or ticks, as shown. Space these so that distance **AC** equals one-half the major diameter where the distance **BC** equals one-half the minor diameter. Keeping **A** constantly in contact with the minor axis and keeping **B** constantly in contact with the major axis, plot enough points for **C** to insure being able to sketch a fairly accurate ellipse.

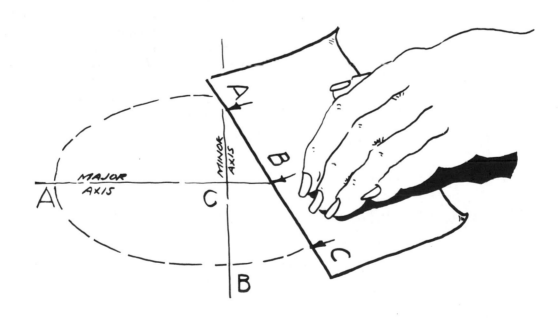

Fig. 10 Trammel construction.

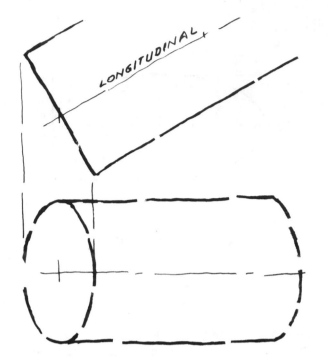

Sketching Cylinders. To avoid the stilted appearance presented by a regular cylinder when seen in orthographic it is customary, in sketching, to tilt the longitudlnal axis until the cylinder ends appear elliptic and its length forshortened. The degree of tilt, or turn, is usually an arbitrary value.

When the length of a cylinder is not great, when compared to its diameter, it is usually best to give it a relatively small degree of turn toward you *(Fig. 11)*.

Fig. 11 Foreshortened cylinder.

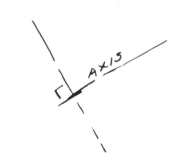

Fig. 12 Selecting the axis.

General Sketching Procedure. Select a convenient axis position and sketch a straight line perpendicular to it *(Fig. 12)*. On this line tick off the equispaced lengths **A-B** and **B-C**, **AC** to equal the diameter of the cylinder to be sketched. Through **A** and **C** sketch lines parallel to the axis *(Fig. 13)*. To either side of **AC** mark off the smaller equispaced length **DB** and **BE** corresponding to the reduced radii of the minor diameter *(Fig. 14)*. Sketch small fragments of narrow radius arcs of **A** and at **C**. Sketch larger, but much flatter ones through **D** and **E**. Fill in the balance of the ellipses fairing each line as you progress *(Fig. 15)*.

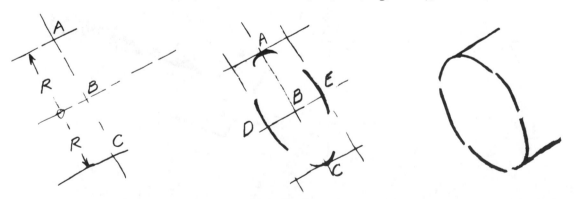

Fig. 13 Major cylinder diameter. Eig. 14 Establishing the ellipse arc. Fig. 15   Completed sketch.

Alternate Methods. One other method for control of sketched ellipses is the so-called parallelogram method *(Fig. 16)*. Using this method you proceed, as before, to sketch the enclosing diamond-shaped form making the ratio of diagonal lengths approximately 1.6 to 1.0.

Mark any convenient number of equispaced ticks as 1 to 10, but there must be the same number on each leg *(Fig. 17)*. From **B**, lightly sketch radial lines through points 5-4-3-2-1 and another group, from **A** through points 6-7-8-9-10. Their intersections determine one-quarter of the curve *(Fig. 18)*. Repeat the general procedure but this time sketch radial lines from **A** through points 5-4-3-2-1 and from **B** through points 6-7-8-9-10. This determines the end quarter *(Fig. 19)*. Complete the figure by transfers of conjugate radii *(Fig. 20)*.

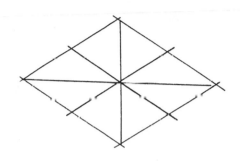

Fig. 16   Parallelogram.

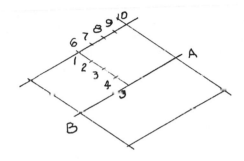

Fig. 17   Equidistant spacings.

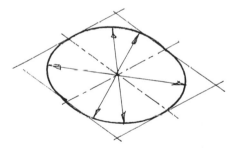

Fig. 20   Completed ellipse.

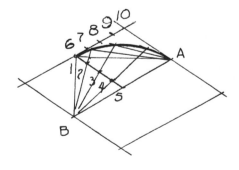

Fig. 18   Radial rays.

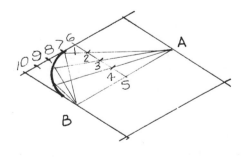

Fig. 19   Radial rays.

While the above method provides a very accurate means for setting out large ellipses you may not always have a card or other straight-edge. In this event the following substitute method may suffice provided you have developed an eye for proportion, chiefly, and for straightness and parallelism of lines.

Ratios of ellipse diameters will, of course, vary with the degree of tilt of the plane in which the ellipse lies. One fairly good result occurs when the major axis is made a little greater than 1½ times that of the minor ratio, say, of about 1.6 to 1.0. By methods of similar triangles mark off seven equispaced divisions on each side of the diamond *(Fig. 21)*. Through these points sketch the grid as shown and, through the grid one unit from each apex as shown, lines paralleling the axes and forming a rectangle. Sketch in the ellipse so as to pass through the points indicated by circles.

Major Axis of Ellipse. Sketch a longitudinal axis at a slight angle *(Fig. 22)*. Perpendicular to this sketch, the line upon which the ellipse major diameter will fall. This will give the degree of tilt of the object *(step 2)*. Mark off equispaced ticks for the ends of the major diameter of the given cylinder. You now have set the scale for the sketch *(step 3)*. The spread of the ticks for the ellipse minor diameter sets the desired degree of turn and the ellipse may now be sketched in *(step 4)*. Tangent to this ellipse, sketch in a pair of vertical lines and note the **T** *(for tangency)* points *(step 5)*. A line through these **T** Points, and through the ellipse center is a horizontal line *(Step 6)*. Parallel to that line **T-T'** draw tangent lines to the ellipse at top and bottom which will define with the tangent at **T** and **T'** the figure into which the ellipse fits. With this figure we can determine the proper construction for other ellipses of the same tilt.

There are innumerable geometric controls for the production of reasonable-appearing ellipses. This, perhaps, is because this particular curved outline is so prominent in science, architecture and engineering. You cannot, unless engaged in some endeavor where the treatment of such outlines is of fairly frequent occurrence, be expected to remember all methods but a mastery and remembrance of at least one is most desirable.

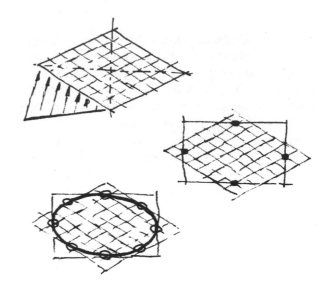

Fig. 21   Grid method for ellipses.

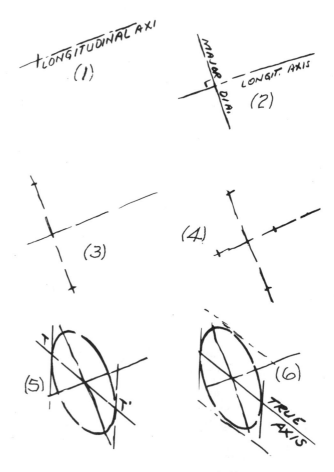

Fig. 22   Find tangency of ellipse.

88

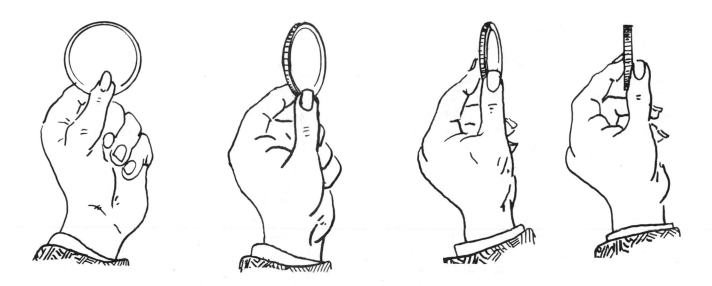

Fig 23 Circle viewed at varying angles.

In pictorials, circles usually appear elliptic. Note that the ellipse major diameter always equals the true circle diameter. The minor diameter, which is perpendicular to the major, depends upon the angularity of direction of sight.

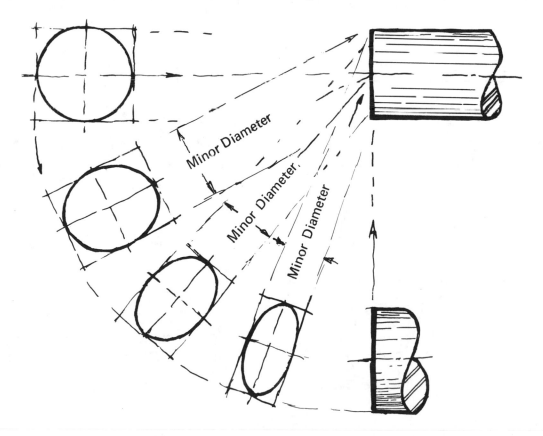

Fig. 24 End of a shaft viewed at varying angles.

Sketching Cylindrical Tubes. The transition between the techniques of sketching a solid cylinder and a tube of comparable size requires the careful observance of two simple facts. One of these is that the major diameters of the ellipses representing the inner and outer diameters of a tube appear equal in size to the actual diameters of the tube and that, as a result, true wall thicknesses for tubes become apparent along the line upon which the major axes fall. A cylinder may be enclosed in a square *(Fig. 25)*. When the plane of its end is turned in regard to your line of observation the square becomes rectangular and circles elliptic *(Fig. 26)*. Use may be made of this fact, if you have developed an eye for geometry, to secure accurate minor diameters for concentric ellipses, as shown below. Note how the proportionate reductions of minor diameters are controlled geometrically and accurately by the diagonals *(Fig. 26)*. In any sketch of a cylinder, the line of the major diameter is always drawn perpendicular to the axis of the cylinder *(Fig. 29)*.

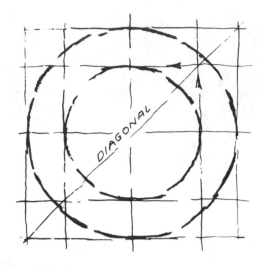

Fig. 25 Orthographic cylinder.

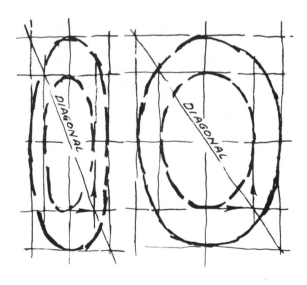

Fig. 26 Reduction controlled by diagonal.

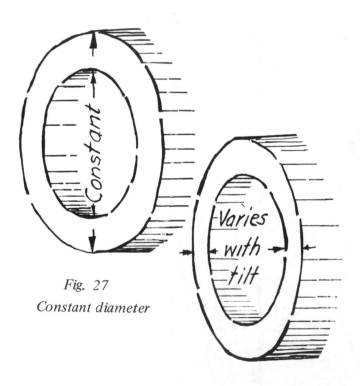

Fig. 27

Constant diameter

Fig. 28 Minor diameter.

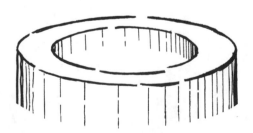

Fig. 29 Completed sketch.

Steel. To visualize the construction of steel, it is often helpful to sketch the construction, particularly the joints. Start with a definite shape *(S beam, T beam, etc.)*. It is best to draw first the end view of the member, using an angle of 30°. Keep the lines light and work up a good sketch of the member in cross section. From the corners draw the long lines of the edges of the member *(Fig. 30)*. Now sketch the connecting members, again starting with an end view of each piece. Sometimes you will have to change the drawing so the end view of an important piece will show or to break off a special member so you can see the cross section. Care with the cross sections will make the drawing look as you intend. You may have to start over with another angle, as if you stood at a higher or lower viewpoint to get the effect you want. Sometimes hidden lines help and sometimes you must exaggerate one of the mem-

bers to give the pictorial effect. For sketching ends of trusses, the slope may be as slight as 10° for the bottom chord; the top chord will still rise at a rather steep angle. Gusset plates, rivets and welds can be treated by section lining, shadow lines, exaggeration, or labelling in order to be differentiated from the rest of the sketch.

Sketching Welding. We can easily sketch the basic weld symbols which represent the natural shape of the weld. A sketch will help to visualize the arrangement of parts, the accessibility to the welder, the depth of penetration of the weld and its aesthetic quality. Gas welding melts the pieces to be joined as well as adding more metal. In sketching these welds in section draw wiggly lines both in the metal parts and on the surface of the bead *(Fig. 31)*. In sketching lengthwise welds an approximation of the welding torch motion is used *(Fig. 32)*.

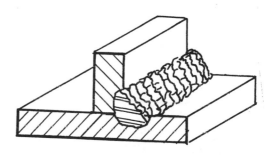

Fig. 31 Weld in section.

Fig. 30 Steel members.

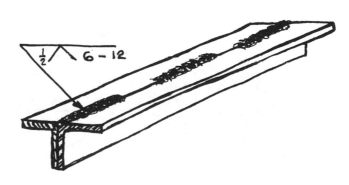

Fig. 32 Lengthwise weld.

Wood Sketching. In first sketching wood start directly in isometric drawing. Use a 30° triangle to draw the members *(Fig. 33).* As in steel sketching, extensive use is made of showing the ends of the members wherever possible. This fixes the shape of the member in the mind. For small details such as sill or plate the scale is the same for all sides but for sketches of joists, girders or any large structural piece of lumber that is used with the long side vertical, an exaggeration of 1½ or 2 times the vertical scale is often used *(Fig. 34).* Drawings that show the members going from floor to ceiling would be too large vertically with this exaggeration so these members are drawn with interrupted or broken sections.

Conventionally wood as a material is depicted by the grain drawn freehand as long slanting lines not quite parallel to the edges of the piece of lumber *(Fig. 33).* Commercially available pressure sensitive sheets include prepared section line symbols (of the type formerly used to denote cast iron in mechanical drawing) to use as wood grain by turning the section lines not quite parallel to the long edge of the board. The end grain of lumber is drawn to resemble sections of the annular rings *(curved parallel arcs) (Fig. 33).* Vary the arcs, for two or more end grains next to each other, by curving the arcs in different directions *(Fig. 34).*

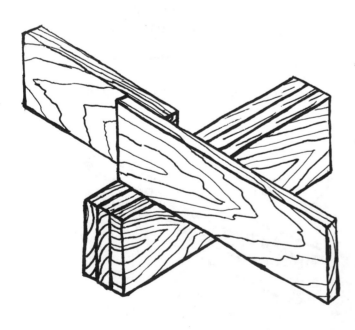

Fig. 33   Wood grain

Fig. 34 Vertical wood members.

Simple Sketching. So far our sketches have been constructed in geometric solids and multitudes of objects can be sketched using this type of geometrical construction. Not all things can be sketched in this fashion, but may use other simple abstract forms of sketching.

Stick Figures. In technical drawings you often need a figure next to a machine or structure to give a clue to the actual size. There are several methods of giving this human measurement and although the human body is difficult to draw we can't spend even a semester practicing artistic figure studies. Children usually begin drawing people as stick figures. These stick figures are valid for some technical drawings, need little skill and can be drawn very quickly. Stick figures can vary in bodily proportion without seeming unnatural. Start sketching figures about ¾" tall beginning with the head as a small circle or ellipse. The body is a straight line with four short lines for arms and legs *(Fig. 35).* You can make this kind of figure assume different positions and actions without a great amount of skill. This type of sketching is not exact but is useful to give scale to drawings of objects. Naturally the figure can be enlarged or reduced, but drawn more than 2" high it looks ridiculous. Draw a series of stick figures: running, climbing a ladder, pointing, reaching, stooping and kneeling *(Fig. 36).*

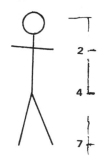

Fig. 35   Proportions for stick figures.

Fig. 36   Stick figures in action.

93

Solid Stick Figures. Adding some thickness to the stick figure we get a more realistic body. They are hard to draw but if done with care, are good enough for professional drawings. Body proportions should be considered in this type of figure. Although individual bodies vary in proportion for simplicity use the vertical length of the head as a basic unit of measurement with the entire figure seven units tall *(Fig. 37)*. Start **small** with the head and a vertical layout line for the rest of the body. Draw the rest of the body within the remaining six units of measurement. The torso is a trapezoid with the waist at the three unit height measured from the top of the head. The top of the trapezoid *(the shoulders)* draw two units wide, the bottom *(the waist)*, make one unit wide. Start the fork of the legs at the four unit mark. If you have trouble, look at yourself in a mirror to establish body proportions. Finish the figure by drawing the toes as points *(Fig. 38)*. Like the stick figure, this figure can be drawn in varied positions but it does take more skill in drawing. Do not attempt to draw hands.

The solid stick figure seen from the profile has the same proportion, seven heads high. Start with the head again, drawing next to the previously drawn front view. The torso seen from the side is drawn as a rectangle two heads high. It is a little wider than the head. Taper the waist front and back and slightly round the shoulder. The hips *(four units down)* have the buttocks protruding while the front line from waist down is almost a vertical line. Draw toes and arms to complete the figure.

Eyes. It is sometimes convenient to sketch an eye in indicating a station point on a drawing. Copy some of these eyes *(Fig. 39)*, and try to memorize the basic shapes. The distance between the eyes is usually equal to one eye width. Draw both right and left eyes *(Fig. 39)*. The eye in profile is also a shape to be memorized *(Fig. 40)*. There is a slight suggestion of a cap over the eyeball. Sketch several of these from the right and the left, large and small.

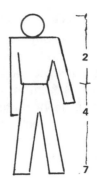

Fig. 37 Proportions for solid stick figures.

Fig. 38 Stick figures in action.

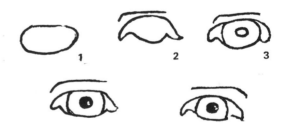

Fig. 39 Sketching the eye.

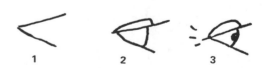

Fig. 40 Sketching the eye.

94

THEORY OF PERSPECTIVES

Introduction. Perspective is the drawing of objects so that they appear natural. For the engineer, architect and urban planner as well as the artist the drawing of objects in perspective is a necessity. Highways, cities, exteriors and interiors of buildings, all use perspective drawings. In some cases the best aesthetic solution, before the object is built, can be found only in perspective drawings.

Procedure. Imagine yourself on a vast desert. The sand under your feet stretches out and out, but not to infinity. In the distance some fifteen miles, the sky and the sand seem to come together, to meet. A little experimenting shows that as you kneel down or stretch up this meeting place appears to move. It was a good many years before man realized that this meeting place varied according to his own eye level. In perspective drawing we call this position in space the **horizon**, labeled **H** *(Fig. 1)*. Because of eye level, the

tal lines appear to vanish to a point. This point is always on the horizon. Another set of level train tracks, going a different place, will appear to vanish at another point on the horizon.

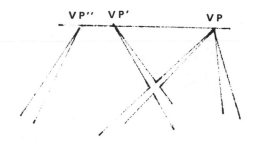

Fig. 2 Multiple vanishing points.

We also remember from drawing that the railroad ties which are perpendicular to the parallel lines appear to get smaller. We can easily imagine a line drawn thru the left top edge of the railway ties. It would be parallel to the steel rails and, while on a different level, it is also horizontal and will vanish to the same point on the horizon. We call this point the vanishing point, labeled **VP**. There can be many vanishing points on the same horizon *(Fig. 2)*.

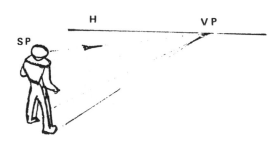

Fig. 1 Vanishing point on the horizon.

horizon is different for small children; for anyone who raises himself above his normal eye level, the horizon also rises. Most of the time this horizon appears as a line, a horizon line.

We are all familiar with some elementary rules of perspective, and we know that railroad tracks as lines seem to get smaller and meet at the horizon line. We should also notice that the railroad track lines are parallel and are on level ground. We can make a rule that parallel horizon-

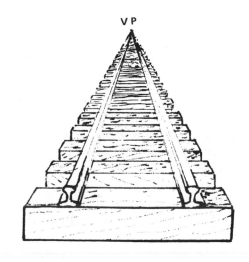

Fig. 3 Horizontal lines vanish to the vanishing point.

Imagine a freight car on the tracks. The top and bottom of the car are horizontal and parallel to the tracks. The top and bottom lines used to draw freight cars will also vanish to the VP. Imagine the letters on the sides of the box cars; if the letters are horizontal, the top and bottom of the letters obeying the same laws of perspective can be drawn to the same vanishing point (Fig. 4).

Fig. 4 Horizontal lines vanishing to the horizon.

What about a railway track that changes direction on our desert? It has now swung around into a new position and, while still parallel and horizontal, will have a new vanishing point (Fig. 5). This new direction can be drawn to the same horizon and a new **vanishing point VP$_2$**

Fig. 5 Changing horizontal lines, changing vanishing points.

Generally urban people do not have the experience of seeing the tracks or highways vanish to a point and this is the reason you should study the rules to draw correctly objects in perspective even when you can't see the vanishing point in nature or on your drawing.

Practice sketching several highways and streets with vanishing points and turning roads. Try your hand at sketching, on these tracks, simple box shapes that could be cars or trains. Try placing them at close and far distances.

Suppose there is a town at the edge of our desert with a church at the south end and a grain elevator at the north; at the west edge is a small airport tower and at the east end a water tank. Imagine the view that you will have approaching this town from each cardinal direction by highway. With a quick sketch actually verbalize by saying, "the road from the south shows the highway getting smaller and coming to a point where the church seems to sit; directly behind the church a large grain elevator can be seen. On my left is the airport tower and on my right is the water tower. All appear to be on the horizon and rising above it." Describe and sketch this town from the other directions, the north, east, and west highways into town. Then imagine, verbalize and sketch the town approaching from the north east.

Perspective is a powerful help aiding you to imagine and visualize. A good perspective drawing can describe objects better than a photograph.

Lines Off the Horizontal. Sky lines obey the same laws of perspective. Imagining a railroad track in the sky, we would draw the tracks vanishing to a point on the horizon. In like manner subway tracks underground, if they are level, appear to the eye to rise to a point on the horizon (Fig. 6).

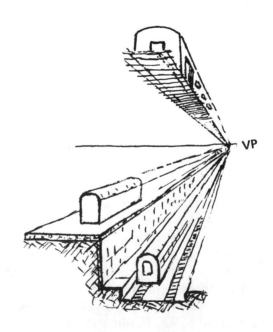

Fig. 6 All level lines vanish to the horizon.

Perspective Measurements. Measurements in perspective are similar to ordinary measurements in that we use height, width and depth. In our previous perspective drawings we had the heights and widths of objects, for the heights appear to be made up of horizontal lines which vanish to the vanishing point. The widths also diminish as they approach the vanishing point.

Depths are harder to measure although they obey the same rules. Again visualize the railroad tracks. The space between the track ties *(the wood that supports the steel rails)* is equal. Draw the first tie with the front side facing you; the ends of the top surface are made up of two parallel horizontal lines which vanish to the vanishing point, as do the bottoms *(Fig. 7)*.

you are standing, where the eye is. In perspective this place is called the **station point (SP).** Naturally it is arbitrary and can vary from drawing to drawing depending on our position and what view we want for the finished drawing, but will remain fixed for a given drawing *(Fig. 9)*.

Notice in the same figure there is an edge view of the drawing sheet. In perspective drawing this is the **picture plane (PP)** and is similar to a movie screen, a sheet of glass or drawing paper upon which we project the perspective picture. The further the object is behind the picture plane the smaller it appears *(Fig. 9)*. We have a top view *(Fig. 9)* of the railroad tracks in which all the labels are subscripted sub$_T$ for top view.

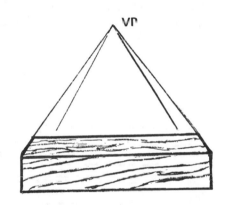

Fig. 7 Railway tie in perspective.

To get perspective depths we need a view of the top surface, a top view. A mechanical drawing of the top view *(Fig. 8)* shows the tie with correct width and depth although the height is missing.

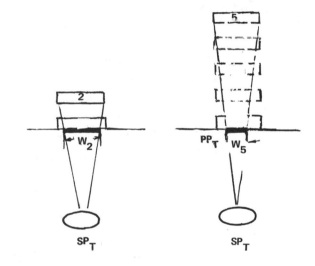

Fig. 9 Widths in perspective.

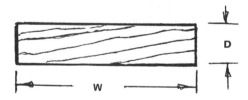

Fig. 8 Tie-orthographic top view.

In perspective the widths of the receding ties becomes smaller. In order to determine the diminishing from tie to tie you must know where

Fig. 10 Spatial sketch of perspective.

97

In our drawing *(Fig. 11)* we place the first tie in the picture plane. This, as it touches the picture plane, is not really in perspective but is the true scale measurement of its width. Draw the second tie in its proper mechanical drawing position. Looking through the picture plane you find that the second tie which is further away is smaller in perspective. We can measure the width (W_2) on the picture plane in its diminished size. The remaining ties can be measured on the picture plane in the same fashion.

The measurements are brought into the perspective drawing.The widths were needed to complete the perspective drawing. This is the basic theoretical method of perspective measurement which we will use to draw any object in perspective.Standard books on perspective show additional ways using tricks and shortcuts.

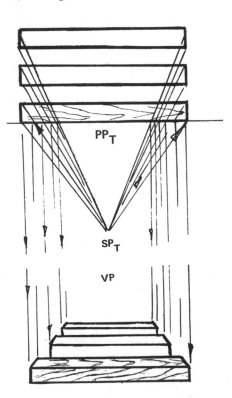

Fig. 11 *Finding perspective widths.*

The perspective width is made by drawing lines from your eye **(SP)** with a straight edge to each point on the object. The line pierces the picture and gives us our desired perspective widths.

Most standard perspective books show the top view *(mechanical drawing)* lined up with the front view, the front view below the top on the paper. After two or three drawings, you realize that the distance from the picture plane to the station point shown in the top view determines if the perspective is pleasing. Putting the station point close to the picture plane results in a correct but distorted perspective drawing. To get a more natural perspective drawing, move the station point (SP_T) to almost the bottom of the drawing paper. This means that the top and front mechanical drawings overlap. At first it seems confusing, but the perspective drawing is our goal; the other drawings will be discarded after we get our perspective drawing. If you pay careful attention to the subscripts *(Fig. 12),* $_T$ meaning a top view, and subscript $_F$ meaning a front view, the drawing will be easier to orient spatially.

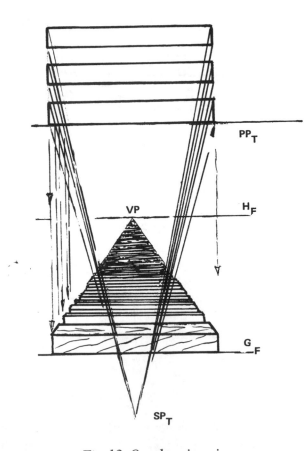

Fig. 12 *Overlapping views.*

Cone of Vision. As you study the top view you can see that the lines from the station point to the object form a cone of vision. Different people have different cones of vision, but in perspective a 30° cone is generally suitable for most drawings. You vary the cone of vision by moving the station point closer to or further from the picture plane.

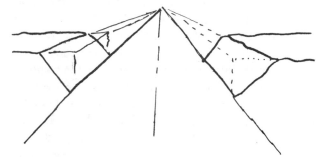

Fig.15 Perspective of highway construction.

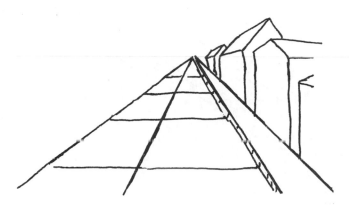

Fig. 13 Perspective sketch.

What we have done is to present an exact mathematically scaled diminished drawing of what an object would look like from a given station point.

Perspective is the most naturalistic method of looking at objects in two dimensional form. However, the human eye really sees things in perspective only in a very small cone and field of vision, for the eye moves and sees a rapid succession of perspectives, focusing fleetingly on a myriad of small parts of the scene. The eye never sees the succession of railroad ties and tracks, but focuses on one or two ties, registers them, moves to others, registers them, and with the help of the mind puts the scene together.

We can now draw in perspective any right rectangular object if we know its height, width and depth. Other objects can be boxed in and the shapes given a very accurate portrayal in perspective. The first few drawings will go slow because you are just learning. In addition, you have had to draw the top and front views of the object. In the working world where industry has billions of top and front views of their products and architects have their house plans, these top and front views are pulled from the files and taped to the drawing board; then the perspective can be started directly.

You should practice a series of boxes and angular planes in perspective. Roofs of buildings are good beginning subjects. Box the roof in (*Fig. 16*), sketching dormers and gables from various station points.

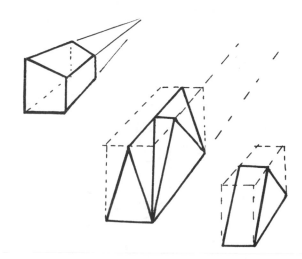

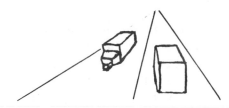

Fig. 14 Highway in perspective.

Fig. 16 Roofs and dormers in perspective.

Vanishing Points Not On The Horizon. Previously the lines that determined our vanishing point were horizontal, so the vanishing point was on the horizon. If we have a sloping set of railroad tracks, and the slope is uniform, the new vanishing point (VP_2) is above the horizon. If the railroad tracks continue in the same compass direction, but instead of being level, slope up, the VP_2 will be directly above the VP_1 of the level tracks *(Fig. 17)*. The tracks are still parallel in nature and still vanish to a point, VP_2, but above the horizon.

When the tracks slope downhill *(Fig. 18)* the vanishing point (VP_3) will be below the horizon. Again if the tracks have not changed compass heading, the new vanishing point (VP_3) will be directly below the other vanishing points (VP_1 and VP_2).

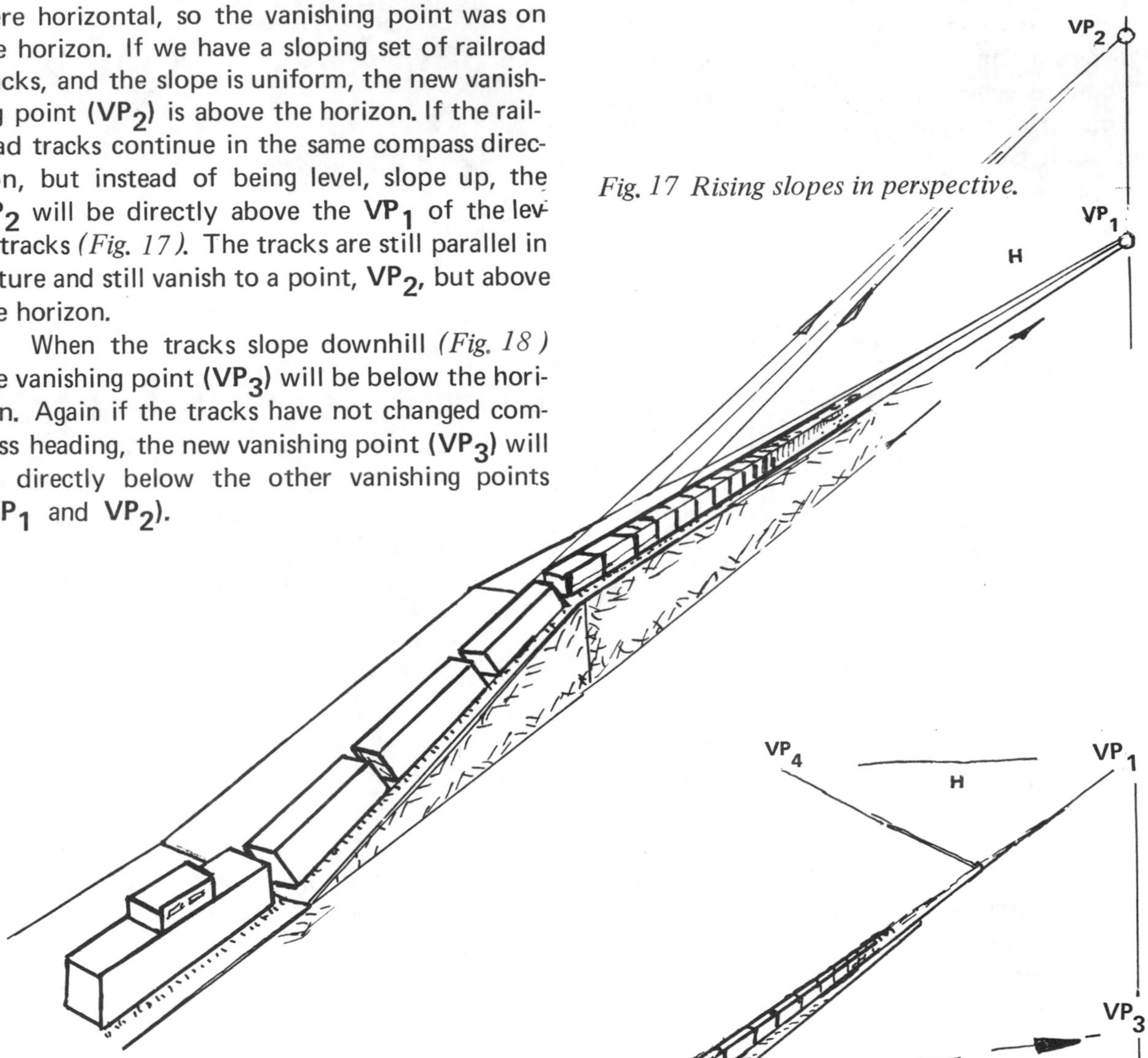

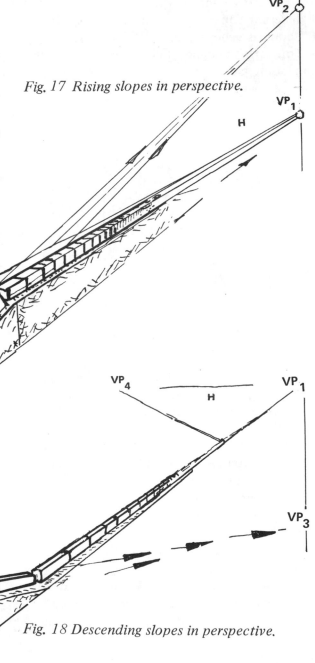

Fig. 17 Rising slopes in perspective.

Fig. 18 Descending slopes in perspective.

Tracks Changing Directions on the Level. When the tracks change to another direction and take a new compass heading they will not be in our original set of vanishing points but will have a new **vanishing point (VP_4)** *(Fig. 18)* for that heading. Each change of direction will have a new vanishing point.

100

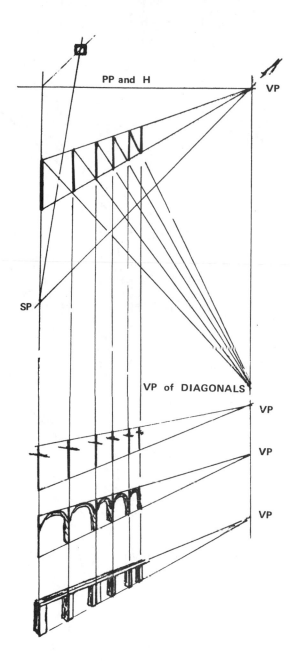

PP and H

VP

SP

VP of DIAGONALS

VP

VP

VP

Fig. 19 Locating the spacing
and height of receding verticals.

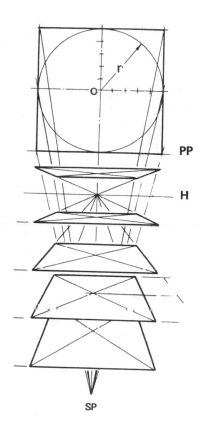

r

O

PP

H

SP

Fig. 20 Plane above and below the horizon.

Fig. 21 Arch in perspective.

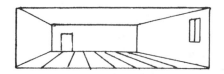
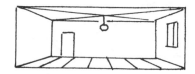

Fig. 22 Perspective sketches.

Summary. While we have drawn many vanishing points above, below and on the horizon there has been a similarity of method. The object was always parallel to or in the picture plane. Whatever the change of vanishing point, we have used only one vanishing point at a given time, although for a given drawing there may be more than one vanishing point. The previous set of rules produced a single vanishing point for one set of horizontal parallel lines. This set of rules is called the **One Vanishing Point in Perspective.**

TWO POINT PERSPECTIVE

Introduction. In using one point perspective, we place the front of the object in or parallel to the picture plane. In two point perspective we place the object turned away from the picture plane, so that only one corner of the block is in or parallel to the picture plane.

In one point perspective we found the vanishing point by drawing lines parallel from the eye to the vanishing point, extending the lines of the object to the horizon. In two point perspective we do the same (*Fig. 23*). Since the box or object has two sides which are parallel and vanish to the right, and two sides which are parallel and vanish to the left, we have two vanishing points.

Right and Left Vanishing Points. We draw parallel lines from the station point parallel to the lines on the object to the right vanishing point (**RVP**) in space. The right vanishing point is not an infinite distance away, but again a finite dis-

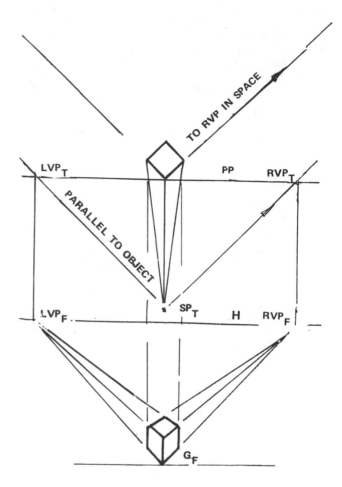

Fig. 24   *Separated views of cube in two point perspective.*

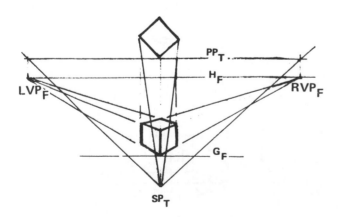

Fig. 23 Cube in two point perspective.

tance that we can see, fifteen miles. To find the RVP we draw from the **SP$_T$** a line parallel to the right horizontal lines on the object and vanishing to the right vanishing point in space. This line appears parallel for small systems. Where it pierces the picture plane in the top view is the right vanishing point (**RVP$_T$**). However, the vanishing points are on the horizon (*for horizontal lines*) so we project the **RVP$_T$** into the front view by coming down perpendicular to the picture plane and stopping at the horizon line (*Fig. 24*). We do a similar construction to find the left vanishing point (**LVP**). This construction is fundamental to all two point perspective. It sounds complicated, but can be executed in a few seconds with drawing instruments.

102

Applications. There are many variations of two point perspective. We can change the angle the block makes with the picture plane, we can change the station point putting the vanishing points off the paper, we can work with complicated irregular figures, circles and curves if we box them in. Thus we can add doors, windows, furniture and floor tiles as well as dormers, chimneys and porches to our buildings. There are enough problems in two point perspective to fill a lifetime of drawing.

A real test of perspective drawing is the correct representation of a telephone. An elliptical room with a parabolic mirror reflected in a circular pool with steps and uniform waves would be a semester's work. Add floor tiles and shadows if you wish.

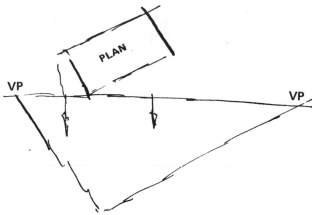

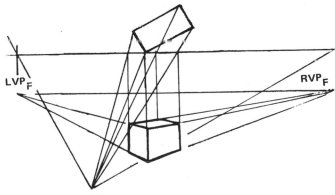

Fig. 25 Rectangular block in two point perspective.

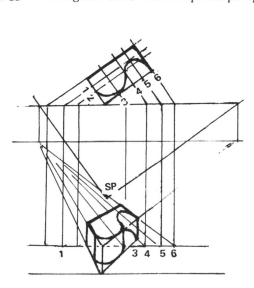

Fig. 26 Curved figure in two point perspective.

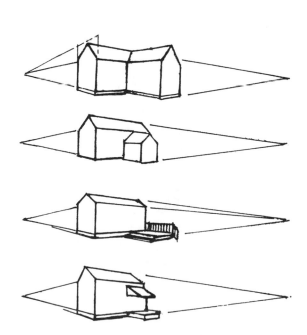

Fig. 27 Proposed alterations in perspective.

103

THREE POINT PERSPECTIVE

Occasionally a large architectural drawing with tall buildings requires a perspective drawing of three points. In theory this means none of the object lines are parallel to the picture plane. In practice viewed from above this produces vertical lines of the building that vanish to a point below the drawing *(Fig. 28)*. Since seen from overhead or underground the vertical lines will not look natural drawn geometrically parallel, the perspective can be changed to be more naturalistic by having a new vanishing point for the vertical lines. Any photograph of high buildings will show this three point perspective. Perspective books go into greater detail, but you can use three point perspective in sketching with just this brief explanation.

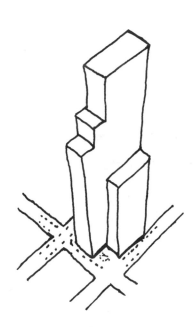

Fig. 28
Three point perspective sketch, from above.

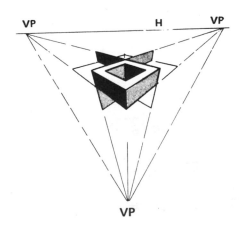

Fig. 29 Geometry of three point perspective.

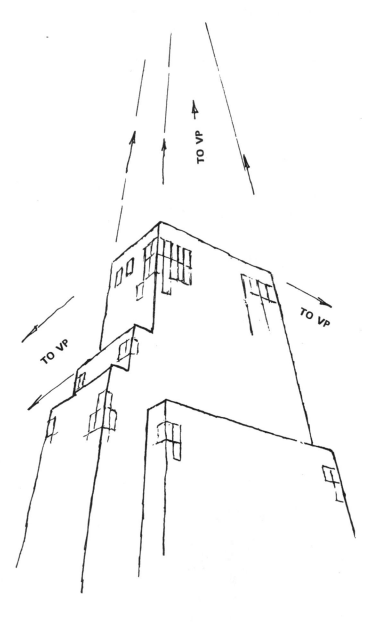

Fig. 30 Three point perspective sketch, from below.

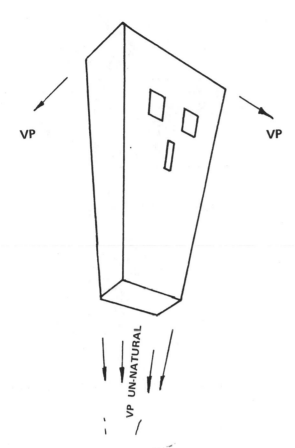

VP

VP

VP UN-NATURAL

Fig. 31   Distorted perspective.

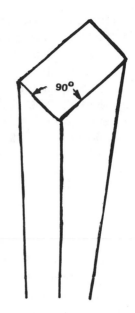

90°

Fig. 33   One point perspective using a vertical vanishing point.

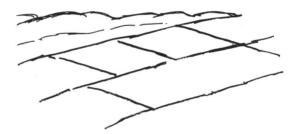

Fig. 34 Bird's eye view.

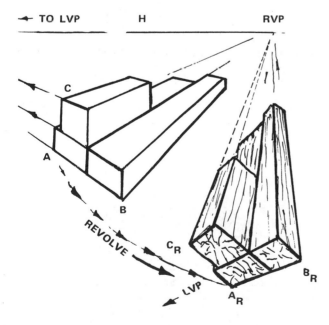

TO LVP   H   RVP

C

A

B

REVOLVE

C_R

LVP

A_R

B_R

Fig. 32 Two point perspective, false three point perspective.

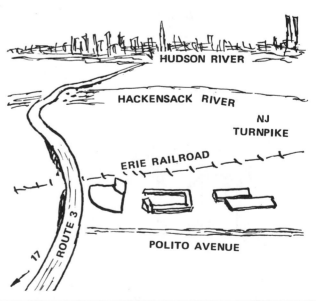

HUDSON RIVER

HACKENSACK RIVER

NJ TURNPIKE

ERIE RAILROAD

ROUTE 3

17

POLITO AVENUE

Fig. 35 Perspective sketch of aerial view.

105

True Measurements on the Ground Line. Establish a horizon *(Fig. 36)* and draw a semi-circle with the horizon as the diameter. At any place on the semicircle establish a station point. Let the ends of the circle's diameter be the left and right vanishing points in the customary layout *(Fig. 37).* Use the left and right vanishing points as pivots for a pair of arcs drawn *(as dotted lines)* through the station point to the horizon. Where these intersect the horizon *(Fig. 38)* two new secondary vanishing points are found. These are vanishing points for actual linear measurements of the object *(Fig. 39).* On the ground *(Fig. 40)* through the station point lay off to the left the right measurements of the object and to the right the left measurements, using true scale. The measurements are projected toward the secondary vanishing points until they reach the edge lines and from there are projected toward the primary vanishing points. Heights can be added by laying off true heights on a vertical line perpendicular to the ground through the station point *(Fig. 42).*

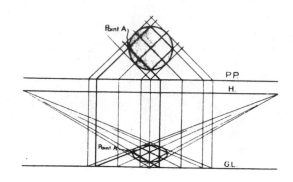

Fig. 41 *Circle in perspective, measured on ground.*

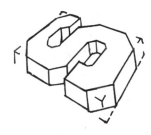

Fig. 42 *Added heights to letter on ground.*

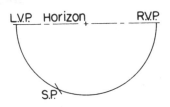

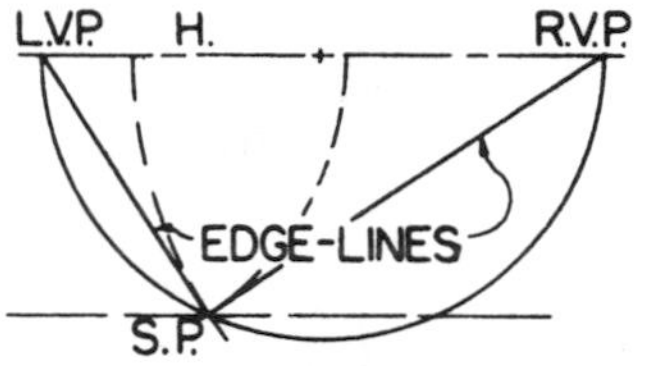

Fig. 36 *Semicircle.*

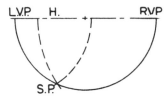

Fig. 37 *Establishing the arcs.* (Fig. 38 *Secondary vanishing points.*

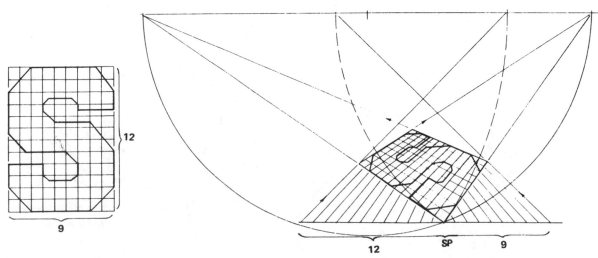

Fig. 39 *Orthographic figure.*

Fig. 40 *True measurements.*

106

Reflections in Perspective. Reflections are the reverse image of the actual object and obey the same laws of perspective. The student should remember that the object has no true measurements unless the measurements are brought into the picture plane. For the first example we have a square monument sitting in the water *(Fig. 43)*. We have turned it 45° to the picture plane with the front corner touching the picture plane. To draw the reflection of this shaft, lay off BT_R equal to TB and directly below it. The remaining lines are out of the picture plane and not true length. In perspective the top, T, of the monument vanishes to the right and left. The reflected top, T_R, also vanishes to the right and left. To find the remaining reflected lengths extend the vertical lines of the monument sides until they intersect lines, $B_T LVP$ and $B_T RVP$. This completes the reflection of the monument in perspective, the other lines being hidden.

Objects off the reflective surface and set back from the picture plane can be boxed in to develop the proper reflections (Fig. 44).

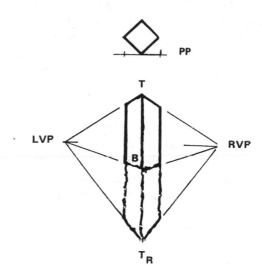

Fig. 43   Monument in reflection.

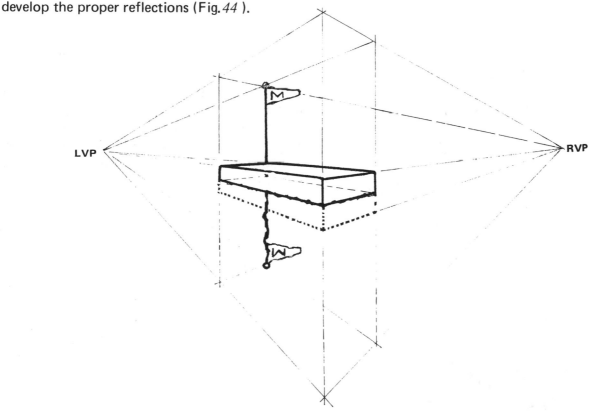

Fig. 44   Flag in reflection.

107

Introduction. Before we can do shadows in perspective we should be able to do simple sketching of shadows. We have learned that the sun is so far away and so big that for practical purposes the rays come to the earth in parallel beams.

If we put a stick into the ground, the sun will cast a shadow of that stick. Assume that the ground is level, and the sun moves. The shadow will vary in length and angle as the sun moves, and can be used to tell time. In most sketching, drawing and drafting we assume the sun rays are parallel to the picture plane and make an angle of 45°, coming from above and down to the right. The 45° angle is arbitrarily chosen because there are 45° triangles, and because this angle yields a shadow of the stick which is the same length as the height of the stick. *(Fig. 45).*

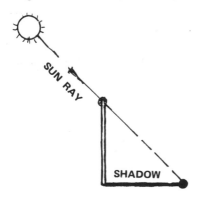

Fig. 45 Shadow of a vertical.

A box resting on the ground can be thought of as consisting of four vertical sticks and since we can find the shadow of each stick we can join the tops to get the shadow of the box, either

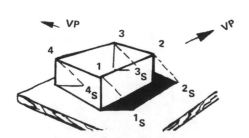

Fig. 46 Shadow of a box.

on the ground or on paper *(Fig. 46)*. We assume the ground is level and we see the ray of sun shining over the tip of the stick and piercing the ground where the ground appears as an edge.

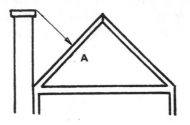

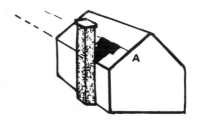

Fig. 47 Sketch of a shadow on a sloping surface.

If the ground slopes, find a view of the slope as an edge *(Fig. 47)* and find the sun rays through each point on the object to find where it pierces the edge. Curved grounds are handled this way as well as broken surfaces made up of planes *(Fig. 48)*.

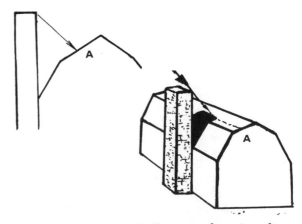

Fig. 48 Sketch of a shadow on changing slopes.

Shadows of abutments, buildings and overpasses will mean that some places can never support plant life. Shadows might also completely obscure warning and information signs.

Architectural renderings and artistic presentations use shade and shadows for detailing buildings which have not yet been constructed.

Study has shown that people do take visual cues from shadows both in art and life. As you drive along the highway notice how much visual information comes to you from shadows alone. A shadow of a tree or pole across a ditch next to the highway gives the only visual cue as to the depth and slope of that ditch *(Fig. 49)*.

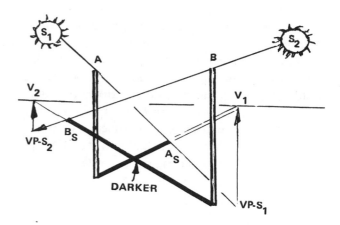

Fig. 51 Shadows from two suns.

If cars are continually running into a specific curb, is it because the curb does not contrast with the horizontal road or does not cast a shadow? If this is so we could paint the curb slightly darker to fool the eye and give the illusion of a shadow making the curb more visible.

In presentation drawings we often use shadows to darken portions of drawings that are in themselves uninteresting or not part of the main communication. The shadow is always made up of uniform tone and the edge is no darker or lighter than any other part unless altered for artistic reasons. Internal lines do not exist in shadows, all we see is the silhouette *(Fig. 50)*.

Where we have shadows crossing each other the crossing is darker. *(Fig. 51)*.

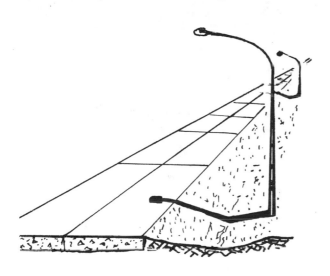

Fig. 49 Visual cues from shadows.

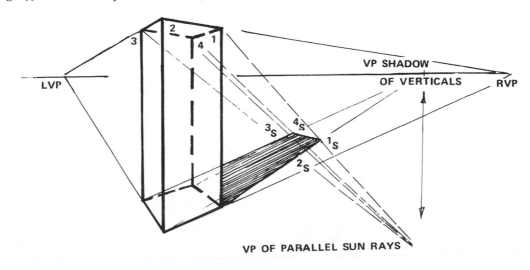

Fig. 50 Shadows cast by oblique sun rays.

As you are passing from home to school, or from class to class, observe the shadows. They are fascinating in themselves, quickly becoming complicated yet logical. Shadows of odd shaped buildings on sloping ground, shadows on steps, or shadows of buildings on other buildings can, with simple visualization, be traced backwards to find the line and point that define the shape of the shadow and be logically proved correct. Shadows are intriguing because of the changes caused by the passing of time.

Shadows have an important utilitarian use too. In architecture it is necessary to know if the sun hits the children's desks in the classroom, or if the sun will shine on and fade the rugs in houses. In northern climates where the sun is wanted, it is desirable to design buildings to catch the sun. In highway design, places on the highways that are in shade often freeze and in some places never thaw throughout the winter.

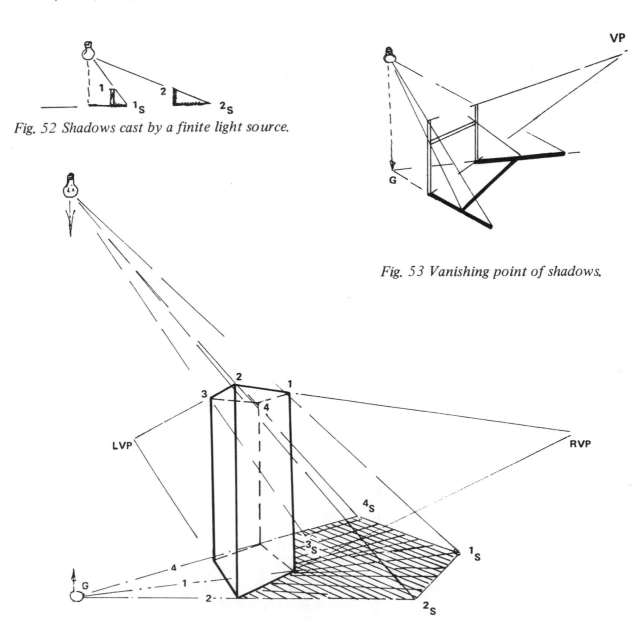

Fig. 52 Shadows cast by a finite light source.

Fig. 53 Vanishing point of shadows.

Fig. 54 Shadow of box, cast by finite light source.

110

CARTOGRAPHY

10

Cartography, the making of maps, falls within the province of the civil engineer. The earth is an oblate spheroid which means, merely, that it is a slightly flattened sphere, hence any attempt to draw its surface on a rectangular plane requires distortion of some lines. This is the point to be emphasized here since students may take measurements from maps without knowing the corrections to be applied if results are to be accurate. It should be remembered from earlier studies in geography that for purposes of time and space measurements a series of circles are passed about the earth so as to pass through the geographic North and South poles. By arbitration, the one passing through Greenwich, England, was selected as the zero datum and these meridians, as they are called, were spaced in degrees along a great circle that crosses them at right angles at their plane of greatest separation. This line, also a great circle is the Equator and parallel to it are a series

of smaller circles, equally spaced, between it and the poles on either side. They are known as parallels of latitude.

Common projections of the earth's surface are the Mercator, used chiefly in navigation, the Polyconic used in land surveys, and the Gnemonic.

In the Mercator, the spherical earth is considered enclosed in a cylinder and the projections of its outlines reproduced on the cylinder which is then unrolled, the meridian lines appearing as parallel vertical lines and the parallels of latitude as parallel horizontal lines. Distortion is, of course, greatest at the poles. This projection method is convenient in mapping small areas.

Gerardus Mercator was a Flemish mathematician and geographer who published his first map on this projection in 1569 (Fig. 1 & 2).

In Polyconic projection, sections such as those that lie between parallels of latitude are

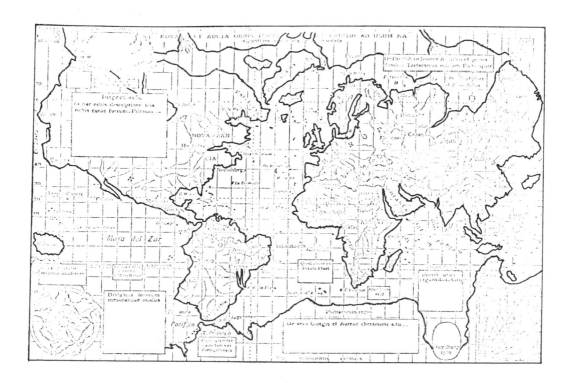

Fig. 1 Mercator's Chart of the World (1569).

111

projected onto surfaces of cones that are tangent to the earth's surface midway between the two parallels under consideration. The resulting charts are not quite rectangular *(Fig. 3).*

In Gnemonic, the procedure is the same as for Mercator except that the parallels of latitude are shown properly spaced *(Fig. 4).*

Contour maps are an ingenious means of indicating three dimensions on one plane which is that of the paper. To clarify this, remember that water normally seeks it's own level, therefore, we can use this as zero for a datum *(which means level for tides)* and can construct shore outlines. If we take another level, such as water would have if raised say 10' higher, we can again trace on our maps the new intersection of the earth and water. Continuing until all had been submerged we would have laid onto the earth's surface a series of contours, or intersection outlines for horizontal planes with the earth's surface.

For investigation of contours at right angles *(perpendicular)* to those just described a vertical plane is imagined passed through the earth's sur-face and the outline of the surface drawn upon it. This plane, when rotated to the horizontal position, shows the contour known as the **profile**.

Map, a representation, on a plane and a reduced scale, of part or the whole of the earth's surface. The words map and chart are derived from **mappa** and **charta,** the former being the latin for *napkin or cloth,* the latter for *papyrus or parchment.* Maps were thus named after the material upon which they were drawn or printed.

Maps are always drawn to scale; that is, an inch or fraction of an inch on the drawing represents a stated number of miles, meters or kilometers of earth surface.

Classification of Maps. Maps differ greatly, not only as to the scale on which they are drawn, but also with respect to the fullness or the character of the information which they convey. Broadly speaking, they may be divided into two classes, of which the first includes topographical,

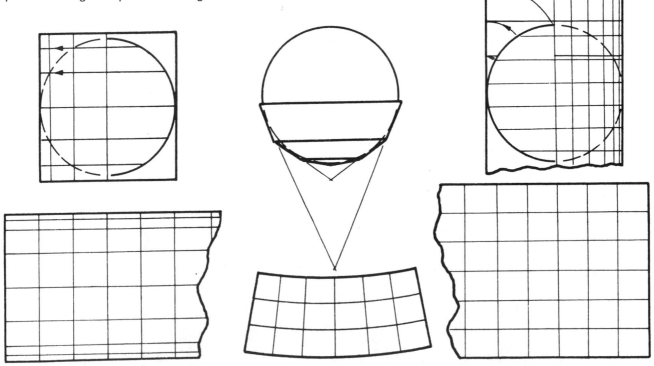

Fig. 2   Mercator projection.   Fig. 3   Polyconic projection.   Fig. 4   Gnemonic projection.

chorographical and general maps, the second the great variety designed for special purposes.

Topographical maps and plans are drawn on a scale sufficiently large to show most objects on a scale true to nature.

Chorographical and general maps are either reduced from topographical maps or compiled from such miscellaneous sources as are available.

The second group includes all maps compiled for special purposes. Their variety is considerable, for they are designed to illustrate physical and political geography, travel and navigation, trade and commerce, and, in fact, every subject connected with geographical distribution and capable of being illustrated by means of a map.

Special Maps

1. Physical maps in great variety, including geological, orographical and hydrographical maps, maps illustrative of the geographical distribution of meteorological phenomena.
2. Political maps, showing political boundries.
3. Ethnological maps, illustrating the distribution of the varieties of man, the density of population, etc.
4. Travel maps, showing roads or railways and ocean-routes, or designed for cyclist, motorist, tourist, etc.
5. Statistical maps, illustrating commerce and industries.
6. Historical maps.
7. Maps specially designed for educational purposes.

History of Cartography

A capacity to understand the nature of maps is possessed even by people whom we are in the habit of describing as "savages". Our arctic voyagers-Sir E. W. Parry, Sir J. Ross and others have profited from rough maps drawn for them by eskimos.

Far superior were the maps found among the semi-civilized Mexicans when the Spaniards first discovered and invaded their country. Among them were cadastral plans of villages, maps of the provinces of the empire of the Aztecs, of towns and of the coast. Montezuma presented Cortez with a map, printed on Nequen cloth, of the Gulf coast.

Peru, the empire of the Incas, had not only ordinary maps, but also maps in relief, for **Pedro Sarmieto da Gamboa** *(History of the Incas)* tells us that the 9th Inca (who died in 1191) ordered such reliefs to be produced of certain areas which he conquered and wished to colonize. These were the first relief maps on record.

The ancient Egyptians were famed as **"geometers,"** and as early as the days of **Rameses II** *(1333-1300 B.C.)* there had been a cadastral survey of the country showing the rows of pillars which separated the nomens as well as the boundaries of landed estates. It was upon such a map source that **Eratosthenes** *(276 - 196 B.C.)* measured the distance between Syene and Alexandria which he required for his determination of the length of a degree. Eratosthenes did much to give man an idea of the limits of his environment. He measured the size of the earth. First at Alexandria, he determined the elevation of the sun at noon on the day of the summer solstice. On the same date but in a different year, he made the same observation at Syene, Egypt. He discovered a difference between the elevations observed at the two different localities, and he measured that difference. Knowing the distance between Alexandria and Syene, he was able to determine the circumference of the earth. His answer was within eight hundred miles of the truth, a lasting testimonial to the accuracy of his work.

A cadastral survey for purposes of taxation was already at work in Babylonia in the age of **Sargon of Akkad**, 3800 B.C. In the British Museum may be seen a series of clay tablets, circular in shape and dating back 2300 to 2100 B.C., which contain surveys of lands. One of these depicts in a rough way lower Babylonia encircled by a "salt water river," Oceanus.

Ionian mercenaries and traders first arrived in Egypt, on the invitation of **Psammetichus I**, about the middle of the 7th century B.C. Among the visitors to Egypt, there were, no doubt, some who took an interest in the science of the

Fig. 5   Ptolemy's Map (1472)

Egyptians. One of the most distinguished among them was **Thales of Miletus** *(640-543 B.C.)* the founder of the Ionian school of philosophy, whose pupil, **Anaximander** *(611-546 B.C.)* is credited by Eratosthenes with having designed the first map of the world.

When Columbus sailed into the uncharted West, certain men had been believing for two thousand years that the earth was round. The spirits of Pythagoras, Aristarchus, and Eratosthenes sailed with him. The *Almagest* of Ptolemy preserved for future students the observations of the Babylonians and the carefully reasoned theories of the Greeks.

History of Map Printing. Maps were first printed in the second half of the 15th century. Those in the *Rudimentum novitiarum* published at Lubeck in 1475 are from wood cuts, while the maps in the first two editions of Ptolemy published in Italy in 1472 are from copper plates *(Fig. 5)*.

Maps and Map Making. A map is a representation, on a flat surface, of any geographical region or expanse. It shows, by means of lines, symbols, and names, the relative extent and the topographic and other features of the area covered.

The earliest map of which there is any record was engraved on a copper plate by **Anaximander of Miletus** about 580 B.C. Of other cartographers of ancient times may be mentioned **Dicaearchus, Posidonius, Hipparchus, Strabo, Marinus of Tyre,** and greatest of all, **Claudius Ptolemy,** who endeavored to fix longitudes and latitudes of worlds chief points. Owing to curvature of the earth, it is impossible to represent any portion of it on a flat surface without the adoption of some type of projection, the extent and location of the territory which will determine the type of projection used. Most maps are made up of parallels and meridians so that all points may have both longitudes and latitudes making it easy to locate all points. On most maps, the north is at the top, the right is east, the left is west, and the bottom is south. All maps that are prepared with any degree of accuracy are made to scale. The scale is an expression of the ratio of distance on the ground to the corresponding distance on the map.

TOPOGRAPHIC MAPS

The United States Geological Survey was established by an act of Congress in 1879 for the purpose of making a systematic study of the geology and natural resources of the United States and for classifying the public lands. A general plan was adopted in 1882 for the production of a standard series of topographic maps. Under this plan each map covers a quadrangle of area bounded by lines of latitude and longitude, by which the location of any point on the surface of the earth is readily determined. Maps with these standard boundaries are usually referred to as quadrangle maps.

FEATURES SHOWN ON TOPOGRAPHIC MAPS

The information shown on topographic maps is generally divided into three main classes that are distinguished by the colors in which they are printed. Water features, such as oceans, lakes, rivers, streams, glaciers, canals, and swamps, are shown in blue. The works of man, such as roads, trails, dams, transmission lines, buildings, airports, railroads, and boundary lines, called cultural features, are shown in black. The features printed in brown depict the shape or configuration of the land surface; this information is called topographic relief or hypsography, and its graphic representation is the characteristic that differentiates topographic maps from other kinds.

The amount of information that can be shown on a map is limited by the map scale. Geological Survey maps are intended to give as complete a picture of the terrain as can be legibly reproduced at publication scale. Many relatively unimportant features are omitted, and many small but important features are necessarily exaggerated in size to make them readable.

MAP PUBLICATION SCALES

Map scale, expressed as a ratio, represents the fixed relationship between linear measurements on the map and corresponding distances on the ground. For example, the scale of 1:62,500 means that one unit, such as 1 inch, 1 foot, or 1 meter, on the map represents 62,500 of the same units on the earth's surface.

Quadrangle maps are published at the following scales:

Scale	1 inch equals
1:20,000	Approximately 1,667 feet
1:24,000	Exactly 2,000 feet
1:30,000	Exactly 2,500 feet
1:31,680	Exactly 1/2 mile
1:62,500	Approximately 1 mile
1:63,360	Exactly 1 mile
1:125,000	Approximately 2 miles
1:250,000	Approximately 4 miles
1:1,000,000	Approximately 16 miles

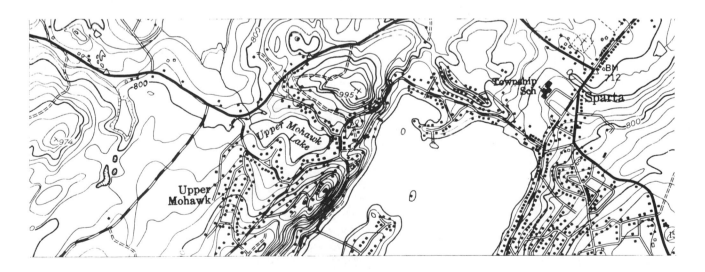

Fig. 6   A portion of the Newton East, N.J. Quadrangle Map. Scale 1:24,000 Contour interval 20 feet. Mapped in 1954.

NATIONAL TOPOGRAPHIC MAP SERIES

Large scale maps (1:20,000, 1:24,000, 1:30,000 and 1:31,680) are especially suitable for densely settled areas and other areas where detailed map information is needed for engineering planning and similar purposes. Medium-scale maps (1:62,500 and 1:63,360) are considered adequate for general use where detailed planning is not contemplated. Small-scale maps (1:125,000, 1:250,000, and 1:1,000,000) cover large areas on a single sheet and are useful in planning statewide and nationwide projects. The quadrangle map series and their essential specifications are given in the following table:

MAP ACCURACY

Specific standards for the horizontal and vertical accuracy of topographic maps were adopted in 1942, and maps that meet these standards carry a statement to the effect in the lower margin. The main provisions of the accuracy standards are (1) that the horizontal positions of at least 90 percent of the well-defined planimetric features must be accurate within one-fiftieth inch on the published map; and (2) that the elevations of 90 percent of the points tested shall agree with the elevations interpolated from the contour lines within one-half the contour interval. The one-fiftieth inch tolerance allowed

QUADRANGLE MAPS

Series	Scale	Quadrangle size (lat. - Long.)	Quadrangle area (sq. mi.)	Paper size (inches)
United States				
7½ - minute	1:24,000	7½' x 7½'	49-68	22 x 27, 23 x 27
7½ - minute	1:31,680	7½' x 7½'	49-68	17 x 21
15 - minute	1:62,500	15' x 15'	197-271	17 x 21
1:63,360 (Alaska)	1:63,360	15' x 20' -36'	207-281	17 x 21, 18 x 21
30 - minute	1:125,000	30' x 30'	789-1082	17 x 21
1 - degree	1:250,000	1° x 1°	3173-4335	17 x 21
1:250,000	1:250,000	1° x 2°	6346-8669	24 x 34
Reconnaissance (Alaska)	1:250,000	1° x 2° -3°	4580-7310	23 x 30
1:250,000 (Alaska)	1:250,000	1° x 2° -3°	4580-7310	23 x 30
1:1,000,000	1:1,000,000	4° x 6°	73734-102759	27 x 27
Hawaiian Islands:				
7½ - minute	1:24,000	7½' x 7½'	70	23 x 27
1:62,500	1:62,500	15' x 15'	282	18 x 21, 19 x 21
1:250,000	1:250,000	1° x 1°30' -1°35'	6730-7104	24 x 29

Fig. 7   Quadrangle map specifications

for horizontal positions is equivalent to 40 feet on the ground for 1:24,000-scale maps and about 100 feet on the ground for 1:62,500-scale maps.

MAPPING PROCEDURES

Most of the modern topographic maps are plotted from aerial photographs with instruments that operate on the principle of the stereoscope. Photographs usually taken from 6,000 to 25,000 feet above the ground are employed with photogrammetric plotters to compile the map detail, including the contours. The method is suited to mass production and makes it practical to prepare maps of uniform quality. Before 1940, most maps were prepared in the field by plane-table methods, and their quality depended on the skill of the individual topographer.

MAP REVISION

Maps are scheduled for revision according to their classification, and the demands of map users. Revision methods vary widely but usually are combinations of photogrammetric and field procedures designed to bring the content of the map up to date and maintain or improve its original accuracy.

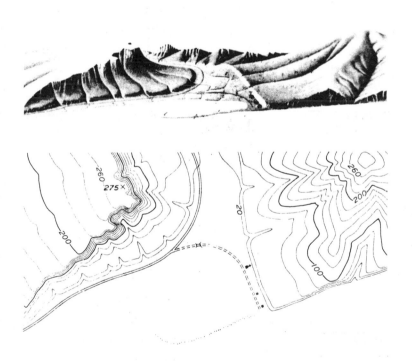

Fig. 8   The lower illustration shows the same features represented by symbols on a topographic map. Elevations are represented by contour lines; the vertical difference between contours in the illustration is 20 feet.

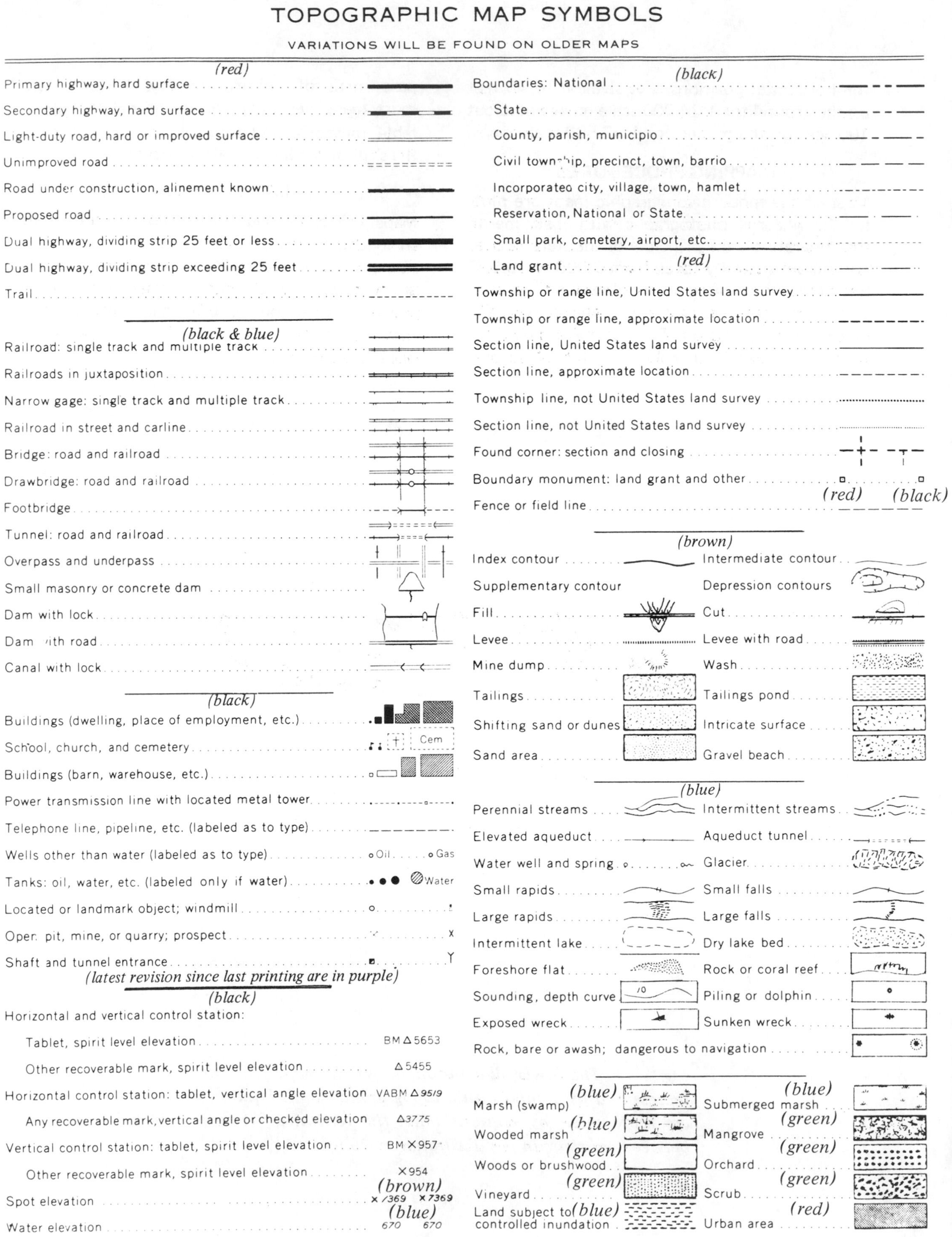

TOPOGRAPHIC MAP SYMBOLS

VARIATIONS WILL BE FOUND ON OLDER MAPS

(red)

Primary highway, hard surface . . . .

Secondary highway, hard surface . . . .

Light-duty road, hard or improved surface . . . .

Unimproved road . . . .

Road under construction, alinement known . . . .

Proposed road . . . .

Dual highway, dividing strip 25 feet or less . . . .

Dual highway, dividing strip exceeding 25 feet . . . .

Trail . . . .

(black & blue)

Railroad: single track and multiple track

Railroads in juxtaposition . . . .

Narrow gage: single track and multiple track . . . .

Railroad in street and carline . . . .

Bridge: road and railroad . . . .

Drawbridge: road and railroad . . . .

Footbridge . . . .

Tunnel: road and railroad . . . .

Overpass and underpass . . . .

Small masonry or concrete dam . . . .

Dam with lock . . . .

Dam with road . . . .

Canal with lock . . . .

(black)

Buildings (dwelling, place of employment, etc.) . . . .

School, church, and cemetery . . . .

Buildings (barn, warehouse, etc.) . . . .

Power transmission line with located metal tower . . . .

Telephone line, pipeline, etc. (labeled as to type) . . . .

Wells other than water (labeled as to type) . . . . o Oil   o Gas

Tanks: oil, water, etc. (labeled only if water) . . . . ● ● ⊘ Water

Located or landmark object; windmill . . . .

Open pit, mine, or quarry; prospect . . . .

Shaft and tunnel entrance . . . .

(latest revision since last printing are in purple)

(black)

Horizontal and vertical control station:

   Tablet, spirit level elevation . . . .   BM △ 5653

   Other recoverable mark, spirit level elevation . . . .   △ 5455

Horizontal control station: tablet, vertical angle elevation   VABM △ 95/9

   Any recoverable mark, vertical angle or checked elevation   △ 3775

Vertical control station: tablet, spirit level elevation . . . .   BM ✕ 957·

   Other recoverable mark, spirit level elevation . . . .   ✕ 954

Spot elevation . . . .   ✕ /369 ✕ 7369
(brown)

Water elevation . . . .   *(blue)*
                                                                            670   670

(black)

Boundaries: National . . . .

   State . . . .

   County, parish, municipio . . . .

   Civil township, precinct, town, barrio . . . .

   Incorporated city, village, town, hamlet . . . .

   Reservation, National or State . . . .

   Small park, cemetery, airport, etc. . . . .

   Land grant . . . . *(red)*

Township or range line, United States land survey . . . . . .

Township or range line, approximate location . . . .

Section line, United States land survey . . . .

Section line, approximate location . . . .

Township line, not United States land survey . . . .

Section line, not United States land survey . . . .

Found corner: section and closing . . . .

Boundary monument: land grant and other . . . .

Fence or field line . . . .   *(red)*   *(black)*

(brown)

Index contour . . . .   Intermediate contour . . .

Supplementary contour . . .   Depression contours . . .

Fill . . . .   Cut . . . .

Levee . . . .   Levee with road . . . . . .

Mine dump . . . .   Wash . . . .

Tailings . . . .   Tailings pond . . . .

Shifting sand or dunes . . .   Intricate surface . . . . . .

Sand area . . . .   Gravel beach . . . .

(blue)

Perennial streams . . . . . .   Intermittent streams . . .

Elevated aqueduct . . . . . .   Aqueduct tunnel . . . . . .

Water well and spring o ~~   Glacier . . . .

Small rapids . . . .   Small falls . . . .

Large rapids . . . .   Large falls . . . .

Intermittent lake . . . .   Dry lake bed . . . .

Foreshore flat . . . .   Rock or coral reef . . . . .

Sounding, depth curve . . .   Piling or dolphin . . . . . .

Exposed wreck . . . .   Sunken wreck . . . .

Rock, bare or awash; dangerous to navigation . . . .

(blue)   *(blue)*

Marsh (swamp) . . . .   Submerged marsh
(blue)   *(green)*
Wooded marsh . . . .   Mangrove
(green)   *(green)*
Woods or brushwood . . . .   Orchard
(green)   *(green)*
Vineyard . . . .   Scrub
Land subject to *(blue)*   *(red)*
controlled inundation . . .   Urban area

Fig. 9   Topographic map symbols.

118

1:24,000 scale,
1 inch = 2000 feet.
Area shown,
1 square mile.

1:62,500 scale,
1 inch = nearly 1 mile.
Area shown,
6¾ square miles.

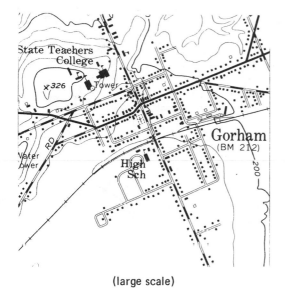

(large scale)

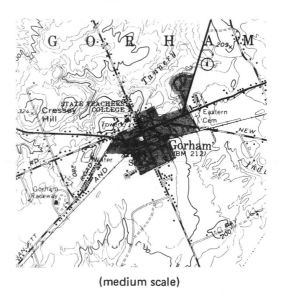

(medium scale)

1:250,000 scale,
1 inch = nearly 4 miles.
Area shown,
107 square miles.

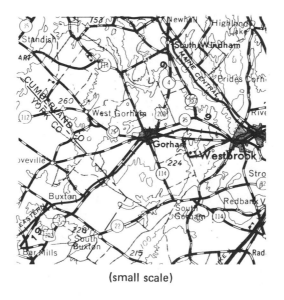

(small scale)

Fig. 10   Contrast between large--, medium--, and small scale maps.

BLUE CREEK GRID SURVEY

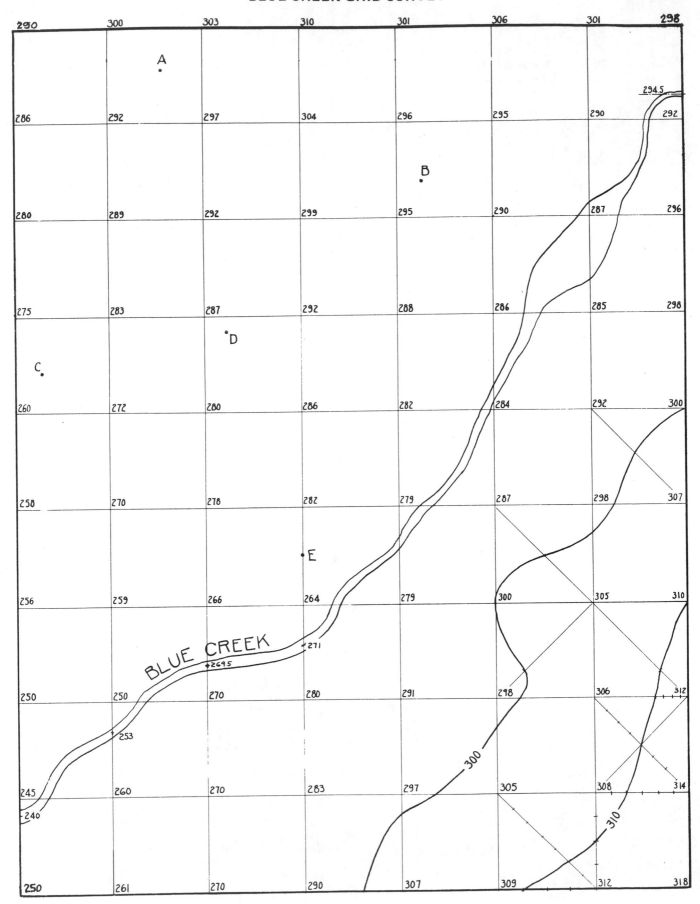

Fig. 6   Blue Creek Grid Survey

11

TOPOGRAPHY

In mapping it is customary to secure elevations at a number of points and to draw contour lines through all successive points of like elevation. In other words, pass horizontal planes at varying elevations through the earth's surface and draw the outline produced when the planes break out into the open or pass again into the earth. Intervals between contour lines may be 1, 2, 5, 10, 20, 50, or 100 feet, etc., measured vertically. Interpolation of intermediate points must be used to secure finer gradations.

When vertical planes are run through the earth's surface and the resulting contour drawn on these planes or parallel ones, the outline is known as the **profile.**

Contours and profiles are used to describe the surface conditions but when we penetrate below the surface new terminology must be used.

The first reason for penetration is usually to reach an ore vein for extraction of minerals or fuel. Other reasons are tunneling for water supply or waste purposes.

A **tunnel** is an opening that is nearly horizontal and may not necessarily be the opening that contacts the vein. It is usually sloped slightly upwards so that there will be good drainage but not enough so that boulders may roll down it.

A **shaft** unlike a tunnel, is more nearly vertical and may run from the end of a tunnel rather than from the earth's surface.

Since most ore bodies are laid down by nature as infiltrations into fissures in rock where minerals leach over a period of time until the enriched vein occurs or are formed by deposits that are later overlaid they have roughly two parallel walls of rock or earth. The uppermost of these is known as the **hanging wall** and the lower as the **foot wall.** Perpendicular to these walls the thickness of the vein is measured. Should the body of ore break out of the surface of the earth the lines formed by the hanging and the foot walls are known as the **lines of outcrop.** Often, when a body of ore is discovered or suspected as being present, holes are drilled with hollow bits that bring to the surface samples of the earth as they penetrate. These cores are laid on racks and the depths of the various sands, rocks, silt, etc., traversed may be readily measured. In this matter locations of the ore body walls at various points can be determined and by projecting the body on the maps a point can be determined where the least amount of excavating will reach the ore body.

Any entry that follows the dip of the vein is called an incline, dip being the amount of variation from the horizontal made by the vein. In addition to the dip it is necessary to specify one other deviation from an established point or direction. This, called the **strike,** is the amount by which a horizontal line in the vein swings away from or towards the North-South direction. A horizontal passage in the vein is a drift and a grade is an expression of slope in terms of feet of rise per foot of run, expressed usually in percent.

Where two veins of ore intersect enrichment of the ore body may be expected. The location is known as a **shoot.**

Ore refuse, dumped on a hillside, will slide down and come to rest at the "**angle of repose**" for that particular material. In problems of this type investigation of the dump will indicate how much material may be discarded into a gully without interfering with stream flow at the bottom. It is stated in degrees or as a ratio.

Establishing Contours. Land is gridded for whatever accuracy we wish the elevations to have. In hilly land the grids are close together, in flat land grids may be several hundred feet apart *(Fig. 1).* The elevations are found at the grid crossings and entered, as well as the most important or primary stations, in this case along the stream. Inspection of the map shows that the country varies from about 130 to 210 feet in

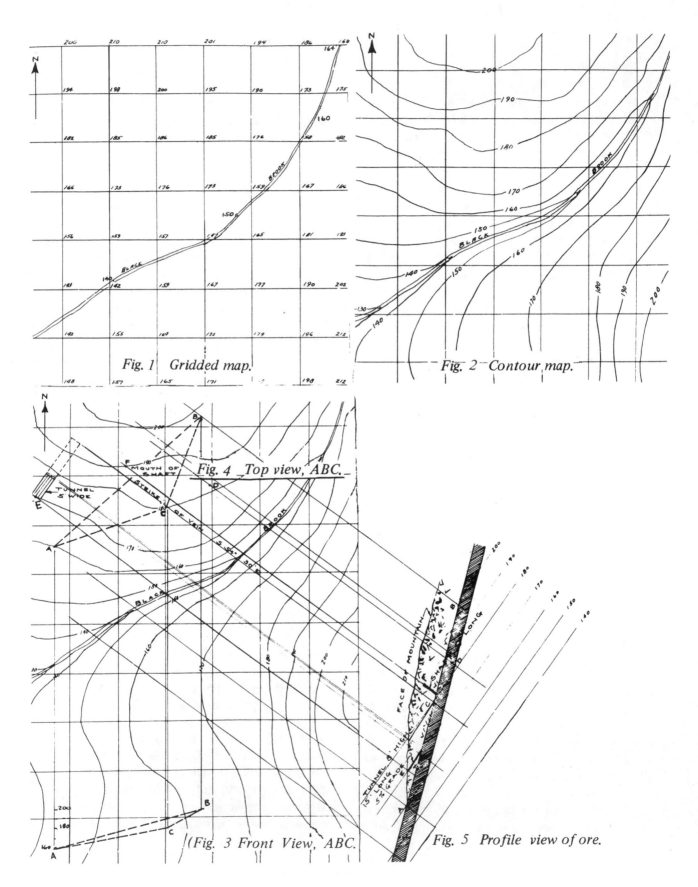

Fig. 1 Gridded map.

Fig. 2 Contour map.

Fig. 4 Top view, ABC.

(Fig. 3 Front View, ABC.

Fig. 5 Profile view of ore.

elevation. There is nearly 70 feet difference between the low and high points so a contour interval of 10 feet seems appropriate. Start at the top of the map with the 200 foot mark and, using the grid lines, find all other 200 foot contour levels in that area interpolated on the grids. Lightly connect these 200 foot points which will result in the 200 foot contour. With practice this sketching becomes easier and smoother. Practice sketching on the earlier map *(Fig. 1)* and the results should be the contour map *(Fig. 2)*.

Profiles. Vertical cuts, as if the earth were opened by a giant knife, will slice through the surface of the ground. An observer looking perpendicularly at the cut will see the true surface of the ground as a line. We call this view a **profile.** The term **profile** in Descriptive Geometry refers only to the right and left side views. In highway design, mining, and architecture profile means any vertical cut including those labeled, in Descriptive Geometry, front and rear views, right and left views and all auxiliary elevations. Draw a line in the top view representing the **profile cutting plane.** To draw the profile view place one edge of your right triangle along this line and, perpendicular to that line, draw down a set of parallel lines. Establish a **base plane** starting with the highest elevation of the profile, the base plane being parallel to the profile cutting plane. Select a suitable scale and draw the rest of the contour lines which is the profile view. In the profile view contour lines will all be parallel, straight and equidistant. From the point where each contour line crosses the profile cutting plane on the map view, drop down lines perpendicular to the profile cutting plane ending each line at the point on the profile view corresponding to its contour on the map view. Circle these points and connect them for a **face view** of the hill profile.

Points A, B, and C on the map are points in the hanging wall of a vein. Point D is a point in the foot wall and all are outcrops. Plot A, B, and C on the profile and draw any horizontal line as C-1. The horizontal projection of this line is the strike of the vein.

Draw an edge view of the plane A, B, and C by passing a horizontal line through it in the plan view and then taking an end view of the line and the plane with it. This view will indicate the dip of the plane below any horizontal line. Plot point D on this view. Assume the vein to be of uniform thickness and draw a line through D parallel to that containing A, B, and C. From this, vein thickness is apparent and the amount of material in the body may be estimated.

To find the line of outcrop of the walls various elevations are selected in the auxiliary elevation and located in the plan view. It is not necessary that these points be on even contours and it is frequently necessary to interpolate between contour lines to determine accurately the line of outcrop.

In figure *#4* point E is a station from which entrance to the ore body is to be made. It is not always the case that the shortest tunnel or shaft is the most economical as accessibility is also important. The selection of such a point, then, is determined by the practicability of the project. From point E it is desired to run a tunnel on a 5% grade and it is necessary to find the length of the tunnel and amount of excavation to be done so that costs may be figured beforehand. The tunnel is to be 5' wide and 8' high through solid rock.

Plot point E on the auxiliary elevation and draw a horizontal line from E toward the edge view. Since the grade is 5% lay off 100' on the horizontal line and at that point erect a perpendicular 5' high. The plane of the base of the tunnel will run along the line of this 5% grade. Draw in the face of mountain by locating contours on the auxiliary elevation and complete the layout of the tunnel by drawing the width and the height.

In figure *#4* point F is the mouth of the shaft and its length is desired.

Visualizing Water. Water is easy to visualize for if flooding occurs the water surface will be the shape of the contour on the map for that level. Many people find it amazing that you can know where a new lake will be, what will be flooded and what the shore line will be. Also since water forms a level surface, it is straightforward to tell what can be seen from any place on the shore.

Drainage of Areas. In figuring the amount of water being drained from a designated region we need to know the area and the slope of the region. We also need to know the material and roughness of the slope surface. Tables are available showing different amounts of rainfall for different years and the extreme conditions for 10, 50 and 100 years. There are several reliable formulae which can be found in engineering texts on drainage, some for quick use, some more complex, but as always in engineering experience from past situations helps. These problems of drainage are particularly acute in urban areas where every drop of rain water must be collected and carried away through man made structures. In some rural areas and along highways it is often not objectionable to have a pool of water backed up behind a culvert but a pool of water in urban areas could completely disrupt subways and commuter traffic.

Flooded Areas. Blue Creek *(Fig. 6)* runs southwesterly. You are to place a dam across this creek to enclose enough water to make a lake. Complete the contours and imagine a dam at various places along the creek. At the same time note the contour line at the level of your imagined dam to 'see' the new lake. With the dam about 6 feet high consider what location would yield the deepest lake and what location would give the biggest lake.

With this kind of simple problem there are many practical applications. In case you need to treat the lake for weeds, you must compute the volume of the lake. To find the number and kind of fish this lake will support, you need, in addition to the volume, to know the size and depth of the deepest and shallowest spots, the rate of flow and the temperature of the water. You may need to know where and what sort of secondary dams will be needed.

The value of the benefit of the dam must be greater than the cost of the construction in order for the dam to be economically feasible. Some locations are impractical because of geological problems or their inaccessibility. The location also depends on its major use: erosion control, water storage for people or farm animals, irrigation, fire protection for remote areas, fish farms or recreation. These uses are valuable and can make a profit if properly managed in the proper location.

Fill, Dams and Dumps. Loose common material if dumped from a point will form a natural cone. The slope of this cone is called the angle of repose which is measured from the horizontal plane to the material slope. The cone will have a different slope depending on the type and condition *(wet, lumpy, weathered)* of the material. For class, measure the angle of repose of dry instant coffee, cornflakes or cornmeal. This simple experiment forms the basis for many practical problems in engineering. It is important to know the angle of repose of coal because you may design delivery chutes where the chute angle must be greater than the angle of repose of coal, or you might need to know the volume of coal left in your coal pile to determine how many days' electricity are left as indicated by the volume of the coal pile.

Roads and dams are often built up of soil dumped along the line of the roadway. For a road going along the side of a hill some of the hill must be cut away and may be used to fill a nearby valley segment of the road to make a level area *(Fig. 7)*. We find these areas by taking an edge view of the road and drawing our contour lines in profile. In that profile view establish the lines of the cut and fill and

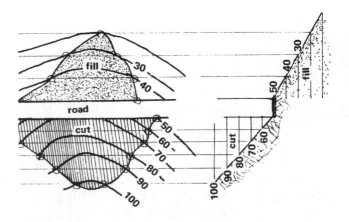

Fig. 7 Cut and fill.

124

draw in the desired width road showing the cut and fill as sloping lines. Where they intersect the contour lines will be the place where the cut will begin or where the dirt will stop. To bring them back into the map view merely project back and where they cross the contour line in the map view put a little circle and, proceeding systematically, build up the area of cut and fill *(Fig. 7)*. Dams also follow this pattern.

Given the map *(Fig. 9)* draw a profile view looking along one edge of the rectangle. In this view the rectangle appears level. Use this as a base plane and draw other contour lines to some suitable scale. At the hill edge of the rectangle use a 1:1 slope for the cut, at the valley edge of the rectangle use a 1:2 slope for the fill. To plot the cut and fill for the corners, think of the contour lines being projected from the profile view as going around the corner in a quarter circle matching the other projections for that level *(Figs. 8 & 9)*.

Culverts. In the profile view we can construct level tunnels and shafts or drainage and culverts. Run a culvert with a slight slope from the deepest part of the lake for draining it or to drain the area behind the fill for a building or highway.

Formulae for runoffs are commonly found in handbooks and are concerned with the size and slope of the culvert, the coefficient of roughness of the pipe surface and the area and kind of watershed slope. The history of rainfall of an area is found from local records and inspection of the area will show high and low water marks often visible several years later. Some consideration should be given to possible future changes for the watershed, such as farmland being converted to residential or industrial uses. In designing culverts the engineer tries to recommend a size that is economical yet able to discharge a 10-year flood without static head at the entrance and even be able to operate with slight to moderate damage at the flood stage expected once in a hundred years. Culverts for highways very seldom operate under full head for to do so they need the outlet submerged. In designing culverts consider such things as the load of fill above the culvert and the loads imposed by the traffic, trucks or trains, over them. The length of the culvert can be estimated on simple graph paper. Some kinds of pipe are made in two foot increments, others much longer and several different lengths may be fitted together to get the necessary length.

Bevelled end sections are available on some standard pipes saving costly construction of concrete headwalls and abutments, retarding scouring and eliminating extremely hazardous concrete wingwalls.

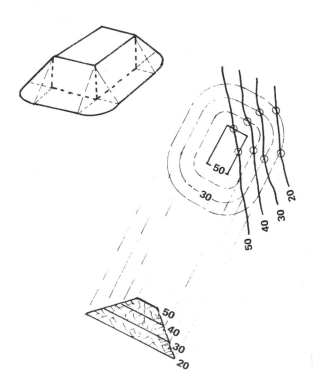

Figs. 8 & 9 Cut and fill of a rectangular area.

Introduction. In the past, field sketching was always taught as part of the training of engineers, military men and geographers. Many Civil War scenes executed by regular army scouts are shown only by field sketches which were better than photographs for pinpointing the location of battles and buildings. In some cases the field sketch has been used for the reconstruction of older buildings. The sketch often conveys more information than a photograph because the vertical scale can be exaggerated and minor details omitted.

Another advantage to learning field sketching is that it gives you a feel or an eye for the land. A six inch hill sounds insignificant but it has saved many lives on the battle field.

Field sketching is an inexpensive avocation as supplies, paper and pencils, are economical and can be packed in a waterproof container and carried at all times in a jacket pocket.

The Corps of Engineers require their topographical students to sketch the terrain, memorize their sketch, destroy it and then resketch it from memory.

Actual Field Sketching. Start with a small paper *(8½ x 11 typing paper is too large)* a board or cardboard for backing, H and 2H pencils, a scale and a protractor. Select some vantage point where you can see some distance, and choose a prominent object or point as center of interest for your sketch. Include a cone of vision of about 30° which will seem to be too narrow a view. Place the prominent object in the center of your sketch and draw a vertical line through it lightly with the 2H pencil. Draw a horizontal line also through this point. Working with the pencil as a guide for the horizontal line, hold the pencil at arms length and by proportion thumb off widths and bring them to the sketch *(Fig. 10)*. With the pencil held vertically do the same but instead of giving an exact proportion, vary the heights, by exaggerating them even to the point of doubling or tripling them near the bottom of the paper.

For all field sketches work from the main features of the landscape, hills, passes or rivers. Don't add foreground or details and don't show individual trees. Sketch the land forms correctly and suggest trees by various freehand lines, water by wavy lines, houses by a couple of roof blocks. If there is one important structure in the town, such as a bell tower, take time to sketch it in, exaggerating its size. Do not add bases even if visible.

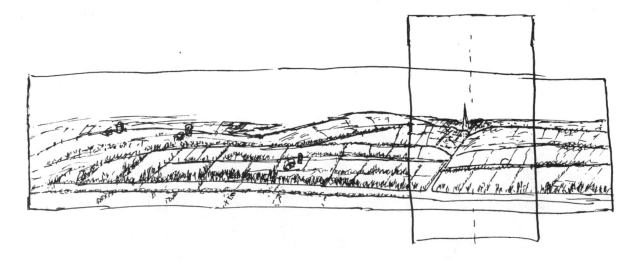

Fig. 10 Selecting field sketch from panoramic view.

Block Geological and Topography Sketching. Block drawings start with a cut-away section of the earth facing you and the sides of the blocks going back some convenient angle like 30°. Isometric sketching paper or the 30° triangle may be used. Draw as much of the front face as needed but it often is smaller than the sides. The land is blocked in and forms added by geometrical construction. In sketching you learned how to do pyramids, cones, cylinders and prismoidal (cut) blocks. Start with some imaginary land *(Fig. 11)*. Do some simple triangular land forms, then cones and cylinders *(Fig. 11)*. Combine some forms to get some imaginary land forms.

Sketching from Contour Maps. Pick a contour map with enough hills and valleys to make an interesting sketch. As in the section on visualization, select various vantage points on the map which will yield good views. Obviously looking down a valley sloping to you with hills on either side will make a good sketch as most of the terrain can be seen. Sketching slopes which recede and drop from the foreground is too hard. The method used is similar to block sketching in that we draw the front of the block parallel to us. Draw the base of the block as in the previous sketch and keep the cone of vision about 30°, a nearly normal view for eastern land, or 45° for the loftier view of the western part of the country. Lay off the grids on the contour map, adding grid lines by pencil on the original contour map if necessary. Redraw the map with its contours but distorted in plan *(Fig. 12)*. Starting from the very back base line measure perpendicularly up from each point on the grid, again exaggerating the vertical heights, in flat rolling country even up to 10

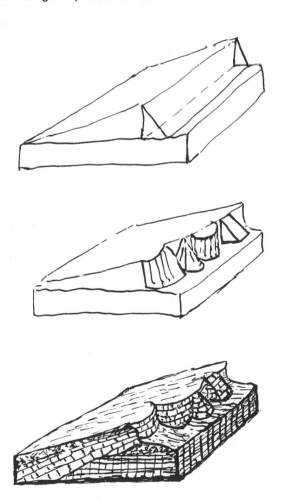

Fig. 11 Steps in geological sketching.

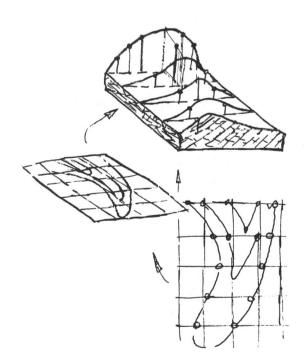

Fig. 12 Section developed from contour map.

times the other scale. Using 5 times for your first drawing, lay off heights along each east-west grid, giving a section for that grid line following the ground. For each grid do the same which will result in a series of ground sections cut parallel to the front surface. Some will appear to overlap *(Fig. 12   )*. Fill in the land surface by sketching light lines following the shape of the land surface, placing the lines closer together where the land is steeper. Use short curved strokes. For the edge of the drawing the block of land should be a solid unbroken line. The front of the block where it appears sectioned should have section lines. The side has less lines *(Fig. 13)*. If you know the geology of the land you can replace the section lines with simplified representation of stone, earth or sand *(Fig. 11)*. Such blocks are extremely useful in showing land forms and give an appreciation of the landscape formed by geological forces.

The entire drawing above was done in pencil and should be redrawn with drafting ink using a ruling pen for the straight lines and a crow quill pen for the others. Afterward the penciled construction lines are erased. Excellent results can be obtained from tinting this sketch with watercolors. When using watercolors, try the special watercolor paper that takes ink and watercolor. The colors used should be thinned so that merely a hint of the color is used. Pick conventional colors, green for woods, blue for water, brown for earth, gray for rocks, with man made objects in black. The whole can be lettered if you like. Naturally field sketching would not have these refinements but the lettering and name place should be on all topographical sketches as well as your name, the date and some scale. On field sketches the scale is often indicated by arrows between objects *(steeple to crossroads)* with an approximated or estimated mileage.

Well known geographical forms can readily be sketched by a series of vertical and horizontal lines by proportions *(Fig. 15)*.

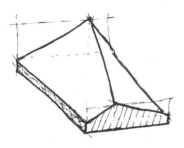

Fig.13 Landform developed from section.

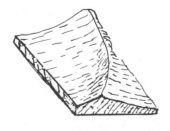

Fig. 14 Topographical sketch.

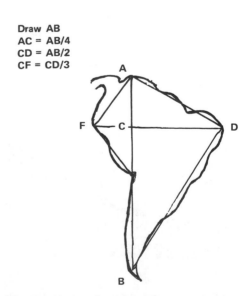

Draw **AB**
AC = AB/4
CD = AB/2
CF = CD/3

Fig. 15 Landform sketching by proportions.

Introduction. Engineers need to know how to find many areas and volumes of varied things: surface area for water runoff, area for aerial spraying, absorbtion area of filters, areas to be paved, painted and cleaned, volumes of cuts and fills, volumes of coal or ore, volume of machine parts for casting, volumes of water for lakes. There are many ways to find areas and volumes and men have spent time in finding other practical yet accurate methods.

Counting Squares. A piece of commercial graph paper is laid over the area to be measured, and the squares are counted. One inch blocks are counted, then the little blocks for the rest of the area. It is often used because it is economical, accurate and takes almost no equipment. It takes a lot of patience and is slow.

Simpson's Rule and Others. These men have discovered a fast yet accurate graphic method of finding areas. The area under a curve is divided into intervals which are juggled about with factors which yield an approximate answer. Simpson's rule seems to be the best and is in most of the texts. It is not a rule that is easily memorized, but can be written down in a note or field book *(Fig. 16)*.

Simpson's Rule. This process is very accurate for smoothly curved outlines. In the figure draw an odd number of parallel equispaced lines. Measure each line giving the outermost two their full values. Give the remaining odd number lines twice their value and the even numbered lines four times their value. Add these values and multiply this sum by one third of the width of an interval.

Durand's Rule. This method is good for very irregular outlines. In any irregular figure draw a number of parallel equispaced lines. Measure each line, giving full value to all lines except the first two and the last two. To the first and last line give a 5/12 value. To the second line from each end give a 13/12 value. Add the values of all these lines and multiply this sum by the width of one interval *(Fig. 17)*.

Rule for Trapezoids. In the figure draw a number of parallel equispaced lines. Assign half values to the first and last lines and full value to the remaining lines. Add these values and multiply the sum by an interval width. The results are sufficiently accurate for estimates of a general nature.

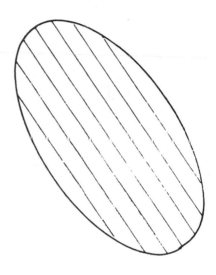

Fig. 16   *Area ruled for Simpson Rule.*

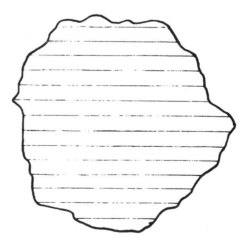

Fig. 17   *Area ruled for Durand's Rule.*

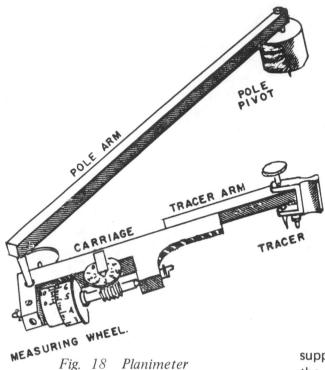

Fig. 18 Planimeter

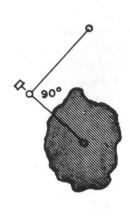

Fig. 19   Pole arm at right angles.

Planimeter. *(pla-nim'e-ter)* A small machine primarily used indoors for measuring areas by tracing around the outside curve, the planimeter is fast, accurate and expensive. It will last for years with zero maintenance, and some, 30 to 50 years old, are still in daily use.

All planimeters have in common a pole-arm and a tracer arm pivoted or hinged together. The two arms are stored apart. The free end of the pole has a pole pivot *(needle point)* and weight combined *(Fig. 18)*.

To use the instrument, open the box and take out the two pieces. The pivot fits in a hole in the carriage. At all times handle the instrument with care, do not force anything, or use much pressure on any part. Tape the map or paper with the area to be measured to a level table, move the tracer point to the center of the area to be measured, then move the pole arm to an approximate right angle with the tracer *(Fig. 19   )*. Lightly press the pole pivot point into the drawing board.

To measure the area, move the tracing point to any point on the area boundary that you will be able to recognize later. Adjust the support pin that rests on paper and is next to the tracer point until the tracer point barely touches the paper; adjust the wheel and dial to zero. When setting the dial raise the carriage and turn the measuring wheel touching only the plastic part. The best way to operate the planimeter is to hold the wing shaped handle of the tracer by pinching it with your thumb and middle finger while the index finger rests on the head of the tracer point. After checking to see that the tracer is still on your initial starting point and the dial reads zero, guide the tracer along the curve clockwise stopping when you return to your initial point. The circumference of the wheel is made so that one revolution is a number of square inches. The conversion of your figures depends upon the scale of the original drawing. Most planimeters can be read to the nearest hundredth of a square inch by a venier. Check your work by remeasuring counter-clockwise. There shouldn't be too much difference.

Most students like to start learning the use of the planimeter by measuring the piece of commercial graph paper and trying it over and over. It takes a bit of mechanical skill to keep the tracer point on the curve, but this comes with practice.

Measurements. All our measurements are relative, paper frequently varies in size due to moisture, temperature and age, and sometimes both dimensions will shrink, but one more than the other. Student scales are seldom extremely accurate and 90° triangles are seldom 90°. Plastic scales left in the sun become useless for accurate measurements at that time.

Precision of Measurement. Assuming that you can measure accurately and can lay off exact right angles and straight lines, construct a 4 inch by 5 inch rectangle as accurately as you can. A skilled man should be able to measure accurately to 0.02 per inch. To find the resulting error in this area, let:

Area = A = xy x and y being the sides of the rectangle.

Error in area = dA = xdy + ydx

For a 4" by 5" rectangle

Error in area = dA_{20} = (4) (0.02) + (5) (0.02) = 0.18 sq. in.

Percentage error in area = $\frac{0.18}{20}$ (100) = 0.9%

All this means is that with a very good man and an accurate instrument it is very likely that areas of 20 square inches will vary by at least 1%. A way of measuring the precision of an instrument and the operator is to measure any constant area many times and calculate the deviation from the mean by the method of least squares. The test is more reliable if done at a standard temperature with a solid which is used as a guide for the tracing point of the planimeter for the guide gives far better accuracy than hand tracing.

Graphic Calculus. Graphical integration is often used for finding the area under a given curve. Often the curve, if taken from field problems, has no known equation and the planimeter or graphical calculus can find the answer quickly. Both methods are not as accurate as traditional calculus, but somewhere the initial measurements were graphical.

Graphical Integration. Calculus is concerned with the change of value of functions due to finite changes in the variables. Integral calculus is concerned with finding the total change, a process of summation. Graphical integration

provides not only the area under the curve but the curve of integration itself. The deflection of a loaded beam *(a specific engineering problem)* can be obtained by making four successive integrations of the load curve, either graphical or mathematical.

Method. The given curve is placed on a sheet of paper with enough space above it for constructing the integral curve. It is customary to line up the abcissas of the x-axis of both curves *(Fig. 20)*.

The area under the given curve is found by dividing the area into small vertical rectangles. The height of the rectangles are laid out by eye so that the area outside the curve equals the area inside the curve. Matching the two little triangles, one above and the other below the curve, can be done quite accurately if the width of the rectangles is kept small. All of these rectangles added together equal the area.

To add them we use a graphical addition. On an extended x-axis, usually to the left, select a convenient polepoint, **P**. The tops of each rectangle are carried across horizontally to the y-axis. A fan of lines is then drawn from P to each y intercept: PA, PB, PC, etc. *(Fig.20)*.

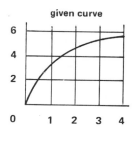

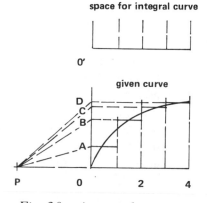

Fig. 20   Area under curve.

131

Start the construction of the integral curve by projecting the x abcissas up to the blank area of the paper, drawing x' and y' axes. In the new graph (the integral curve) draw lines from 0'0' parallel to PA, PB, PC, etc., to correspond to the intervals in the first graph (the given curve). The new graph consists of small straight line segments which are faired or smoothed out into one continuous line which is the integral curve *(Fig. 21)*.

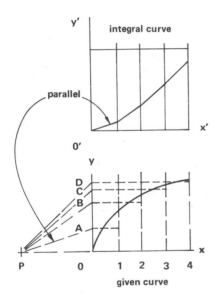

Fig. 21   Finding integral curve.

So far we have the curve but we have no values for the integral curve. To find these values, go to the given curve graph, selecting from it any known rectangle *(say 2 x 5, giving an area of 10 units)*. From the y intersept of this rectangle draw 5 to the pole P. This gives us a 10 unit ray which we can transfer to the integral curve. Starting inside the graph from 0'0' draw 0'M parallel to P5 which yields a 10 unit rectangle which on the y' intercept gives a value of 10 *(Fig. 22   )*.

There are various refinements of this procedure. To estimate the height of the integral curve before starting *(to see if it will fit on the*

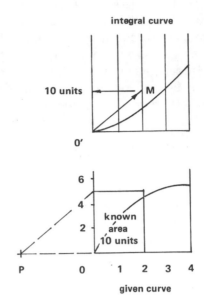

Fig. 22   Finding units on integral graph.

paper or will be too flat an angle), by eye draw one horizontal line in the given curve which, like the little rectangle, will divide the area above and below the curve into equal areas. With practice this can be done by eye, but you may want to count the large squares on the graph paper the first few times. This rectangle gives the approximate total area under the curve, and tells the approximate height of the integral curve.

After selecting a polepoint and finding the scale value for the y' axis in the integral curve, you may find that these values do not coincide with the grids of the graph paper. You may then refine the problem by moving the pole P so that the y' value is readjusted to coincide with the grid lines of the graph paper.

A constant of integration must also be added to the equation to provide for initial conditions. This moves the integral curve up the y' axis so that it does not start at 0'0'. The actual value may be determined by knowing any fact that will fix the value on the integral curve.

GLOSSARY

Angle of Repose The base angle of the right circular cone developed when rock or any other loose material, dumped from a point onto a horizontal surface, comes to a natural halt and the pile remains stable. Stated either in degrees or as a slope ratio.

Base Plane A plane from whose edge view measurements are taken perpendicularly above and below.

Block Drawing A sketch of relief models showing three dimensions in a rectangular box.

Contour Line An imaginary line that represents on the land or contour map all equal elevations connected in sequence.

Contour Map A map showing elevations and surface configurations (a top view of the surface of the ground) by means of contour lines.

Cut and Fill The cut is the cubic space from which material must be excavated (cut away) to reduce higher elevations to the specific level needed. The fill is the cubic space into which material must be dumped to raise (fill) the lower elevations to the specific level needed.

Dip The average inclination of a stratum or vein measured downward at right angles to the strike, expressed in degrees of the dihedral angle below the horizontal plane.

Drift The horizontal passageway driven on the course of the vein.

Elevation The height, in feet or meters, of any location measured from sealevel above or below.

Foot Wall The surface of rock below the vein.

Grade The degree of inclination or slope in terms of feet or rise to feet of run, expressed usually in percent.

Hanging Wall The surface of rock above the vein.

Incline A sloped passage that follows the dip of the vein.

Interval The distance between two elevations usually in multiples of 10 or 100 feet.

Isometric Paper Paper gridded at a 30° angle so that drawings can be made of figures and maps showing the three dimensions, not in perspective.

Lines of Outcrop Visible segments of the vein of mineral on the surface of the earth, particularly the edge view of the hanging and foot walls.

Profile A side view of an object or structure. An outline drawn of the vertical planes cutting through the earth's surface.

Shaft A vertical or slightly inclined opening for finding or mining ore, may be begun from any point along a tunnel.

Shoot A rich streak of ore in a vein.

Strike The degree of swing of a horizontal line of a vein from a North-South meridian.

Tunnel A nearly level or horizontal passage into the earth from a surface opening or daylight. All horizontal passages are labeled lateral drives.

Vein A regularly shaped and lengthy occurrence of an ore.

Yorktowne I Subdivision

LAND SURVEY AND DESCRIPTION

12

Introduction

Every legal description of property is based upon a land survey. In order to prepare a legal description of a parcel or tract of land, someone at some time must have measured and marked the land---made a survey---upon which the description is based

The subject of land descriptions and surveys is centuries old. The earliest records of man refer to the skillful measurements and calculations with respect to land, but it is impossible to assign the birth of the science of surveying to any particular year or even country. The Chinese, at an early date, and the ancient Egyptians practiced the art of surveying. In Egypt, it appears that it was necessary every spring to re-establish corners and boundary lines altered by floods of the Nile River.

Today, the transfer of land ownership and the mortgaging of property require legal land descriptions by which the location and boundaries of land parcels can be determined. Descriptions must be referenced to established systems of field marks and measures. Hence, a general knowledge of survey systems is necessary to understand the description of land in writing.

This section describes the several general systems of survey and types of legal land descriptions used in the United States today.

A survey is the measure and marking of land, accompanied by maps and field notes which describe the measures and marks actually made in the field. The lengths and directions of boundary lines are established between reference points on the ground. The reference points may be natural marks, such as rivers, or they may be stone, concrete or other artificial markers located and set in the field by a surveyor, and permanent markers set in the field by surveyors are called **monuments.**

Today, survey measure of lengths commonly is made in feet and decimal parts of feet. However, terminology based on measures no longer used is encountered often in surveys and legal descriptions. For example, early surveys were based on lengths such as **chains** and **links.** Surveyors actually made field measurements with a metal chain made of 100 links. The chain was 66' long, and 80 chains equaled one statute mile *(5,280')*. Some of the various measures used and their equivalents are shown in *(Fig. 1)*.

LAND MEASURES AND EQUIVALENTS

1 mm	= 0.039 370 1 inch	1 km	= 0.621 371 mile
1 inch	= 25.4 mm	1 rod	= 16.5 feet
1 link	= 7.92 inches	1 rod	= 25 links
1 foot	= 304.8 mm	1 furlong	= 10 chains
1 foot	= 0.3048 meters	1 furlong	= 40 rods
1 yard	= 0.9144 meters	1 mile	= 80 chains
1 meter	= 3.28084 feet	1 mile	= 320 rods
1 meter	= 1.09361 yards	1 mile	= 8 furlongs
1 chain	= 100 links	1 mile	= 1.609 344 k m
1 chain	= 66 feet	1 section	= 1 square mile
1 chain	= 4 rods	1 section	= 640 acres
1 chain	= 20.1168 meters	1 acre	= 160 square rods
1 km	= 49.7097 chains	1 acre	= 43,560 square feet

Fig. 1 Land Measures and Equivalents

Two general systems of survey are used in the United States; the **metes and bounds system,** evolved from Colonial days, which is based on tracing the boundary lines surrounding an area; and the **Rectangular System** of the Federal Government Survey used in most of the states,which is based on a modified grid of north-south and east-west lines.

Though the following discussion of survey systems may appear to be a rather exact basis upon which land can be described, it is not. Inaccuracies in surveying, which may or may not be avoidable, may present difficulty and disagreement in the legal description of land.

Metes And Bounds System

Survey by metes and bounds *(Fig. 2)* consists of beginning at a known point and "running out" the boundaries of the area by **courses** *(directions)* and **distances** *(lengths)*, and fixing natural or artificial monuments at the corners. The place of beginning *(P.O.B.)* must be a known point that can be readily identified. The point must be

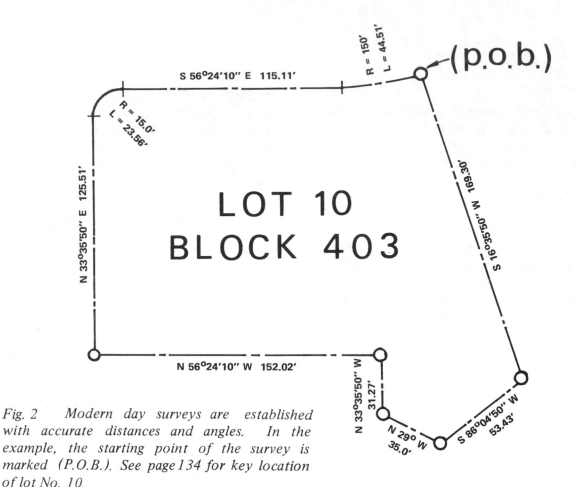

Fig. 2   Modern day surveys are established with accurate distances and angles.   In the example, the starting point of the survey is marked (P.O.B.). See page 134 for key location of lot No. 10.

established and witnessed so that it can be relocated with certainty if the **monument** which identified it is destroyed or removed. The survey description "must close"; that is, if the courses and distances of the description are traced in order, one must return to the starting point.

The metes and bounds system is one of the oldest known manners of surveying and describing land. The system evolved from the early practice of "settlement first, survey afterwards." Land being bought, claimed or inherited would be identified by known natural points such as trees, rivers, and artificial points such as roads, structures or other manmade marks.

Early metes and bounds surveys and descriptions often were based on monuments that lacked permanency. Surveying of large and irregular tracts of land without regard to any system or uniformity, and the failure of the surveyors to make their survey notes a matter of public

record, created situations that gave rise to frequent boundary line disputes . and litigation. Today, metes and bounds surveys do not have the uncertainty as to place of beginning that existed in Colonial days. Present day surveys and descriptions may refer to government survey sections lines and corners *(see Rectangular System)* as monuments, in addition to permanent artificial marks placed by surveyors.

Metes and bounds surveys and descriptions still are used in 20 states, which include the states of the New England area, the Atlantic Coast states *(except Florida)*, and Kentucky, Tennessee, Texas, Virginia and West Virginia. The metes and bounds system may be used anywhere to survey areas which are irregular in size and shape *(Fig. 5)*.

Rectangular System

After the Revolutionary War, the federal government found itself with huge tracts of undeveloped and uninhabited land, with few natural characterics suitable for use as monuments in metes and bounds descriptions. It was necessary to develop a new standard system of describing land so that parcels could be located readily and permanently for land office sales. A committee headed by Thomas Jefferson evolved a plan, which the Continental Congress adopted in 1785, for dividing the land into a series of rectangles. This plan, designated the **Rectangular System** *(also called the Government System)* of survey, is in use today in the other 30 of the 50 states.

Meridians and Base Lines. A map of the world *(Fig. 3)* shows a series of north-south lines called **meridians** of longitude extending

LINES OF LONGITUDE AND LATITUDE

(Meridians & Parallels)

NORTH POLE

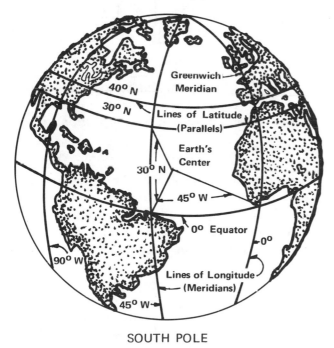

SOUTH POLE

Fig. 3 The rectangular system of survey is based upon a modified grid of meridians and parallels measured from the Greenwich Meridian and the Equator.

from the North to the South Pole. One of these lines, the **Greenwich Meridian,** passes through the Royal Observatory at Greenwich, England and is designated as 0° longitude. Locations on the globe east or west of Greenwich are measured in degrees from that meridian.

The reference lines running around the globe due East and West are called **parallels** of latitude. The **Equator,** which circles the center of the globe, is designated as 0° latitude. Locations on the globe north and south of the Equator are measured in degrees from that parallel of latitude.

The Greenwich Meridian and the Equator are the lines of reference used in navigation. The position of a ship or plane relative to these lines of reference can be determined by taking an instrument reading of the position of celestial bodies. The position, or location, is stated in degrees, minutes and seconds north or south of the equatorial line *(latitude);* and in degrees, minutes and seconds east or west of the Greenwich Meridian *(longitude).* For example, O'Hare Airport Tower, Chicago, is located at $87^o57'28''$ West Longitude and $41^o59'10''$ North Latitude.

The rectangular system of survey is based on a series of **principal meridians** and **base lines** located by surveyors using methods similar to those used in navigation. The meridians run north and south, the base lines run east and west. Their position is established by longitude and latitude.

Principal Meridians. In establishing the rectangular system of survey, surveyors first selected a substantial landmark from which a start could be made in surveying an area of land. Usually a place was selected that could be identified readily, such as the mouth of a river, and wherever possible a monument was placed. From this point the surveyors ran a line due North and South and designated it as the **principal meridian** for that particular state or area. The location of the principal meridian *(its longitude)* was fixed by a reading measured in degrees, minutes and seconds west of the Greenwich Meridian.

As territories were opened and surveyed by the government, principal meridians were established for each area opened. Some of the principal meridians were referred to by number, such as the **First, Second, Third** Principal Meridian. The Third Principal Meridian is the line located 89°10'15" west of Greenwich and extends from the mouth of the Ohio River to the northern boundary of Illinois. Other principal meridians were named for the states, such as the Michigan Meridian which covers the survey of that state.

Base Lines. After the principal meridians for a particular area were fixed, a point on the meridian was selected from which a line was run at right angles, due East and West. This line was designated as the **base line** for the area, and its location *(its latitude)* was established in degrees, minutes and seconds north of the equatorial line *(Fig. 4)*.

In certain instances the base line for a new territory was established by extending the base line of an adjoining territory, previously surveyed. For example, the base line for both the Second and Third Principal Meridians is a parallel of latitude 38°28'20" north of the equatorial line *(Fig. 5)*.

Correction Lines. All meridians meet at the North and South Poles. They are not parallel lines. This fact is not observable from a point on the earth's surface without the aid of surveying instruments, but an accurate measure of a midwestern area 6 miles square would show its north line to be nearly 50' shorter than the south line. To compensate for the convergence of the meridians, it was necessary to establish additional reference lines to measure equal east-west distances. East and west lines, parallel to the base line, were located at intervals of 24 miles north and south of the base line. These lines were designated as **correction lines.**

Guide Meridians. After the east-west correction lines were set, **guide meridians** running due North and South at 24 mile intervals on each side of the principal meridians were established. Guide meridians extend from the base line to the first correction line, and then from correction line to correction line. The guide meridians and the correction lines form a square approximately 24 miles on each side as shown in *(Fig. 4)*.

DIVISION OF LAND BY RECTANGULAR SURVEY SYSTEM

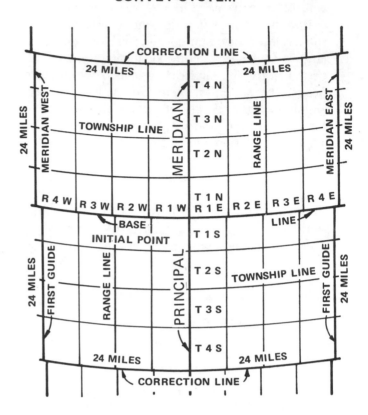

Fig. 4   In the rectangular survey system, 24 miles square are divided into 16 townships and each township is divided into 36 sections.

Township and Range Lines. The 24 miles square were then divided into 16 smaller tracts by township lines and range lines. **Township Lines** were run east and west *(parallel to the base line)* at 6 mile intervals. **Range lines** were run north and south at 6 mile intervals. This cross-hatching resulted in a grid of squares, called **townships,** approximately 6 miles on each side *(Fig. 4)*.

Two reference numbers were assigned to each square---a township number and a range number. Rows of squares *(tiers)* were numbered consecutively to the north or south of the base line. Thus, each square in the first row north of the base line is called **Township 1 North** *(T. 1N);* each in the second row, **Township 2 North** *(T. 2N),* etc. Similarly, each square in the first row south of the base line is called **Township 1**

MERIDIANS AND BASE LINES OF THE UNITED STATES RECTANGULAR SYSTEMS

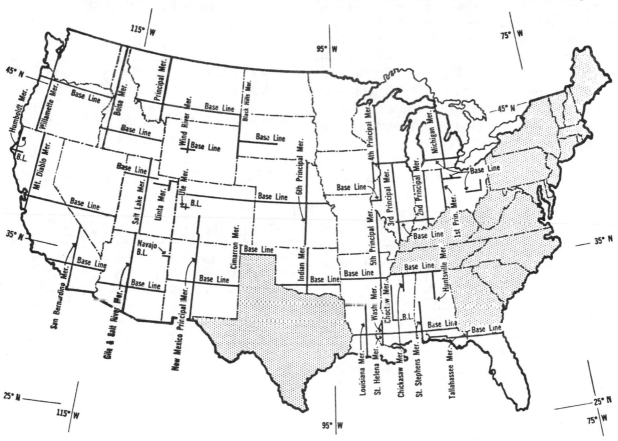

Meridians.	Governing surveys (wholly or in part) in States of—	Longitude of principal meridians west from Greenwich. ° ′ ″	Latitude of base lines north from Equator. ° ′ ″	Meridians.	Governing surveys (wholly or in part) in States of—	Longitude of principal meridians west from Greenwich. ° ′ ″	Latitude of base lines north from Equator. ° ′ ″
Black Hills	South Dakota	104 03 00	44 00 00	Navajo	Ariz. & N. Mex.	108 32 45	35 45 00
Boise	Idaho	116 24 15	43 22 31	New Mex. Principal	New Mexico	106 52 41	34 15 25
Chickasaw	Mississippi	89 15 00	34 59 00	New Mex. Principal	Colorado	106 53 36	
Choctaw	Mississippi	90 14 45	31 54 40	Principal	Montana	111 38 50	45 46 48
Cimarron	Oklahoma	103 00 00	36 30 00	Salt Lake	Utah	111 54 00	40 46 04
Copper River	Alaska	145 18 42	61 49 11	San Bernardino	California	116 56 15	34 07 10
Fairbanks	Alaska	147 38 33	64 51 49	Second Principal	Ill. & Ind.	86 28 00	38 28 20
Fifth Principal	Ark., Iowa, Minn., Mo., N. Dak., & S. Dak.	91 03 42	34 44 00	Seward	Alaska	149 21 53	60 07 26
First Principal	Ohio & Indiana	84 48 50	41 00 00	Sixth Principal	Colo., Kans., Nebr., S. Dak. & Wyo.	97 23 00	40 00 00
Fourth Principal	Illinois[1]	90 28 45	40 00 30	St. Helena	Louisiana	91 09 15	31 00 00
Fourth Principal	Minn. & Wisc.	90 28 45	42 30 00	St. Stephens	Ala. & Miss.	88 02 00	31 00 00
Gila and Salt River	Arizona	112 18 24	33 22 33	Tallahassee	Florida	84 16 42	30 28 00
Humboldt	California	124 07 11	40 25 04	Third Principal	Illinois	89 10 15	38 28 20
Huntsville	Ala. & Miss.	86 34 45	35 00 00	Uinta	Utah	109 57 30	40 26 20
Indian	Oklahoma	97 14 30	34 30 00	Ute	Colorado	108 33 20	39 06 40
Louisiana	Louisiana[2]	92 24 15	31 00 00	Washington	Mississippi	91 09 15	31 00 00
Michigan	Mich. & Ohio	84 22 24	42 26 30	Willamette	Ore. & Wash.	122 44 20	45 31 00
Mount Diablo	Calif. & Nev.	121 54 48	37 51 30	Wind River	Wyo.	108 48 40	43 01 20

1. Numbers are carried to fractional township 29 north in Ill., and are repeated in Wisc., beginning with south bounaary of the Staie, range numbers are in regular order. 2. Latitude doubtful; is to be verified.

Fig. 5 *Rectangular System is used in states shown unshaded, Hawaii and Alaska. Each principal meridian and its base line is shown on the map with location by longitude and lattitude in table: shaded areas use metes and bounds surveys.*

South; each in the second row, **Township 2 South,** etc. In the same manner, rows of squares *(ranges)* were numbered consecutively to the east and west of the principal meridian. Thus, each square in the first row east of the principal meridian is called **Range 1 East** *(R. 1E)*, those in the second row **Range 2 East** *(R. 2E)*, etc., and on the west of the principal meridian, those in the first row were number **Range 1 West**, those in the second row, **Range 2 West**, etc.

Sections. Townships were the smallest divisions of land provided for in the act of 1785, which created the Rectangular System of survey. In making the early surveys, the outside boundaries of the township were surveyed and monuments were placed at every mile on the township lines.

It soon became apparent that a township six square miles was too large an area in which to describe and locate a given tract of land. In 1796, Congress passed an act directing that townships already surveyed be subdivided into 36 **sections,** each to be approximately one mile square containing *"as nearly as may be"* 640 acres. The corner of each section was to be monumented, and the sections numbered consecutively from 1 to 36, beginning with No. 1 in the northeast corner of the township, ending in the southeast corner with No. 36, as shown in *(Fig. 6)*. This manner of numbering sections in a township has continued to this date. A given tract of land can be located within a particular square mile by giving the section number, the township number north or south of the base line, and the range number east or west of the controlling principal meridian.

Fractional Sections. Due to the convergence of the meridians, each township does not form a perfect square. A township cannot form 36 identical sections in area or shape. Rules had to be established to correct any excess or deficiency in south to north measurements and to add or subtract them from the north portion of the sections in the north row in the township *(namely, Sections No. 1 through No. 6)*. Any excess or shortage in the east to west measurements should be added or subtracted from the west portion of

NUMBERING OF SECTIONS
WITHIN A TOWNSHIP

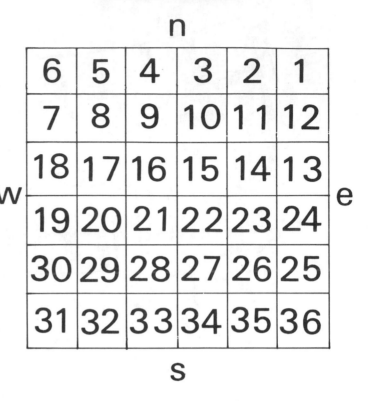

Fig. 6 A township is divided into 36 sections.

the west row in the township *(namely, Sections 6, 7, 18, 19, 30 and 31)*. Such adjustments to these adjusted sections bordering on the north and west sides of a township are called **fractional sections.**

The land that borders on lakes, surveyed areas that do not close perfectly and sections that are less than one mile square are reasons for fractional sections.

Government Lots. Regulations stated that fractional sections were to be divided into equal fractional parts as even as possible. Any remaining portion was to be divided into parts called government lots and numbered consecutively. The intent of the regulation was to divide fractional sections into as many regular parts as possible according to their position in the section, with any left over portions divided into lots of approximately the same size.

Division of Sections

Congress later provided for the division of sections into smaller units *(Fig. 7)*. In 1800, the sections were divided into halves of approximately 320 acres by running north and south lines through the center of the sections. In 1805 regulations provided for quarter sections by running east and west lines through the center of the

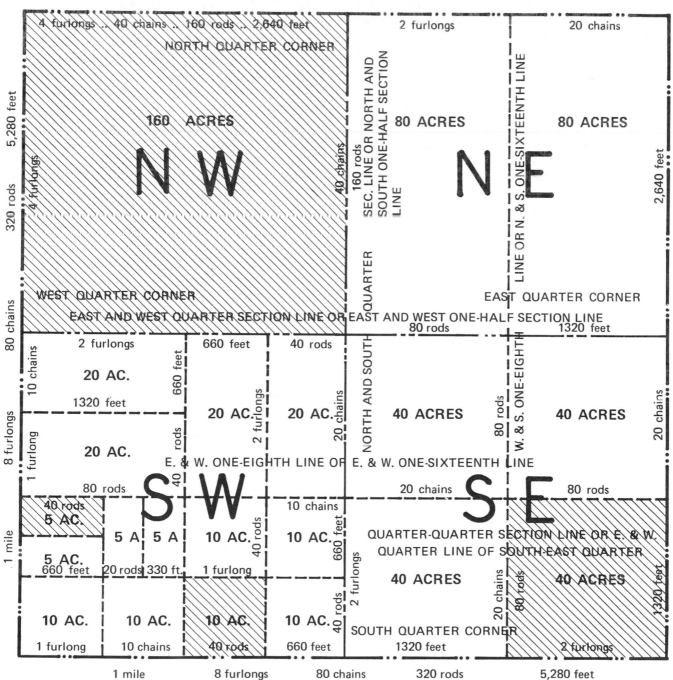

Section = 1 sq. mile = 640 Acres

Fig. 7 Sections, one mile square, are subdivided by federal act down to 40 acre-quarter quarters. Land acreage and distances within the section are shown here.

sections, with the corners of all quarter sections to be monumented.

This act stated that all corners marked in the public survey would be accepted as the proper corners of the sections or quarter sections. That is, monumented corners set by the government surveyors would *stand as true corners* whether or not the monument was actually placed as described in the field notes.

Congress later provided for the further division of quarter sections in *half quarters* and finally *quarter-quarters*. These subdivisions were made by running east-west lines and north-south lines through the quarter sections. The quarter-quarter section of 40 acres is the smallest statutory division of regular sections in the rectangular survey system *(Fig. 7)*.

EROS MAPPING

The United States Government operates the Earth Resources Observation Systems (EROS) with its primary location at Sioux Falls, South Dakota. This is the Data Center which acts as the library for maps, conducts discipline oriented courses in mapping for agriculture, forestry, geology and hydrology, and sells maps. Visitors to the Data Center can also obtain specialized help in the operation of equipment such as densitometers, additive color viewers, zoom transfer scopes, stereo viewers, computer multispectral systems, etc.

EROS Data Reference Files have also been established at various locations throughout the United States, but scientific assistance is only available at the Center in Sioux Falls.

The Data Center has a central data computer on all geographical areas of the world. Retrieval is based on latitude and longitude, or the name of large cities.

There are millions of imagery available, maps, aerial photos, satellite mapping and tapes which would yield maps, multi-band spectrum, false color, computer enhancement of maps, etc. The computer search is free, and they will advise you of the many maps, imagery available for your selected location and the cost. The computer tapes are also available at a nominal fee.

Information is generally divided into: Landsat Data, Skylab Data, and NASA Data.

Landsat Data, from an orbital satellite, gives new coverage every 18 days. Each pass yields 5 different maps, band 4 is generally for water, band 5 for cultural features, band 6 generally for vegetation, band 7 for landforms, band 8 senses emitted (not reflected) thermal radiation, and can discriminate between temperature emissions as small as 1.5 degrees C. Each frame covers an area of 115 x 115 miles.

Skylab (various ones in orbit from 1973 to 1974) takes photos in natural color with a coverage of 70 x 70 miles (110 x 110 km). Coverage is only between latitudes 50 degrees N. and 50 degrees S., and some photos have scattered clouds which obscure the land.

NASA aerial photography is available in a wide variety of formats from low level flights (altitudes of a few thousand feet, 1000 km.) to the U-2 flights at altitudes above 60,000 feet (18,000 km). Each frame (9 x 9 inches, 230 mm) shows an area of 17 miles (27 km) on a side. Individual roads and some buildings can be picked out. In addition some Gemini-Apollo hand-held camera photos are available.

Many maps and photos are attractive and suitable for framing.

COMPUTER MAPPING

Computer mapping is now in general use for most surveying projects. The computer will handle all the mathematics, bearings, set backs, lengths of utilities, etc., and generate plot plan, survey plans, site planning and sub-division layout and design.

13

The objective of a legal description is to identify, locate and define a specific piece of land and distinguish it from all other existing tracts of land. A **legal description** in the United States is based on: (1) the metes and bounds survey system, (2) the rectangular survey system, and (3) reference to recorded maps and plats. It is not unusual to find several of these methods in one description.

Metes and Bounds Description. This consists of a series of statements describing each portion of the boundary around the parcel of land that is being described. Starting from a *place of begin-*

ning (P.O.B.), the direction and distances of the property lines are called, **bearings,** until the entire perimeter has been traced around the property, returning to the starting point. Each leg of the perimeter is described first by the direction and then by the length *(Fig 1)*.

Direction. When the directions *(courses)* agree with the major compass directions, they are so named. Courses that are not due North, South, East or West *(cardinal points)* are called **angular courses.** Angular course direction is stated in degrees, minutes and seconds as an angular deviation east or west of due North or South *(Fig. 2)*.

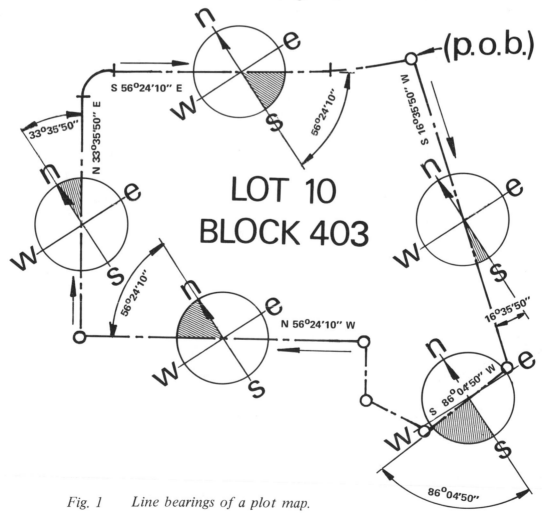

Fig. 1   Line bearings of a plot map.

The direction is always written with the general statement North or South, followed by the angle of eastward or westward deviation from North or South. "North 25 degrees East" defines an angular course direction 25° eastward of due North. A call "South 47 degrees 20' West" defines a direction 47°20' westward of South.

Prolongation. Occasionally a course direction is described by stating the amount of deviation from the preceding course line. An angle is measured from an extension, a **prolongation**, of the previous line, and might be stated: "Northerly 45 degrees to the left of an extension of the last described line."

Curve Lines. A curved line is referred to in a description as "South 75 degrees East 125 feet to a point of tangency; thence along a curve northeasterly and having a radius of 40 feet; a distance of 62.80 feet" *(Fig. 3)*. The point of tangency, or the point of contact between the last described straight line and the curve, is the starting place of the curve. Convex refers to the

outside of the curve; concave refers to the inside of a curve. "Convex northeasterly" means the outside of the curve lies to the northeast.

Distance. Distance is stated in feet and decimal parts of feet. Sometimes it may be stated in feet and inches, or fractions of feet, and rarely in chains, rods, and lengths *(Fig. 3)*. Measure is taken from point to point along straight lines and along the curve of a curved line.

Rectangular System Descriptions

In this system, large unmarked areas of land are reduced to series of small squares; basic lines of survey are established by astronomical measurements; permanent monuments have been located on the ground by surveyors to establish quarter-quarter section corners; and careful survey notes of the description and location of all monuments have been made and filed with the government.

Any tract of land in the government survey is described legally by reference to its prin-

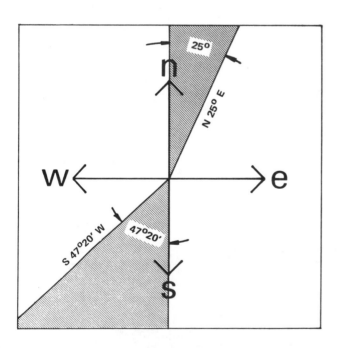

Fig. 2   Boundary line directions are designated by their eastward or westward deviation from North or South.

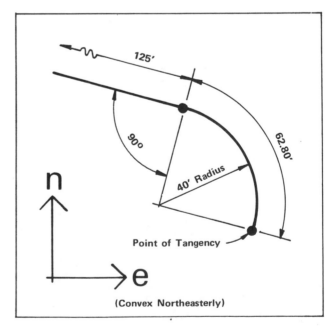

Fig. 3   Curved lines are described by giving the radius and length of the arc, and the direction of the curve.

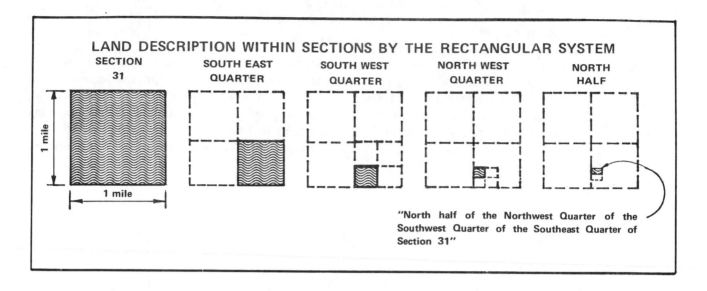

Fig. 4   Land description such as "the North half of the Northwest quarter of the Southwest quarter of the Southeast quarter of Section 31," it is faster to locate the tract of land within the section by reading the land description in reverse; "Section 31, South East quarter, South West quarter, North West quarter, North half.

cipal meridian and base line, township and range numbers, section number, and its location within the section.

A parcel of land might read: "the South West quarter of the North East quarter of Section 31, Township 12 East of the Third Principal Meridian" *(Fig. 4).*

Government lots are described by identifying the lot number and the quarter section in which the lot is located: "Government Lot 2 in the North West quarter of the fractional Section 18, Township 36 North, Range 11 East of the Third Principal Meridian."

The rectangular system is often used to describe the boundaries of a subdivision in which individual lots may then be described by reference to a recorded plat or map. The plat is prepared by a surveyor and recorded in the county records.

Reference to the Recorded Plat

Curved street patterns may produce irregularly shaped blocks and lots. The entire subdivision may be described within the rectangular system or by a metes and bounds description, but it may

be impractical to use these two systems to describe individual blocks or lots. Therefore, many states provide for the legal description of property by the reference to plats properly recorded, generally in the county office.

The plat is prepared by a surveyor. The tract or subdivision may be divided into blocks and then into lots. Lots and blocks may be given consecutive numbers or letters in order to be completely identified in the subdivision, which is usually given a name by the developer and/or owner. An example of a recorded subdivision plat is shown in *(Fig. 5).*

The surveyors plat is headed with the legal description of the land. It shows all boundary lines, all monuments, dividing lines for blocks, lots and streets, the numbering and dimensions of each lot and the setback lines.

Easements and restrictions may also be indicated on the plat. The plat is certified by the surveyor, signed by the owner and/or developer, mayor, municipal clerk, municipal engineer and a notary public seal. Upon approval by the proper authorities, *planning boards, zoning boards and building commissions,* it is recorded in the county recorder's office.

When recorded, the lots in a subdivision may easily be identified legally by reference to lot and block numbers, the subdivision name, and the section, township and range in which the entire subdivision boundaries are described within a rectangular survey or metes and bounds description.

Uncertainties

Mistakes, errors and judgements may result in conflicts and uncertainties in the legal description of land. Whether a recorded subdivision plat, a rectangular survey, or a metes and bounds description is involved, there may be differing opinions as to the exact location of the boundary

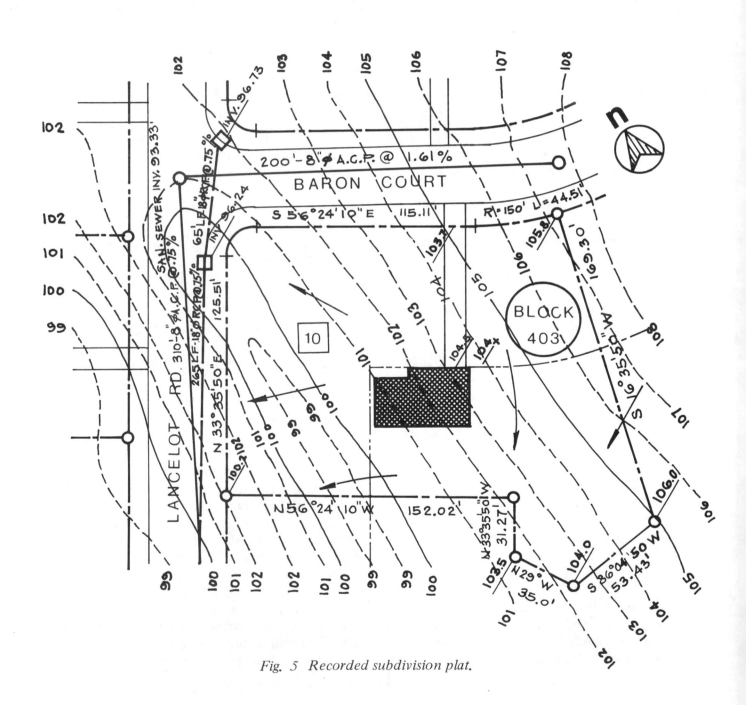

Fig. 5 Recorded subdivision plat.

lines of a tract of land. This exact location of a point on land can be a matter of opinion and subject to interpretation.

Location of Markers. While making the original government surveys, upon which resurveys should be based, section corners are marked; however, through the years, monuments may have been changed or destroyed during the moving of earth, such as road constructions, or in farming. Relocating a missing corner may require measuring from monuments in existing surveys or from other references.

The disappearance of monuments cause uncertainties in surveying. Metes and bounds surveys monumented to a tree or post which is non-existing, may require the surveyor to spend time trying to locate the missing remains.

Roads described in an old survey may have been abandoned and offer no trace of their former location. Many times the surveyor must establish a line on paper that represents that missing road.

Inaccuracies. The measurement of distances called for in some legal descriptions is almost impossible. As written in a description, the distance "133.01 feet" gives an illusion of precision; however, if two surveying crews measured the same distance, they very rarely would observe the same measurement. Minute differences in the tautness of the measuring tape and changes in the length of the tape due to the effect of temperature changes are unavoidable. A point in mathematical definition has neither **length, breadth,** nor **depth.** The ".01" of a foot is equal to a little less than 1/8". It would be amazing if two surveyors would locate this invisible point in exactly the same place. Yet a surveyor must express an opinion as to its location and the opinions of individual surveyors will differ unless the point is monumented in the first place.

In surveying a tract, it is necessary to locate the boundaries of all adjacent tracts as shown in any earlier surveys and to harmonize the perimeter lines of the tract being surveyed with them. Many times the legal descriptions of the abutting tracts must be checked.

Early government surveyors used a measuring instrument that was a 66' chain made up of 100 metal links. Weather changes resulted in expansion or contraction of these chains, and wear and use caused them to stretch. Sometimes surveyors would count the revolutions of the wheel of the vehicle in which they traveled to measure long, straight stretches. Distances were often "stepped off" by the measured stride. Remember, even though these measurements were far from accurate, markers were placed, and they were considered legal points of reference, regardless of their accuracy in being placed.

Mistakes, such as careless observations and inaccurate measurements, are random and unpredictable. Even though the best surveying instruments are subject to a certain degree of error, these errors are predictable and can be allowed for in observing measurements. Keep in mind, **there is always some human judgement involved.**

Recorded Plats

When an individual lot is described by reference to a recorded subdivision plat, the plat together with all information and data shown thereon is part of the lot description. It includes not only dimensions and expressions of quantity and area, but also the notations of the courses and distances of the lines of the subdivision and of the identity and locations of the monuments marking the boundaries.

When this information is included into a legal description, it becomes a metes and bounds description and is subject to rules of interpretation, should any conflict or discrepancy be contained in the data of the plat.

Monuments prevail over courses and distances, courses prevail over distances, and expressions of quantity or area are generally the least reliable.

The systems of survey upon which legal descriptions are based are as precise as is possible. There is always the possibility of uncertainties in separate surveys, and mistakes may occur in the writing and rewriting of legal descriptions. Descriptions may **identify land,** but surveys are necessary to actually **locate boundary lines.**

GLOSSARY

Angular Course Compass direction in degrees, minutes and seconds, stated as a deviation eastward or westward from due North or South; used in metes and bounds surveys and descriptions.

Angular Measure The deviation between two lines which meet at a point, expressed in degrees, minutes and seconds.

Base Line Parallel of specified latitude, used in the rectangular survey system serving as the main east-west reference line with a principal meridian for a particular state or area.

Call In surveyor's language, the statement or mention of a course and/or distance.

Cardinal Points The four major compass headings of North, East, South and West

Correction Lines East-west reference lines used in the rectangular survey system, located at 24-mile intervals to the north and south of a base line.

Course Compass direction from one reference point to the next for each leg of a metes and bounds survey.

Degree Unit of angular measure equal to the angle contained within two radii of a circle which describe an arc equal to 1/360 part of the circumference of the circle; also used to define an arc equal to 1/360 part of the circumference of a circle.

Equator The parallel circling the middle of the earth, all points of which are equidistant from both North and South Poles; designated as the starting line (0°) for measuring north or south latitude.

Fractional Section Any "adjusted" section of land generally containing less (sometimes more) than 1 square mile. The deficiency (or excess) may be the result of the convergence of meridians, the presence of bodies of water, or uncertainties in surveying.

Guide Meridian North-south reference lines located at 24-mile intervals east and west of a principal meridian.

Great Circle Line described on a sphere by a plane bisecting the sphere into equal parts. The Equator is a great circle, as are pairs of opposing meridians.

Latitude Position of a point on the earth's surface north or south of the Equator, stated as an angular measure (degrees, minutes and seconds) of the meridian are contained between that point and the Equator.

Legal Description A written identification of the location and boundaries of a parcel of land. A legal description may be based on a metes and bounds survey, the rectangular system of survey, or it may make reference to a recorded plat of survey.

Longitude Position of a point on the earth's surface east or west of the Greenwich Meridian, stated as an angular measure (degrees, minutes and seconds) of the arc on the Equator contained between a meridian passing through that point and the Greenwich Meridian.

Metes and Bounds System of land survey and description based on starting from a known reference point and tracing the boundary line around an area.

Meridian Imaginary north-south line on the earth's surface described by a great circle arc from the North Pole to the South Pole. All points on a meridian are of the same longitude.

Greenwich (Prime Meridian) The meridian passing through the Royal Observatory at Greenwich, England, and designated as the starting line (0°) for measuring east and west longitude.

Principal Meridian Meridian of specified longitude, used in the rectangular survey system, serving as the main north-south reference line for a particular state or area.

Minute Unit of angular measure equal to 1/60 of a degree.

Monument Permanent reference point for land surveying whose location is recorded; either a manmade marker or a natural landmark.

Parallel Imaginary east-west line on the earth's surface, consisting of a circle on which all points are equidistant from one of the poles. All points on a parallel are the same latitude.

Plat A map of surveyed land showing the location and the boundaries and dimensions of the parcel.

P.O.B. (Place of Beginning) Starting point of a metes and bounds survey or description.

Range Lines North-south reference lines used in the rectangular survey system, located at 6-mile intervals between guide meridians.

Recorded Plat A plat which is recorded at an appropriate government office, usually the county recorder's office. The recorded plat, in addition to location notes and boundary line layout may contain information such as restrictions, easements, approvals by zoning boards and planning commissions, and lot and block numbers for a subdivision.

Rectangular (Government) Survey System Land survey system based on geographical coordinates of longitude and latitude originally established by acts of Congress to survey the lands of public domain and now used in 30 states.

Second Unit of angular measure equal to 1/60 of a minute.

Section An area of land used in the rectangular survey system, approximately 1 mile square, bounded by section lines. The rectangular system provides for the further subdivision of sections into halves, quarters and quarter-quarters.

Section Lines North-south reference lines used in the rectangular survey system, parallel to the nearest range line to the east, and east-west lines parallel to the nearest township line to the south; these lines divide townships into 36 approximately equal squares called sections.

Survey The measure and marking of land, accompanied by maps and field notes which describe the measures and marks made in the field.

Township An area of land, used in the rectangular survey system, approximately 6 miles square, bounded by range lines and township lines.

Township Lines East-west reference lines used in the rectangular survey system located at 6-mile intervals between correction lines.

918   Bargain and Sale—(Cov. Against Grantor).
Individual or Corporation.

JULIUS BLUMBERG, Inc., LAW BLANK PUBLISHERS
80 EXCHANGE PLACE AT BROADWAY, NEW YORK

This Indenture,

Made the 29th day of November , in the year of our Lord
One Thousand Nine Hundred and Seventy-one

Between

COUNTY OF MONMOUTH
CONSIDERATION 43,000 —
REALTY TRANSFER FEE 43 —
DATE 12-6-71 BY _____

and State of New Jersey **party of the first part;**

And

1 Baron Court

and State of New Jersey **party of the second part;**

Witnesseth, That the said party of the first part, for and in consideration of — — — — —
FORTY-THREE THOUSAND ($43,000.00) DOLLARS — — — — — — — — — — — —
lawful money of the United States of America, to them in hand well and truly paid by the said
party of the second part, at or before the sealing and delivery of these presents, the receipt whereof is
hereby acknowledged, and the said party of the first part being therewith fully satisfied, contented and
paid, ha ve given, granted, bargained, sold, aliened, released, enfeoffed, conveyed and confirmed and by
these presents do   give, grant, bargain, sell, alien, release, enfeoff, convey and confirm unto the said
party of the second part, and to their heirs
and assigns, forever,

All That Certain lot, piece,
tract or parcel of land and premises, hereinafter particularly described, situate, lying and being
in the Township of Manalapan **County of** Monmouth
and State of New Jersey, more particularly described as follows:

BEGINNING at a point in the southwesterly side of Baron Court, said point being the
dividing line between lots 10 and 11 in Block 403 on map hereinafter stated from
thence running: (1) Along said dividing line, between lots 10 and 11 in Block 403
South 16 degrees 35 minutes 50 seconds West, 169.30 feet to the dividing line between

149

lots 7 and 10 in Block 403, on map hereinafter stated; thence: (2) Along the same, South 86 degrees 04 minutes 50 seconds West, 53.43 feet to the dividing line between lots 8 and 10 in Block 403, on map hereinafter stated; thence: (3) Along the same, North 29 degrees West, 35.0 feet to the dividing line between lots 9 and 10 in Block 403, on map hereinafter stated; thence (4) Along the same, North 33 degrees 35 minutes 50 seconds East, 31.27 feet; thence: (5) Continuing along the same, North 56 degrees 24 minutes 10 seconds West, 150.02 feet to a point in the southeasterly side of Lancelot Road; thence: (6) Along the same, North 33 degrees 35 minutes 50 seconds East, 125.51 feet, to a point in the curve connecting the aforesaid southeasterly side of Lancelot Road, and the southwesterly side of Baron Court; thence: (7) Along, said curve, in a general easterly direction, curving to the right, having a radius of 15.0 feet, an arc distance of 23.56 feet to a point in the southwesterly side of Baron Court; thence: (8) Along the same, South 56 degrees 24 minutes 10 seconds East, 115.11 feet; thence: (9) Continuing along the same, in a southeasterly direction on a curve to the left, having a radius of 150.0 feet an arc distance of 44.5 feet to the point and place of Beginning.

Premises are also described as follows: BEING known and designated as Lot 10 in block 403, as laid out on map entitled "Section 2 Olde Battleground Village situated in Manalapan Township," and filed in the Monmouth County Clerk's Office on March 20, 1967 as Case No. 87-13.

The above description is drawn in accordance with a survey made by Goodman, Allgair & Scott dated November 10th, 1971.

BOOK 3760 PAGE 649

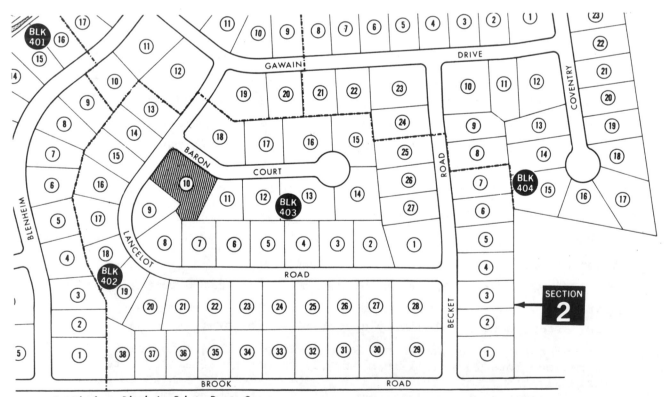

1 Mile from Blenheim Rd. to Route 9

Fig. 6 Developers location map showing sections, blocks, lot numbers and streets.

LOCATION PLAN DESIGN

14

Location plans are very important as they present information about the property. They are composed of a plot plan, the survey plan and the landscape plan. The **plot plan** shows all structures on the property, the **survey plan** shows all the geographical information, and **landscape plan** shows how the various existing and new features will be used to blend the overall design of the property.

The plot plan. The plot plan shows the shape of the lot upon which the structure is to be built, along with the dimensions and bearings. The dimensions of the building are shown, and the building is located from all property lines. The location and size of courts, drives, patios, pools and walks are also shown. Utilities such as electric, gas, sewers and water are represented by straight line symbols. Compass orientation of the plot is shown. The elevations of the corners of the property are listed as well as various parts of the lot. The first floor elevation is given along with the contour lines that express the slope of the land.

Planning and execution of good grading involve basic steps pertaining to street layout, block grading and lot grading. The objective being to establish the street grades, floor elevations and lot grades in proper relation to each other and to existing topography. Set back lines are shown, and a legal description of the lot is indicated *(Fig. 1)*.

The local building codes established by the community control the location of the building on the property by front, side and rear building lines. Restrictions are placed on buildings in relation to the lots on which they are to be built in order:

> To provide for (A) convenient access to and circulation around the dwelling, (B) adequate natural light and ventilation of rooms and spaces, (C) reasonable privacy for each living unit, (D) utilization of the plot for laundry drying, gardening, landscaping and outdoor living, (E) and where individual water-supply

and sewage-disposal systems are involved, adequate areas to assure a safe and sanitary installation.[1]

Use the civil engineer's scale for laying out all dimensions of land measurements in feet and decimal parts of a foot. *(125.75' instead of 125'-9")* Usually a scale of **1" = 20'** is used; however, this depends on the lot size, house size and paper size that is used. The dimensions on architectural features should be drawn in feet and inches *(87'-10")*.

Steps in Designing Plot Plans.
1. Show the legal limits of the property and locate the building from the property lines.
2. Draw the outline of the house. Sometimes the roof plan is shown. Crosshatch the area of the house.
3. Show the dimensions of the house and locate it on the property from two different property line dimensions.
4. Show all driveways, retaining walls, sidewalks, patios, stepping stones and carports, and their dimensions if necessary. Indicate materials used.
5. Indicate elevations of first floor, garage driveway elevations, patios, and pools. List other key elevations if necessary.
6. Label all avenues, boulevards, courts, drives, roads, and streets adjacent to the property. Show centerline of roadway.
7. Show the compass orientation of the lot by the use of a north arrow.
8. Use a civil engineer's scale such as **1" = 20'**, **1" = 30'** for preparing the plot plan.

The survey plan. The survey plan shows the exact size, shape and elevations of the lot. The survey plan that is prepared by a licensed professional surveyor becomes a legal document and

---

1. *Minimum Property Standards for One and Two Living Units*, FHA No. 300, Section 500.

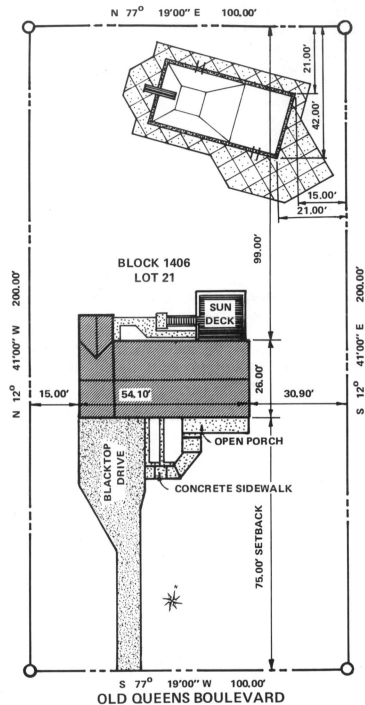

N 77° 19'00" E 100.00'

21.00'

42.00'

15.00'

21.00'

99.00'

BLOCK 1406
LOT 21

200.00'

SUN
DECK

N 12° 41'00" W 200.00'

S 12° 41'00" E 200.00'

15.00'

54.10'

26.00'

30.90'

BLACKTOP
DRIVE

OPEN PORCH

CONCRETE SIDEWALK

75.00' SETBACK

S 77° 19'00" W 100.00'
OLD QUEENS BOULEVARD

Being known as Lot 21, Block 1406 as shown on a map of
Yorktowne at Holiday North, Section 8, Manalapan Township,
Monmouth County, N.J.

Filed: Sept. 11, 1964, Case No. 74, Sheet No. 26.
File No. 64M002
Book H-9 Page 76   SCALE: 1" = 30'

Fig. 1   Plot plan design.

is recorded along with the deed in the court house, town hall, or the municipal building. The survey plan will list the lengths of each side of the property, elevations of the corners, contours, tree locations and trunk size, total acreage, utility easements, streams, ponds, roads or streets and utility lines such as electric, gas, sewer lines, storm sewers and water. The name of the owner and the names of the owners of adjacent properties are listed. A survey plan must completely describe the features of the plot *(Fig. 2)*.

Steps in Designing Survey Plans.

1. List and show the elevations of all corners of the property.

2. Indicate the bearing and distance of all property lines (degrees, minutes and seconds).

3. Show the compass orientation of the lot by the use of a north arrow.

4. Show all lot corners by using small circles.

5. The elevations of the contour lines are inserted, by breaking the contour.

6. Select a heavy dash and dot line to represent the property line.

7. Existing contours are shown by dotted lines while new contours are solid lines.

8. Place the name of the owner inside the property lines and the names of adjacent property owners outside the property lines.

9. Show the different utilities by using different line symbols and listing their purposes *(electric line, gas line, sewer line, and water line)*.

10. Use a civil engineer's scale such as **1"** **= 20', 1" = 30'** for preparing the survey plan.

11. Label all avenues, boulevards, courts, drives, roads, and streets adjacent to the property.

The landscape plan. The landscape plan shows the different types of trees and vegetation that are existing and new trees, shrubbery, flowers, etc. that are to be added to enhance the appearance and function of the site. The landscape architect specifies the type of trees, shrubs, flowers, bushes, hedges and their location on the site. *(Fig. 3)*.

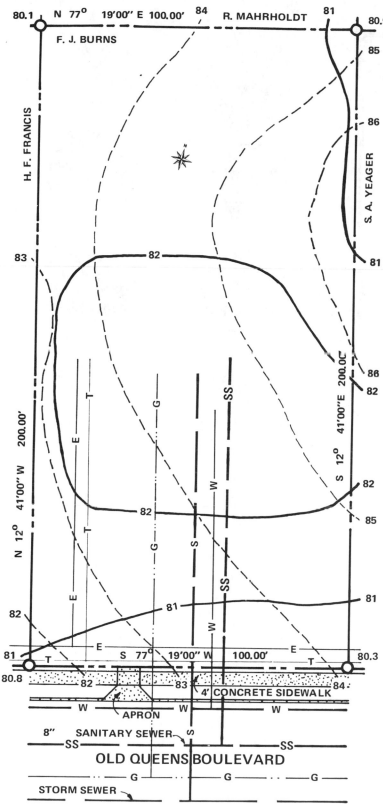

The image includes the following labels and markings:

80.1 N 77° 19'00" E 100.00' 84 R. MAHRHOLDT 81 80.9

F. J. BURNS

H. F. FRANCIS

S. A. YEAGER

85

86

81

83

82

86
82

82

82

85

81

82

81

N 12° 41'00" W 200.00'

S 12° 41'00" E 200.00'

S 77° 19'00" W 100.00'

80.3

81

80.8

82   83   84

4' CONCRETE SIDEWALK

APRON

8" SANITARY SEWER

SS   SS

OLD QUEENS BOULEVARD

G   G   G

STORM SEWER

Fig. 2   Survey plan design.

Steps in Designing Landscape Plans.

1.   The elevations of all trees are noted as they are indicated on the drawing by circles which represent the spread of their branches, irregular lines which represent their spread or by preprinted pressure acetate sheets which are transferred to the tracing by hand burnishing *(Fig. 4).*   A plus sign (+) indicates the location of the trunk.

2.   The property lines of the lot are shown.

3.   Trees are planted in order to take advantage of the orientation of the sun's angle, to provide windbreaks and to enhance the appearance of the lot.

4.   Carports, outdoor fireplaces, patios, retaining walls, sidewalks, stepping stones and swimming pools are identified on the lot.

5.   Shrubbery is placed according to design which will define boundaries, conceal foundation walls, hide irregular slopes and outline walks and paths.

6.   The names of trees and shrubs are listed on pages 160-161. The landscape architect will use the botanical *(latin)* names of all trees and shrubs on the drawings and they may be indexed to a planting schedule.

7.   The house is outlined, crosshatched, or shaded.

8.   Hedge planting is used as a screening method which adds privacy, controls traffic flow and helps to serve as a wind break.

9.   Use a civil engineer's scale such as 1" = 20', 1" = 30' for preparing the landscape plan.

Some lots take several years to complete the landscaping scheme due to a lack of time in planting time or because of economic reasons. When the landscape plan is phased, the final plan or scheme is drawn, and then different colors or materials are added for each years planting and then different shades of color are used to show what is planted in each year. A phasing plan can be expressed over a period of several months or several years.

153

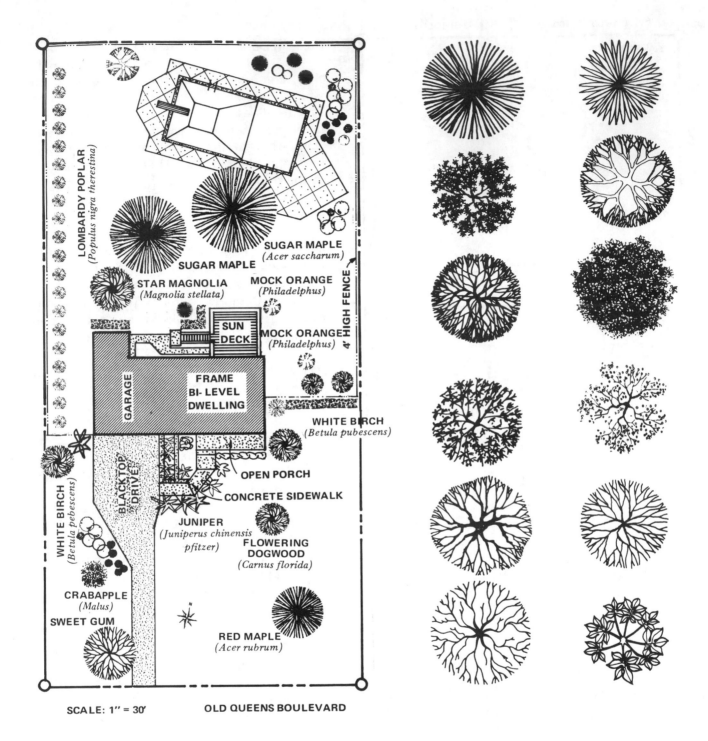

LOMBARDY POPLAR
(Populus nigra therestina)

SUGAR MAPLE

SUGAR MAPLE
(Acer saccharum)

STAR MAGNOLIA
(Magnolia stellata)

MOCK ORANGE
(Philadelphus)

MOCK ORANGE
(Philadelphus)

4' HIGH FENCE

SUN DECK

GARAGE

FRAME BI-LEVEL DWELLING

WHITE BIRCH
(Betula pubescens)

OPEN PORCH

BLACKTOP DRIVE

CONCRETE SIDEWALK

WHITE BIRCH
(Betula pebescens)

JUNIPER
(Juniperus chinensis pfitzer)

FLOWERING DOGWOOD
(Carnus florida)

CRABAPPLE
(Malus)

SWEET GUM

RED MAPLE
(Acer rubrum)

SCALE: 1" = 30'

OLD QUEENS BOULEVARD

Fig. 3   Landscape plan design.

Fig. 4   Landscape Graphic Art Aids

154

15

LANDSCAPING

Planning lawns. The first step in landscaping your plot is to make an overlay or tracing of your plot which is drawn to scale. By ruling 1 ft x 1 ft. squares, locate your house properly along with sidewalks and drives, trees and other important features. The first point to bring up is the front lawn. This is very important in making your house attractive. It should be large enough to provide a well balanced setting for the house, but not so large that it is too time consuming to keep up. By being too large it will demand most of the weekends cutting grass. Your front lawn should be large enough so that it will be a pleasure to look at and take care of rather than a dreaded chore. When designing your front lawn, make it as broad and as open as possible. Do not cut the lawn up with walks and driveways, unless it is impossible to avoid. A small unbroken front lawn will be more effective than a larger size lawn that is divided into several small sections.

Making a Lawn. Don't make the lawn absolutely flat if there are natural slopes to the site. Avoid steep slopes, however; these will make cutting the grass difficult. The topsoil should be free of weeds, roots and stones. Four to six inches of topsoil will be sufficient for a seed bed. Before you go any further, have the soil tested so that you will know what and how much fertilizer must be added to it to make it suitable for grass. You can purchase a small soil-testing kit and make the test yourself, or you can send a sample of your soil to the county agent or the state department of agriculture and they will make the test for you. Next, a lawn fertilizer should be applied.

The best way to plant seeds so that you will get uniform coverage is to sow one-half the amount of seed to be used in parallel strips and then sow the remaining seeds at right angles to the first half.

After the seeds are sown, rake lightly and then go over the lawn with a roller. Finally, the lawn should be watered lightly and kept damp until the seeds have rooted. The grass should be cut only after it is four inches high.

Trees. Trees are used to provide a background or frame to the house, to provide shade for various sections of the house, and also as screens and windbreaks. Some types of trees are better for these jobs than others. Trees, for the purpose of landscaping, are divided into two groups, **evergreens** and **deciduous**. Evergreen trees keep their leaves or needles on all year around, while deciduous trees shed their leaves in the fall. One of the mistakes many homeowners make in using trees around the house, is that they forget that trees are going to grow. Many times, trees intended for shade purposes have been planted too close to the house so that by the time they reach full growth, they must be cut down. Another mistake is that too many trees are planted close together while they are small. Before you select a tree for any purpose, find out what its width and height will be at maturity. When trees are used around the house to provide shade during the summer months, deciduous trees should be chosen. Their leaves will provide shade in the summer and when they drop off in the fall, it will allow the winter sun's warmth to reach the house. Shade trees are not required on the south side of the house. Trees used for screens or windbreaks can be either evergreens or deciduous.

Shrubs. Shrubs of varying sizes can be used for foundation planting, for screening and for many other landscaping purposes. They can be either evergreen or deciduous and very often the two types may be mixed. Around the foundation, a few deciduous shrubs mixed in with the evergreens produce a highly pleasing effect.

Screen Planting. This type of planting can be used either to insure privacy or to hide an unpleasant view. If you want all year round screening, evergreens should be used and they should be high enough to do the job. These can be used as screens or to divide sections of the plot into separate pieces. If you have part of your plot set aside for recreation, you might use a hedge between this and the lawn or backyard.

SKETCHING TREES AND SHRUBS

Trees and Shrubs in Plan. These trees and shrubs are represented by simple figures quite easy to sketch. Shrubs are cloud-shaped forms showing the extent of the leaves *(Fig. 1)*. Trees are circular-shaped forms again showing the main expanse and spread of the leaves *(Fig. 2)*. Often a coin may be used as a pattern for the circular form.

Evergreens seen individually can be sketched with the pencil held flat. Starting with the tip of the tree, move the pencil left and right in wider and wider strokes *(Fig. 3)*. They can also be represented by pyramidal shapes with spears sticking out and up giving the line small indentations *(Fig. 4)*. Show some spears facing you.

Fig. 1 Shrubs in plan.

Fig. 3 Strokes for evergreens.

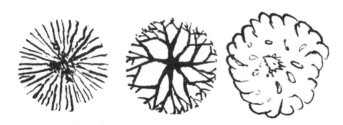

Fig. 2 Trees in plan.

Trees and Shrubs in Elevation. Trees and shrubs are difficult enough to draw correctly that art schools have classes in tree drawing. However, you can develop the ability to sketch recognizable tree forms. In general remember that even the tree with the densest growth is open enough for a bird to fly through. In forests we often see bits of the sky over head through the leaves of many trees. Most trees have such a characteristic form that they can be identified a half mile away by this shape: bushy, round, conical, or fan-shaped. These basic shapes can be used in sketching tree forms. While sketching trees and shrubs darken one of the interior sides. See the section on tree forms which follows:

Fig. 4 Evergreen silhouettes.

Deciduous trees can be sketched individually with a cylindrical trunk and cloud masses representing groups of leaves on one branch, the pencil keeping near the given shape with no

Sketching Specific Varieties of Trees. Red cedar *(Fig. 7)* is a medium sized tree with a pyramidal shape and a dark silhouette. Starting at the base and working up, stroke the branches up-

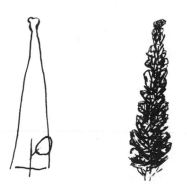

Fig 7 Red cedar

ward, overlapping each stroke. Spruce *(Fig. 8)* is pyramidal also but wider at the base than the

Fig. 5 Deciduous patterns.

straight line longer than an eighth of an inch *(Fig. 5)*. Trees in the distance are often sketched with a trunk and a few irregular lines to create the effect of the outline of the tree.

Shrubs are handled as trees but in a smaller size *(Fig. 6)*. They are often boxed in and many small leaves are drawn on the imaginary box frame.

Fig. 8 Spruce.

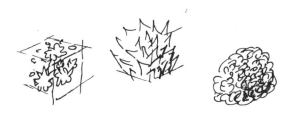

Fig. 6 Shrubs.

red cedar and darker than most other trees. Sketch by drawing the central trunk. Then, imagining wagon wheel spokes as branches, sketch smaller wheels one above the other. Each wheel will have only three or four 'spokes.'

Maple *(Fig. 9)* has a large central trunk, branching from the trunk at a 30° angle. Sketch the many twigs going in all directions at the end of the branches. The Black Walnut *(Fig. 10)* is a massive boxy tree with very few limbs and few small branches, giving the impression of openness to the silhouette. White Oak *(Fig.11)* with massive trunk and branches has a mushroom shaped silhouette. Note that the branches twist and turn with many small twigs at the ends of

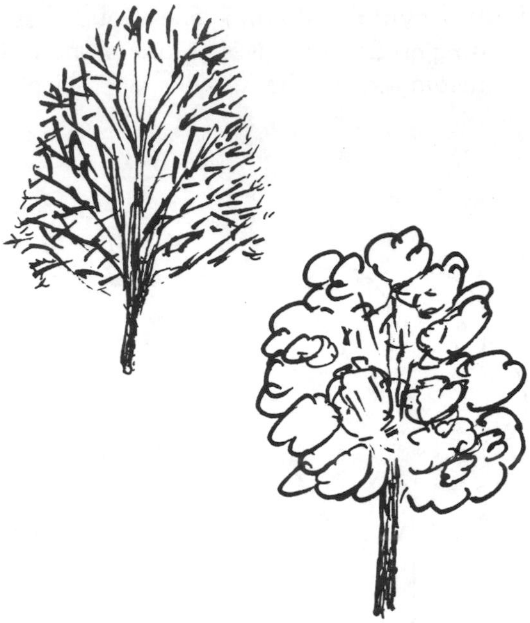

Fig. 9 Maple

Fig. 11   White oak.

Fig. 10   Black walnut.

158

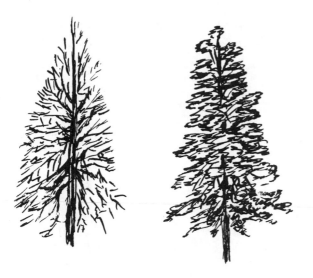

Fig. 12 Pin oak.

the branches. Pin Oaks *(Fig. 12)* have a pyramidal shape with one central trunk tapering to the very tip of the tree, upper branches ascending, lower branches dropping. Elms *(Fig. 13)* have a large trunk with open branches starting at half or three quarters of the total height of the tree and arching gracefully with many small twigs. The Dogwood *(Fig. 14)* is a small tree with horizontal branches and fan-shaped twigs. Pine *(Fig. 15)* has very sparce branches and needles, high up on the trunk. It is often seen in marshes and scrubland.

Various companies specialize in providing graphic symbols of all kinds, including trees, for use by architects, artists, engineers, or anyone doing similar layouts.

Fig. 13 Elm.

Fig. 15 Pine.

Fig. 14 Dogwood.

159

TREES AND SHRUBS

Large Deciduous Trees		Mature Height (in feet)	Dia. Trunk (in feet)	Spread (in feet)	Spaced (in feet)
Apple	Malus, pumila	20-40	1-2	20-40	25
Beech, American	Fagus americana	50-75	1½-4	40-50	30-40
Birch, White	Betula pubescens	50-75	1-3	30-50	30-40
Elm, American	Ulmus americana	80-100	4-8	70-80	60-70
Locust, Black	Robinia pseudoacacia	40-70	2-4	30-40	30-40
Magnolia	Magnolia acuminata	70-90	3-4	60-70	50-60
Maple, Norway	Acer platanoides	60-80	2-3	60-70	50-60
Maple, Red	Acer rubrum	50-75	2-3	40-50	40-50
Maple, Sugar	Acer saccharum	70-100	2-4	50-60	50-60
Oak, Pin	Quercus palustris	60-80	3-4	40-50	40-50
Oak, White	Quercus alba	80-100	3-6	80-100	100
Poplar, Carolina	Populus canadensis eugenei	75-100	3-5	40-50	30-40
Poplar, Lombardy	Populus nigra therestina	75-100	2-6	20-30	20-30
Sweet Gum	Liquidambar styraciflua	80-120	3-5	40-50	40-50
Tulip Tree	Liriodendron tulipifera	100-120	3-4	50-60	50-60
Walnut, Black	Juglans nigra	75-150	3-5	50-75	50-60
Weeping Willow	Salix babylonica	30-40	1-2	30-40	30-40

Small Deciduous Trees

Birch, Grey	Betula populifolia	20-30	under 1'-0''	15-20	10-20
Crabapple, Flowering	Malus	15-20	under 1'-0''	20-25	20-30
Dogwood, Flowering	Cornus florida	20-25	under 1'-0''	25-35	20-30
Hawthorn	Crataegus	15-30	6''-1'-0''	20-40	20-30

Small Evergreen Trees

Arbor Vitae	Thuja occidentalis	25-50	1''-2''	10-20	10-20
Box Tree	Buxus sempervirens	20-30	1''-2''	25-30	20-25
Holly, American	Ilex opaca	40-50	1''-2''	25-35	30-40
Juniper	Juniperus virginiana	25-50	1''-2''	10-15	20-30

Hedges

			(Single row)	(Double Row Staggered)
Privet	Amurense	3	1'-6''	2
Yew	Hicksi	2	1	1'-3''

Large Evergreen Trees

Cypress, Sawara	Chamaecyparis	20-40	9-15	15-20	20-30
Fir, White	Abies concolor	100-150	3-4	50-60	50-60
Hemlock, Canada	Tsuga Canadensis	60-100	2-4	40-60	40-50
Larch, European	Larix decidua	50-60	1-3	30-40	40-50
Magnolia, Southern	Magnolia Grandiflora	70-80	2-3	50-60	50-60
Live Oak	Quercus Virginiana	50-60	4-6	60-70	60-70
Pine, Austrian	Pinus nigra	60-80	2-3	30-40	40-50
Pine, Monterey	Pinus radiata	50-60	4-6	50-60	50-60
Pine, Red (Norway)	Pinus resinosa	60-80	2-3	30-40	40-50
Pine, White	Pinus strobus	80-100	4-5	60-80	50-60
Spruce, Colorado	Picea pungens	70-90	1½-3	30-40	40-50
Spruce, Norway	Picea abies	50-100	2-3	40-50	40-50

Deciduous Shrubs

		Height	Season	Spread
Azalea	Rhododendron calendulacea	3-9	May	4-6
Barberry	Berberis	4-5	May	4-6
Bittersweet	Celastrus scandens	Vine	Fall	Vine
Blueberry Highbush	Vaccinium corymbosum	6-8		6-8
Cardinal Shrub	Weigela vaniceki	5-6	June	5-6
Firethorn	Pyracantha coccinea	6-10	May	1-6
Forsythia	Forsythia intermedia	6-8	April	6-8
Honeysuckle	Lonicera	6-12	May	6-12
Lilac, Common	Syringa vulgaris	12-15	May	10-12
Mock Orange	Philadelphus	8-10	May	6-8
Myrtle, Crape	Lagerstroemid indica	15-20	July-Aug.	15-25
Privet, Regel	Liqustrum obtusifolium	5-6	May	4-5
Rosa Multiflora	Rosa multiflora	6-8	June	6-8
Rose of Sharon	Hibiscus suroacis	10-12	July-Sept.	8-10
Snowball, Japanese	Viburnum tomentosum	6-8	June	6-8
Spirea, Van Houttei	Spirea van houttei	5-6	May	5-6
Sweet Shrub	Calycanthus floridus	3-9	June	4-6
Trumpet Vine	Bignonia radicans	Vine	May to Sept.	Vine

Evergreen Shrubs

		Height	Spread	O.C.
Box, Dwarf	Buxus suffruticosa	10-12	10-15	variable
Holly, Japanese	Ilex crenata	15-20	10-15	8-10
Juniper, Pfitzers	Juniperus pfitzeriana	6-8	6-8	5-10
Mountain Laurel	Kalma latifolia	4-10	4-8	4-8
Oleander	Nerium oleander	7-15	7-12	6-10
Pine, mugho	Pinus mugho muahus	6-8	8-12	10-15
Rhododendron	Rhododendron	6-30	6-15	5-15
Yew, Japanese	Taxus cuspidata	12 15	12-16	variable

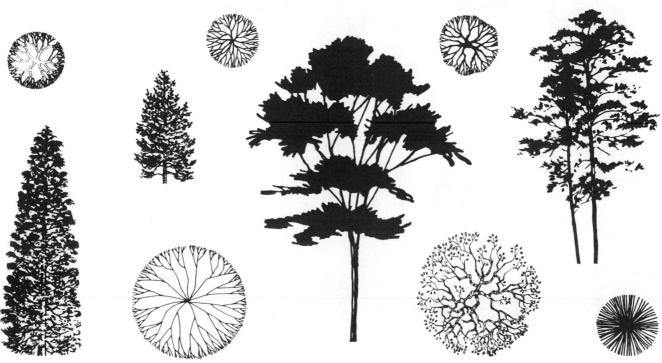

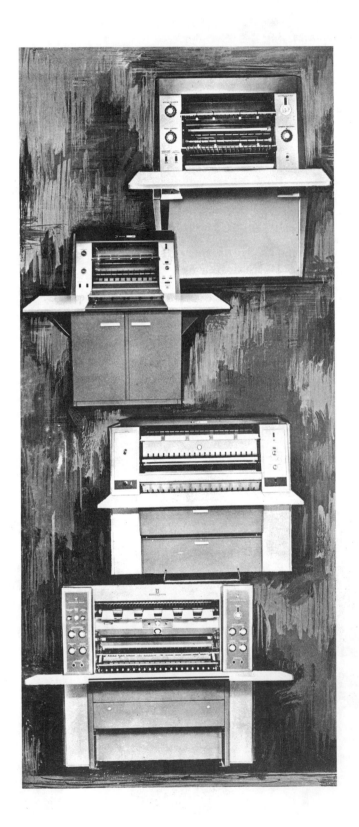

The term "Drawing Mediums" as used herein is applicable only to the material on which the drawing is manually made. A description of common mediums follows:

Tracing Paper or Tracing Vellum. These serve as an inexpensive medium for the preparation of drawings that are not subject to excessive handling or rough usage. They are suitable for ink or pencil work and will permit good quality reproductions by all of the commercial printing processes. Paper stocks vary from 100% rag content to no rag, and translucence and transparency are obtained by processing with a plastic resin or oil. Papers treated with oil have a tendency to decrease in translucency and transparency with age. Paper which is made from clean white rags has better keeping qualities and will not become brittle with age. As a general rule, thinner papers are more translucent; however, the heavier papers possess more strength and will withstand repeated erasures more satisfactorily.

Ink Tracing Cloth or Pencil Tracing Cloth. Tracing cloth may be used when a more durable medium than tracing paper is desired. It consists of a high grade closely woven cloth material, chemically treated to provide translucency and transparency. The working or drawing side of the ink tracing cloth has a dull matte surface suitable for taking ink and permitting erasures. The matte surface on the pencil tracing cloth has a sufficient *"Pencil tooth"* to insure a firm reproducible line and reasonable erasures. All pencil cloths permit ink work; however, they are slightly more expensive than the ink type. Selection of the suitable grade of cloth is determined by translucency, transparency, erasure qualities, suitability of working surface and ability to withstand handling.

Drawing Paper. This is frequently used in the preparation of the drawing for tracing or photographing. The selection of the grade of paper is governed by the following qualities:

(a) **Surface:** Degree of smoothness should be suitable for pencil, ink, pastel sticks or water colors as applicable.
(b) **Erasing Qualities:** Should permit redrawing of ink lines over repeated erasures.
(c) **Strength:** Should resist kinking and tearing, and also permit repeated folding without breaking.
(d) **Permanence:** Should not discolor or weaken with age.

Drawing paper is commonly used as an inexpensive covering for the drawing board surface. A more durable covering called *"drawing board surface material"* is commercially available in white or green colors. Basically this material is a glass smooth surfaced paper, having no irregularities to deflect a pencil or ruling pen. It should be hard enough to minimize pencil scoring yet yield enough to permit a pencil line to take well on the drawing. The surface should be washable to permit cleaning by an occasional sponging or removal of ink stains.

Bristol Board. Bristol Board is a fine quality cardboard having a high grade, smooth, hard surface suitable for taking ink or pencil. It is used for the preparation of illustrations and patent drawings. This material is commercially available in plain sheets *(3-ply, 10" x 15")* having a printed border and title in conformance with the requirements of the United States Patent Office. These boards may be rolled without damage to the board or surface.

Special Drawing Mediums. Special drawing mediums made from plastics, acetates or glass cloth are constantly being developed and improved. Glass cloth is generally used where dimensional stability is a requirement. Polyester base film coated with a drawing surface is frequently used. It is dimensionally stable, tough and water proof. Since these mediums are often limited to a specific application, thorough investigation should be made before adoption.

Drawing Reproductions

There are many different types of reproduction processes available to industry. Selection is governed by the quality, quantity and type of reproduction desired. A description of the common types follows:

Blueprints. Blueprints are low cost paper or cloth reproductions having white lines and a blue background. They are produced from any translucent positive original by the following steps: (a) printing, (b) washing, (c) developing, (d) washing and (e) drying. Early production methods consisted of printing in a frame by exposure to the sun or artificial light, processing the print by hand through developing and washing tanks or trays, followed by drying in air or passing the print through a belt fed gas or electrically heated drying machine. Modern self-contained equipment for production work combines the steps into a continuous automatic progression. The translucent original and sensitized paper go into one end of the machine, the print comes out the other as continuous yardage in roll form. Prints are then cut from the roll and trimmed to size. *(Fig. 1).*

VanDykes. VanDyke negatives are permanent negative paper or cloth reproductions having white lines and brown background from which blue line prints, brown line prints or reproduced tracings are made. They are produced by exactly the same methods as blueprints, using different chemicals and commercially available papers or cloths. When the original is inverted, that is, the line surface of the original is placed in direct contact with the chemical surface of the printing medium, an indirect reading negative is obtained. Direct and indirect reading negatives are equally popular. VanDykes are commonly used as an inexpensive means for supplying subcontractors, suppliers, or government departments with a suitable medium for producing as many prints as they may require.

Blueline Prints. These are positive reproductions made on blueprint paper or cloth with regular blueprint equipment by using a VanDyke or a phototype negative for the original.

Brown Line Prints. These are positive reproductions made on VanDyke paper or cloth from a

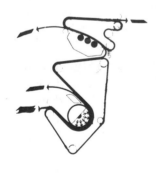

Original and sheet of copying material—matched together in the exposure section—are separated automatically by a jet of air; the original returning to the operator and the copy sheet continuing its travel to the developing tank . . . another automated feature that speeds the print-making operation while adding to operator convenience.

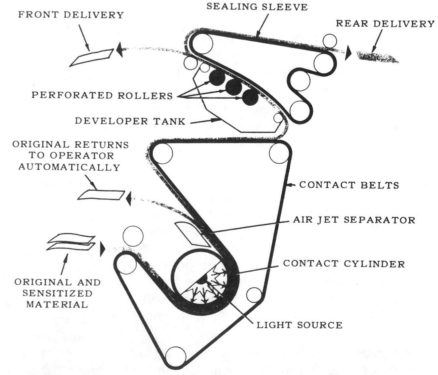

FRONT DELIVERY

SEALING SLEEVE

REAR DELIVERY

PERFORATED ROLLERS

DEVELOPER TANK

ORIGINAL RETURNS TO OPERATOR AUTOMATICALLY

CONTACT BELTS

AIR JET SEPARATOR

CONTACT CYLINDER

ORIGINAL AND SENSITIZED MATERIAL

LIGHT SOURCE

Fig. 1   *Steps in printing a blueprint.*

VanDyke or a phototype negative. They are made by the use of regular blueprint equipment using suitable chemicals. When made on thin translucent paper they can serve as an inexpensive form of reproduced tracing. They are also used in the graphic arts industry to make silverprints before plates are made.

Direct Line Prints. Direct line prints are also termed direct process prints, black and white prints, dye line prints or white prints. Positive or negative reproductions may be made on specially prepared paper or cloth from any translucent original. Physically, their appearance may be the same as any of the previously listed reproductions; the color of line or background being determined by the selection of the printing medium. When made on translucent paper, acetate or cloth, the print *(known as a sepia line transparency)* can serve as a reproduced tracing for reproductions by any process. Direct line prints are exposed or printed the same as when making a blueprint. After printing they are developed by applying a solution of developer chemicals to the sensitive side of the exposed print, or as in the dry process, passing a print over a chamber that is emitting aqueous ammonia fumes. Developing equipment ranging from table models to units attachments for blueprint printers is available; however, for quantity productions, more satis-

REVOLUTE 820 (Sit-down Model)

Fig. 3   Bruning 820 Revolute Diazo continuous copier machine.

factory results, coupled with a saving in floor space, will be obtained by the use of commercially available integral machines designed for this process. Direct line printing is a desirable method for printing a single or small quantities of reproductions *(Fig. 2)*.

Reproduced Tracings. These are positive transparent copies of original pencil drawings, tracings, direct line prints or blueprints. They are also called processed tracings, photo tracings, second originals, or photographic translucent reproductions. The process, when compared with hand tracings, is an inexpensive means of producing a translucent or transparent photographic reproduction on cloth, paper or film, having lines of ink-line density, allowing erasures and drawing of ink lines. The steps in making a reproduced tracing consist of first exposing and developing a VanDyke negative or a photographic negative. The negative is then placed in contact with sensitized paper or cloth and exposed in a vacuum printing frame or a continuous copier machine *(Fig. 3)*. This print is then processed through

Fig. 2   Bruning 110 all purpose table-top model for direct line prints.

developing and fixing baths and then washed in water. A minimum of shrinking is obtained if air dried. Reproduction papers, cloths and films are available under various trade names in cut sheets, pads or rolls.

Photocopies. These non-transparent photographic paper copies of an orignal drawing, document, or object are commonly called **photostats**. The commercial cameras used for this process have sensitized paper and the developing process contained as an integral part of the machine and the copy produced may vary in size from reductions to enlargements within the limit of the camera. Photocopies in the negative form are legally acceptable in most courts of law;however, it is a relatively slow method of making reproductions and is seldom used for drawings where scale work or high production is required.

Microfilm. A reduced scale photographic film negative reproduction of a drawing, document or object is called a **microfilm**. It is used primarily to provide a record requiring a minimum of space that may be stored in a fireproof vault, or to provide a means of automating record hand-

Fig. 4   Dietzgen Microfiche Reader E-4315 for viewing microfiche or microfilm.

ling for current or obsolete material. Camera equipment and film viewers are commercially available *(Fig. 4)*. Microfilm is also a working tool for making reproductions, through such mediums as photographic or electrostatic processes.

Microfilm enlarger-printers are commercially available for making prints. They have quick change enlarging heads. These machines will accommodate 35mm. aperture card-mounted or roll type microfilm.

Photo Offset Prints. Positive printed paper reproductions made on commercial offset printing presses are also termed planograph prints or lithograph prints. In this process the drawing is photographed and a print is made from the negative on a sensitized metal or plastic plate. When a reproduction of lesser quality is satisfactory and the drawing is simple, a paper plate is made by typing or drawing directly on it, using special ribbons, pencils or inks. The plate is mounted on a suitable base or holder in the offset printing press, which differs from the direct printing type of press in that the inked pattern of the plate is transferred to a pad and then to the paper rather than transferring directly from the inked plate to the paper. This process eliminates the necessity of engraving and permits copying photographic, hand drawn, or typewritten material at a very fast rate. When drawings are needed in large quantities for advertising or service purposes they are produced economically by this method.

When a photographic type plate is used, the print may be an enlarged or reduced scale reproduction restricted only by the dimensions of the printing press. The size of the print is determined when the photographic negative is made.

Carbon Transfer Copy. A positive paper reproduction of typewritten material, drawings or sketches, that is made from a spirit carbon master, by a liquid duplicating process is commonly called a Ditto Copy. The master is prepared by typing or drawing directly on the master with sufficient pressure to transfer the carbon from the backing sheet to the reverse side of the master sheet. The master sheet is then fastened in a printer and by a contact process copies are rapidly produced. A variety of colors may be printed individually or collectively by interchanging the backing sheet when preparing the master. This method is an inexpensive means for preparing a fair quality type of reproduction of letters, bulletins, and sketches.

Microfiche *(last part pronounced as fish)* is presently widely used for checks, drawings, computer printouts, social security data, etc. The original is photographically reduced and placed on film. The sheet size of microfiche have been standardized at 150 mm *(about 6 inches)* and 105 mm high *(about 4 inches)*. The number of images on one sheet varies, but 60 to 100 pages is average. This means most books can be put on three microfiche sheets.

Microfiche can also be linked to computers as well as indexes. The reproduction cost is approximately five cents, and it allows convenient updating of prices and saves the expense of mailing heavy catalogues.

Since the image is smaller, better drafting is required on the originals. Also one needs an enlarger, called a microfiche reader to view the enlarged image. However, readers are available approximately the size of an attache case, battery or A.C. powered for portable viewing. Projecters also are available as well as reader-printer machines. It has been estimated that an entire library could be contained within a single briefcase.

RESUME OF REPRODUCTION METHODS

TYPE	DESCRIPTION	PURPOSE OR REQUIREMENT
Blueprint	Negative paper or cloth reproduction having white lines and blue background. May be made from any translucent positive original. (Wet Process)	Primarily for shop and file copies of architectural and engineering drawings. For sizes larger than 17 x 24 the least expensive method of reproducing drawings (Unit cost is equal to 1)
VanDyke	Negative transparent paper or cloth reproduction having white lines and brown background. May be made from any translucent positive original. (Wet Process)	Serves as an inexpensive means for supplying customers or outside organizations with a negative for further reproductions (Unit cost is equal to 4)
Blueline Print	Positive paper or cloth reproduction having blue lines and white background. May be made from any translucent negative (usually a VanDyke by using the Blueprint Process).	Same as for blueprint. Desirable type of reproduction when many copies that can be easily marked up are required. (Unit cost is equal to 1.2)
Brown Line Print	Same as for Blueline Print except having brown lines and a white background.	Same as for Blueline Prints. Serves as an inexpensive form of reproduced tracing when made on thin translucent paper. (Unit cost is equal to 4).
Direct Line Print	Positive or negative paper, cloth or acetate reproduction that has same physical appearance as any one of the previously listed reproductions. Color of line or background is determined by selection of the printing medium. May be made from any translucent original. (Dry Process).	Desirable method when single or small runs are required quickly. When cut sheets are used cost compares favorably with blueprinting. (Unit cost is equal to 1.2)
Sepia Line Print	Same as for Transparent Mediums.	Same as for Direct Line Print. (Unit cost is equal to 2.5)
Reproduced Tracings	Transparent photographic image of an original on vellum, cloth or film having lines of ink-like density and the ability to permit erasures and drawing of ink lines.	To supply additional copies of an original, to replace worn drawings, or to reduce drafting time when a new drawing with slight modifications is required. (Unit cost is equal to 30 on cloth, 9 on paper and 30 on film).
Photocopy	Negative photographic paper reproductions of any type of an original.	To provide record or reference copies of an original drawing, letter or document. (Unit cost is equal to 7.5)
Microfilm	Negative reduced scale photographic reproduction of an original on film.	Primarily used to provide a record for reference or storage in a minimum of space and as a reproduction medium. (Unit cost is not comparable)
Photo Offset Prints	Full or reduced positive paper reproduction of any original made on a commercial offset printing press.	Serves economically when a large number of good quality reproductions are needed for advertising or service purposes. (Unit cost is .13 based on a run of 1000 8½ x 11)
Carbon Transfer	Positive paper reproduction of letters, bulletins or sketches made from a spirit carbon master by a liquid duplicating process.	Inexpensive method of preparing quickly a reproduction of fair quality. (Unit cost is .19 based on runs of 100 copies 8½ x 11)

CIVIL ENGINEERING AESTHETICS

Ground Slopes for Buildings and Highways. Good design calls for the blending of the structure to the landscape. When moving a rock into the garden you want the rock to appear to be part of the garden. You want some feeling that the rock belongs there although it does stick up and is noticeable. You can slope the earth about the rock so that it appears as a slight slope leading up to it, or the rock can be buried slightly. You can also put in some grass taller than the other grass about the meeting of rock and soil *(Fig. 1)*.

Fig. 1 Rocks in place.

We feel the same about our highways, buildings and other man made structures. We can build an elevated highway by the generous use of vertical walls, but the walls stop the eye and the road does not appear to be part of the landscape. Make two sketches, both the same highway, one with a retaining wall and one with grass slopes.

Safety reports show that many accidents on highways are the result of going off the road, so modern highways are designed with generous shoulders, in some cases 20 feet or more for safety. Where possible the slope down from the shoulder is 1.6 which allows cars to recover if they go off the shoulder. This gradual slope, usually in grass, does cost more money for land acquisition *(purchase)* and soil than a steeper slope, but a steep slope will need guard rails and in some cases retaining walls which are expensive to build and maintain. The slope of 1:6 is more pleasing too, it looks natural. Sketch a 1:6 slope as if you were sectioning the road, draw the shoulder and the slope true scale, and by one

point perspective approximate the high slope in space on your sketch. Do the same for a vertical wall and guard rail *(Fig. 2)*.

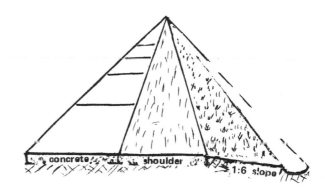

Fig. 2 Highway edge.

A steep slope of 1:4 *(sketch this)* hardly looks different on paper but is quite steep in nature and does not allow the car to recover. Sketch both the vertical wall and the 1:4 slope for the same height of the highway *(Fig. 3)*.

Some highway departments, to save cost, have used a bit of each, resulting in a section called barnroof for the slope. Sketch the highway and shoulder in one point perspective, and for

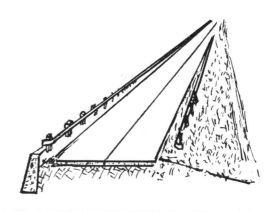

Fig. 3 Vertical wall and 1:4 slope.

20 to 24 feet the 1:6 slope, and then a steeper slope of 1:4 for the rest. Try several sketches, starting with the 18 foot width and going up by 2 foot increments, using the 1:6 slope, and finish with the 1:4 slope in each drawing. Compare all the sketches and decide which is the most pleasing. On these drawings blend the surrounding by breaking the sharp point where the two slopes meet *(Fig. 4)*.

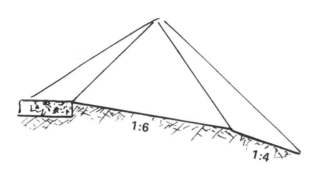

Fig. 4 Barn roof slope.

Buildings. Buildings can be blended into their surroundings with sloping earth. However, buildings can use steep slopes, and of course trees and shrubs as well, for we don't have cars using the slope. The steeper slopes of 1:4 are hard to walk on but are not too steep visually. Sketch several buildings on top of a hill and in section give

them different slope treatments. The very steep slopes of 1:1 are nearly impossible to walk on, and most cars cannot climb them, so they will be used for the backs of buildings or where people will not go. The steeper slopes, either on highway or building landscaping, will need special treatment to stop soil erosion and will increase the costs of cutting the grass. On some highways the only way the grass can be cut on these steep slopes is with a hand mower which is pulled up and down using a rope, for the bottom of the slope is too close to the highway for operator safety. Power grass cutting machinery is unsafe on steep slopes *(Fig. 5)*.

For steep slopes about highways and buildings where you don't want to construct retaining walls, special plants and shrubs can be used. See the chapter on plants. Sketch several treatments of steep slopes, using plants and grass *(Fig. 6)*.

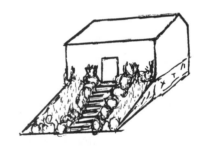

Fig. 6 Slope landscaped with shrubs.

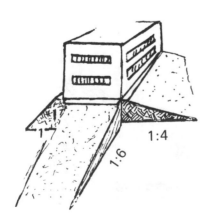

Fig. 5 Foundation slopes.

Fig. 7 Slope landscaped with trees.

On highways these steeper slopes will need the protection of a guard rail. Sketch a section of a highway with the shoulder, and from 2 to 5 feet out from the shoulder, place a guard rail, then a slope of 1:2. Do another sketch using 1:1 slope. *(Compare Fig. 8).*

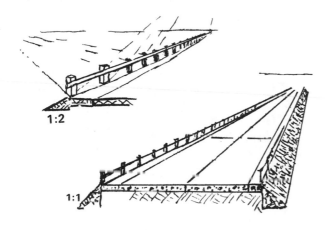

Fig. 8   Highway slopes.

Slopes of 1:1 and Steeper. These slopes are necessary in places where there is need for them, but they are impossible to camouflage. It is impossible to bring a car out of a 45° embankment, in fact most cars can not climb such a slope; even walking on a 45° slope is difficult if not impossible. On grass slopes of 45° you will have severe erosion problems and extra costs in maintenance. Sketch several slopes *(Fig. 9).*

Fig. 9   1:1   slopes.

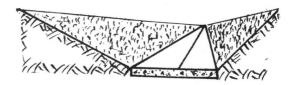

Fig. 10 Grassed slopes.

Fig. 11 Elevated highway slopes.

Fig 12 Depressed highway slopes.

Sketching Rock.

Cut rock does look rather attractive at this steep slope and even greater cuts do not look unsightly. If the rock is left natural it adds to the look of the highway and gives the viewer a feeling of ruggedness and a sense of the geology of the country. A very steep slope in rock going straight up will sometimes curtail the defacement of rocks by not providing climbing holds for such vandals, especially if the rock is in full view of highway traffic.

In loose rock, where falling rock becomes a hazard, these rocks can be used aesthetically to build walls, laid either dry or in mortar. What does not look pleasing is the use of imported, unharmonious rock to build walls that do not match the landscape.

Rocks properly used are an asset to the highway and should not be disguised. They provide visual relief and a sense of the country.

Plan a sketch of a vertical rock wall. Draw a shoulder and from that a downward slope 1:6 with a width of 25 feet. At the bottom put a 3

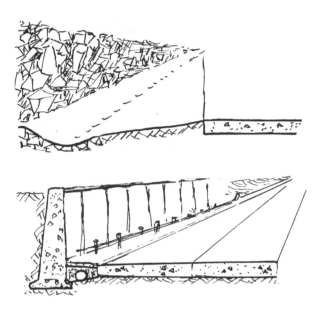

Sketching Hills. Sketch as you did before the vertical wall in perspective. Add a horizontal road with two strokes of the pencil. Now instead of making a vertical wall imagine a cut going through a hill. On the vertical wall take a colored pencil and practice the hill as an upside down V with the top point rounded off. You will need to practice this several times before it looks right. Draw another sketch and make the slope about 45°. Practice making these, both right and left cuts. Sketch several hills one behind the other with a road cutting through them (Fig. 15)

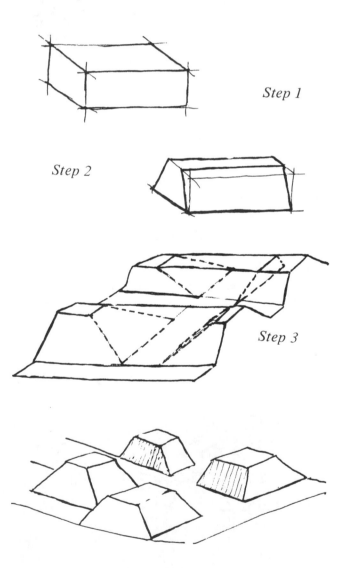

Step 1

Step 2

Step 3

Figs. 13 & 14 Vertical walls.

foot wide ditch, rounding off the bottom. Then start the upward grade of the rock for five feet with a slope of 1:2, followed with an almost vertical wall of rock for a 25 foot rise.

First sketch just the vertical rock wall. Draw the left wall by laying out the top and bottom lines in perspective. Make the top rather irregular, with wavy lines varying about 1/8 in 1 inch. Some of the rock sticks out from the wall in blocks which are irregular in shape. Rock is difficult for artists to draw but try to sketch the rock as blocks getting smaller in perspective (Fig. 13). If you have difficulty doing this after three tries sketch a concrete wall instead.

In your sketch add the ditch, the other slopes and shoulder to give you the feeling of the wall. After finishing the left wall, do the right, combine these two sketches to give you the view the driver will get as he goes through this area.

Sketch several other rock walls with a 1:4 and a 1:5 slope at the base, still using the vertical wall. Compare these sketches.

Fig. 15 Sketching hills

Sketching Exits. Sketch the straight highway in perspective with two lines going to the horizontal vanishing point. Imagine an exit road leading off the highway and dropping down parallel to the highway. Sketch different slopes of each road. If you have trouble sketching in space, go back to drawing the section first with the slopes shown true angle and use perspective to get the lines. Sketch several exit roads, with an increasing angle between the main road and the exit. Sketch different slopes for each road, making about 20 sketches side by side *(Fig. 16)*.

a bridge under the highway with the exit road going under the bridge *(Fig. 17)*. The road does not have the sharp turns of the square as we have sketched, so add the curves of a spiral ramp and use the square only as light guidelines for help in showing how the dirt slopes. You will have to practice many of these to get the drawing to look right. Our main concern is not so much to teach you to draw spirals, which are difficult to draw, but to visualize in space. Do at least ten exit ramps with different slopes and different kinds of spirals. Sketch some small houses and stores on the far side of the exit spiral ramp. The ramp will partially hide the bases of the houses.

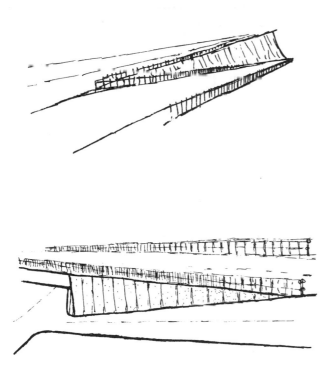

Fig. 16 Sketching exits.

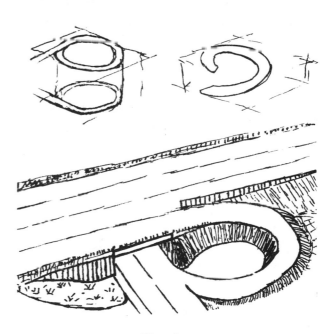

Fig. 17 Sketching ramps.

Sketching Exits that Turn. Sketch the highway again with an exit coming off to the right and dropping down. From the scale of the highway drop about 25 feet. About one-fourth of the height down on the exit road construct a diamond, the basic shape of the square in drawing. Add the road in perspective, and each side of the diamond instead of appearing as a plane appears to be dropping in space with a lower vanishing point. As the road comes back to it, it will appear larger. End the exit road with a sketch of

Sketch some highways with exit ramps parallel and going off to the left and level. Do a series of sketches, starting back a mile, showing signs and the widening of the highway. Using perspective, bring your motorist up to the exit by sketching the view from each ¼ mile and finally show a sketch of the motorist exiting to left. Now sketch some left exits which drop. Draw sketches of the exit as seen by the driver who remains on the highway and as seen by the driver who takes the left ramp.

Slopes under Structures. Bridges and underpasses represent a difficult problem for the highway designer, these areas are places of obstruction where people tend to lose control of their cars. Movies and studies of motorists show they tend to overcompensate in steering away from such obstructions as highway signs and bridge supports. The highway designer has tried to eliminate the bridge support that is close to the road and have the bridge span the highway and the slope. Sketch several views of a highway bridge made of a deep beam and having but one support in the highway median *(Fig. 18)*. To that sketch add a column support adjacent to the shoulder. Not only does it seem to block the view, but it is most dangerous. You will have to add guardrails to direct cars back to the highway. Sketch these *(Fig. 19)*.

Fig. 18 Bridge with median pier.

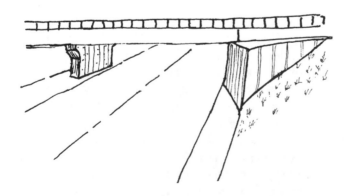

Fig. 19 Bridge with vertical abutment.

Sketching Different Slopes. Using the same deep beam of the highway bridge, sketch several different slope treatments for the area directly under the bridge and next to the highway. Start with a section view, add perspective to give you depth and therefore a better visual sense of the problem. Steep slopes with soft soil need to be surfaced with concrete or cobblestones. Do two sketches, one for each type of surface. Compare for visual attractiveness *(Figs. 18 & 20)*.

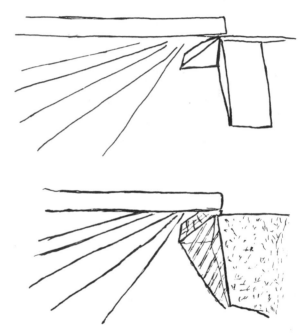

Figs. 20 & 21 Slope treatments at abutments.

Slopes Facing the Driver. We have been sketching the slope which is perpendicular to the highway under the bridge. There is another slope which slopes toward the driver as he uses the highway. This slope is parallel to the highway and comes from the overpass embankment. It too can have different slopes. First sketch a right pyramid, one edge parallel to the road. This is what the dirt looks like to the motorist *(Fig. 21)*. Do four sketches of the mound of dirt that protects the bridge abutment. Give the slope under the bridge a 1:1 slope and the one facing you a 1:6 slope with each slope meeting the level shoulder.

Resketch some of these slopes and add drainage ditches. From the shoulder there is a slight drop into a rounded ditch with a concrete or grass surface for collecting water from the highway and the bridge. The ditch parallels the highway, continuing under the bridge and beyond. Do sketches of the grass and concrete drainage ditches *(Fig. 22)*.

Fig. 24   Offset vertical abutment.

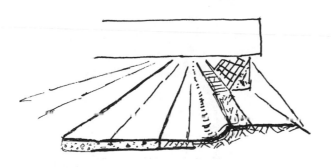

Fig. 22   Highway ditch.

Bridges with Vertical Abutments next to the Highway. Sketch a bridge over the highway with the abutment next to the shoulder. Treat the abutment as a vertical wall, perhaps adding vertical wingwalls. The highway shoulder has a 6:1 slope. You are to sketch several transition treatments of how the slope meets the abutment. You will need a guardrail as part of your solution. Try for a continuous line visually. The guardrail, if flexible, will need stiffening right before the abutment so it won't flex enough to

let the cars hit the concrete abutment. Guardrails are made to give. Sketch the guardrail, adding extra posts or stiffeners. Be aware of grass cutting problems too. Try to make the whole pleasing to the driver. There is nothing wrong with concrete handled honestly, use concrete as a mass in solving your problem. Do not use shrubs as they detract from the basic structure of the bridge and do not belong to the view *(Figs. 23 - 26)*.

Fig. 25 Straight vertical abutment.

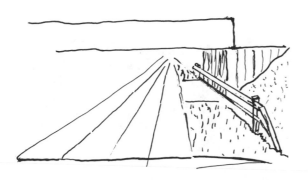

Fig. 23   Vertical abutment with guardrail.

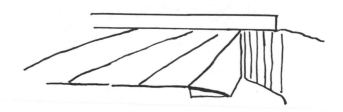

Fig. 26 Vertical abutment with shoulder.

175

Visual Orientation. Bridges are memorable orientation clues and tell the commuter how he is progressing. They are visible, serve as familiar landmarks and are used in giving directions. For that reason they should be identified. Sketch a small sign which can be painted on the bridge structure itself and does not have to be lit. The motorist-commuter will often be able to recall correctly each crossroad. Since bridges are so visually important to people, consider them in this visual sense. There should be a unifying concept to them, this similarity has often been done for reasons of cost. However, this doesn't mean that bridges have to be identical, particularly in urban areas where you may find them every other block. Each bridge can vary slightly as caused by the natural conditions surrounding that bridge *(Fig. 27)*.

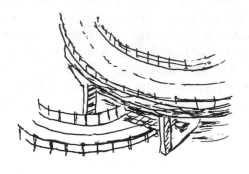

Silhouettes play an important part in highway driving. A bridge, as we see it from the distance, then from a middle range, and from directly beneath, is primarily a silhouette. Visually we remember this silhouette. Draw a bridge over a highway and sketch lampposts, first concrete ones 20 feet apart, then modern lamps of tubing. Change the silhouette by different spacing. Think of the speeding motorist and what he will see. Treat guardrails and posts in the same way sketching many different solutions. Sketch some sort of enclosure, wire, metal or plastic, over the bridge to keep people from throwing things on motorists passing below. Solve the problem by sketching many different materials and shapes. Get a pleasing shape and check to see if the material you used is available.

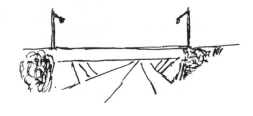

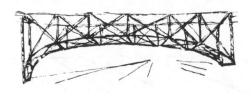

Fig. 27   Bridge treatments.

176

Blending The Road Into The Land. Highway engineers used to butcher the land, smoothing out the valleys with fill and cutting through the hills with ugly gashes. They did this partly because they did not have the money or machines to do more, but also because they were conditioned by years of railway construction where a smooth grade was necessary. A slope of 4:100 is steep for a train *(sketch this)*. Railroads also liked to balance the cuts and the fills so they didn't have to buy or pay to dump dirt when they built *(Fig. 30)*.

Sketch several hills using a space about 2 by 4 inches, drawing the hills as if they were trapezoidal prisms, with the long axis parallel to you *(Fig. 28)*. Sketch a level road thru the hills, balancing the cuts and fills. Because earth will not stand vertically in the cut you will get a slope like a V. Since the relocated dirt will not stand at the same angle as when it was undisturbed in the hill, you will need more dirt for the fill. Sketch this. *(Fig. 29)*.

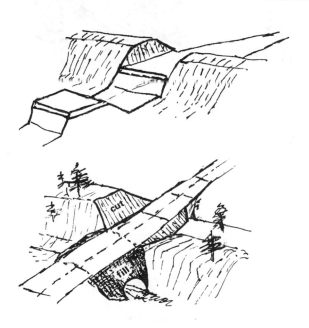

Fig. 28   Highway cuts and fill.

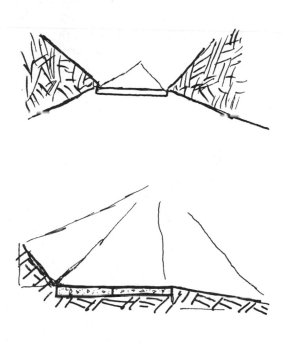

Fig. 29   Diagrams of cut and fill.

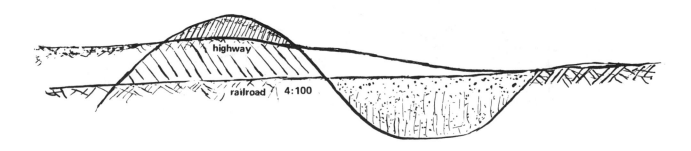

Fig. 30   Profile of cut and fill.

177

Fitting The Highway to the Landscape. Now try to solve this problem by drawing the highway by fitting it into the landscape. Draw the same hills. In doing this problem keep in mind that you are not trying to hide the highway, it is there and it is bold. You don't want to bore straight through the hills, yet you want the highway to predominate visually. Start with a cut through the top of the first hill. With a generous slope rising up, see if you can sketch the hill so that the motorist can see the sky as he moves toward the crest. This means that with a gentle slope of the road you will need to remove more dirt from the hill to the right of the driver *(Fig. 31)*. Sketch this.

As you approach the crest imagine that you are going to cross a valley about ½ mile ahead. The road butcher would go directly across the valley with fill or a bridge. Visually you would not get the idea of a valley at all. Sketch this first, making the road drop by using a lowered vanishing point *(Fig. 32)*.

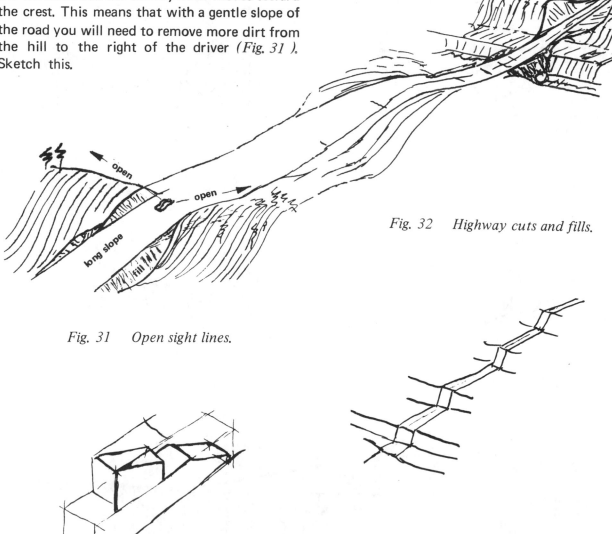

Fig. 32   Highway cuts and fills.

Fig. 31   Open sight lines.

Fig. 33 Sketching cuts and fills.

Instead of filling up the valley, imagine the road descending and crossing the valley with a slight curve. The curve is important visually for it shows the valley to the best advantage and shows the swoop of the road. Keep all the curves wide, and keep the slopes of the highway very slight as highway construction demands.

As he descends, the driver's view will be of the fill *(or bridge and water)* seen to the driver's right. If it is fill he will see the steep slopes and be forced to realize there is a definite valley. Sketch this *(Fig. 35)*, keeping the road small, even at the top of the crest where you first start to sketch. Have the vanishing point down to the left in the valley bed, then straighten the road and make it rise. Sketch the bridge first as it is easier to draw, using vertical piers only Draw in the river with wobbly lines. Draw the next sketch with the same road using fill instead of the bridge and river. Show the fill as sloping lines, the valley as a rounded V in perspective.

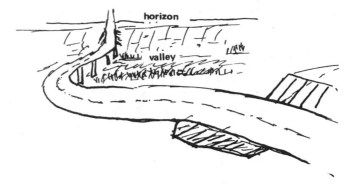

Fig. 35   Highway aesthetics.

Fig. 36   Fitting the highway to the landscape.

Fig. 34   Detail of Fig. 37.

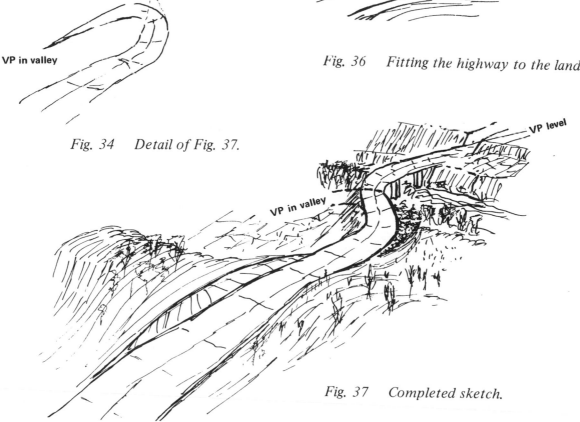

Fig. 37   Completed sketch.

Supportive Scenic Views. As the designer of the highway you can add scenic attractions to the road. There will be a place as you descend where the road will be at the same level as the land, neither cut nor filled. It is a place where the eye dwells and it can be turned into an added attraction by making it a sort of meadow, *(or a man made stream could be seen, crossing under the road)*. Sketch these places and turn one into a meadow. Draw another and put a picnic area with one picnic table and long exit and entrance roads *(Fig. 38)*.

If the country is tree covered, leave some of the trees in the valley to form a cluster directly in line with the road as the driver comes over the crest. It will take a few sketches to get the feel of this, but you should have the curve which we used to reveal the valley also appear to go around the clump of trees. Sketch the same idea except have the road going to the other side. Add trees and meadow growth. Lay out all these sketches together and compare them. As you compare them imagine yourself in a moving car. Sketch the view of the road and the valley as you move down and across the bridge *(Figs. 40 - 43)*.

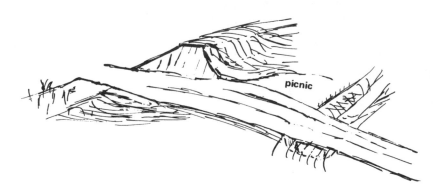

Fig. 38 Developing a picnic area.

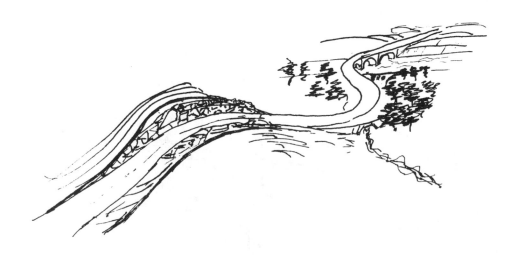

Fig. 39 Scenic view.

Fig. 41 Visualizing from location 1.

Fig. 42 Visualizing from location 2.

Fig. 40   Visualizing the road.

Fig. 43 Visualizing from location 3.

Fig. 44 Existing eastern view.

Scenic Areas. An excellent view often exists a few feet off the road but is obscured by bushes, trees or small hills. Many highway departments routinely eliminate these obstructions both to give the motorist pleasure and to eliminate the roadside obstruction. Several possibilities of treatment exist: the first is merely to open up a new vista by cutting down trees or shrubs or by removing the mound of rock or dirt. This is the economical method and can routinely be done on existing roads with normal maintenance crews. The second is to construct a pull-off where cars can park parallel to the road which accomplishes the same effect and in addition serves as a rest area on long stretches of the highway. This solution is best where

Fig. 45   New vista for eastern view.

182

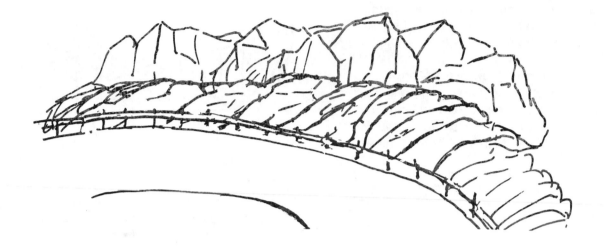

Fig. 46 *Existing western view.*

there is some fill that will provide the extra width for the side shoulder. The third and most costly possibility is to provide a secondary road, or even a loop, with parking alongside this road. In some cases this can easily be at a different level and be relatively narrow for it would be one-way and presumably cars will have slowed down before entering it.

Here are two views *(Figs. 44 & 46)*, one in the East and one in the West. Fig. 45 shows selective cutting so one can see the mountains and an added shoulder. Fig. 47 shows the rocks along side the existing road removed to show the view and a lookout road added. Both open the view to the motorist and allow parking.

Fig. 47 New vista for western view.

183

Highway Sketching from the Driver's Seat. Sit in your car and draw the windshield as a picture window, the metal serving as a frame. Learn to do this in one continuous stroke, practicing at least 20 of them *(Fig. 48)*.

Now imagine your car parked on an airport runway which is so wide and long that there appears in your windshield nothing but sky and runway, everything else being too far away to register. Sketch this. Where is the sky

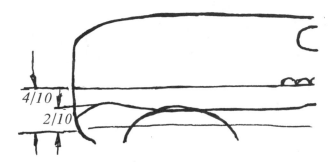

Fig. 48 Runway view through the windshield.

level? What percentage of the sky is within your picture frame? Imagine that you are parked on a six-lane highway, three lanes each way. The road will appear different depending on what lane you are in. Using one point perspective sketch the view from each lane. Be careful not to put the station point too high. The view from the road is mostly sky. The road appears very small and narrows very quickly *(Fig.49)*.

Fig. 50 Two lane highway.

The next time you are on a highway try to memorize the shape and size of the road, shoulder and sky. When you are sitting next to the driver and moving down a highway take a china marking pencil and mark the lines of the shoulders and lane on the windshield and sketch in the angles of the road as it vanishes.

We know that the faster we go, the more narrow our cone of vision as we concentrate on the road. Redraw the windshield and, of the six-lane highway, draw only as much as you will see at high speeds. To help you visualize this, sit in your car with a 45° triangle in front of your eye and draw a circle on the windshield to let you visualize how much you see at these speeds. It is surprising how little the cone is. Of course drivers do see out to the sides but most of this blurred. Since drivers do turn their heads, study a driver the next time, counting the times he turns his head in a mile of city driving and the times he turns his head at

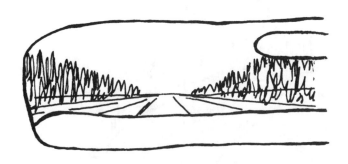

Fig. 49 Six lane highway.

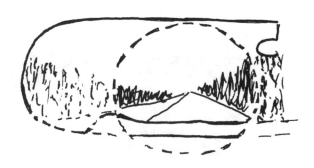

Fig. 51 45° cone of vision.

highway speeds. The driver at high speeds concentrates on the road ahead and you as the designer must present any information, any visual improvements, within this narrow cone of vision. In these exercises it is amazing how little you see of the road. Most of the road view on urban highways is sidewalls and backs of other cars and trucks.

Sketch several signs that obey these rules and can be seen by drivers behind trucks. Sketch several bridges with cars and trucks passing underneath. Make more sketches of the same view as you in the car move under the bridge with cars and trucks ahead in the same relative position. You will need perspective for this *(Fig. 52).*

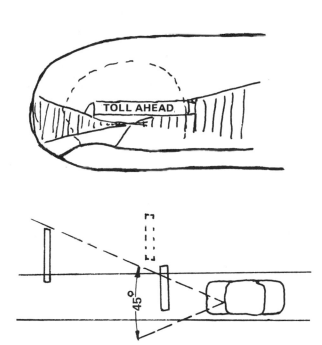

Fig. 52 Signs in the cone of vision.

Make some sketches of signs to be read at high speeds. Show locations on a sketched map, sketch in the 45° cone of vision. Bring pictures or descriptive sketches of highway signs that exist and sketch these showing improvements. Some signs are placed where they are for safety reasons. Don't put the stanchions for signs where they will be a hazard for a runaway car.

Sketch views of Interstate 80 passing through Nebraska: long, flat, farm fields on either side, fences, shoulders and drainage; an over pass of interstate design, with entrance and exit ramps, a little crossroads cluster of eats, gas and rest rooms, all with a huge sign 70 feet high *(Fig. 53).*

Fig. 53 Interstate 80 through Nebraska.

Rhythm or Tempo of Highways. Some highways have tar strips between the slabs of concrete which cause an audible thump giving a rhythmic beat. There is a visual rhythm for highways also. In all of our visual treatments we have had no sense of forward motion and it is hard to get this sense of moving from looking at one or two plans and maps. Sketches sometimes help but again we are looking at one or two at a time.

Visualizing the Tempo. Consider the depressed highway through an urban area with a bridge every block. As you drive along you notice a basic rhythm to the view: dark, light; blank wall, open sky. Given a prescribed speed limit we can find the visual rhythm of a road mathematically. Sketch a plan of the highway with bridges every 1000 feet. What is the rhythm going at different speeds? Given a speed of 60 mph *(88 feet per second)*, bridges 1000 feet apart and 88 feet wide, you will pass a bridge approximately every eleven seconds and be about one second under the bridge. How soon does this repetition annoy you? Guardrails spaced close together register only as a blur. Telephone poles register individually. To make the motorist visually aware of what you have designed you must make it big and spaced far enough apart to register. Then you can establish the tempo of the view. Guardrails, lights, culverts are often presented to the motorist in an even tempo. A different lamppost, one with a sign on it, can be out of tempo. Sketch several of these. Sketch a view of concrete panels, each one to be visually presented as a unit for a vertical wall of a highway with a speed limit of 45 mph. Sketch the same vertical wall but give each panel a slight turn so that from the top the wall appears serpentine. Sketch some of these *(Fig. 52)*.

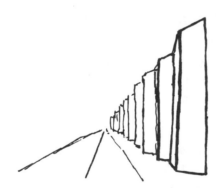

Fig. 52 Serpentine wall.

Building New Vistas. So far we have been sketching vistas that already exist but one of the most rewarding designs we can do is to make a vista where none appeared before. Home owners do this by selective trimming of bushes around a picture window. One owner of a mountain cabin hired treemen to take out and trim trees which obstructed his view, supervising them through binoculars and directing them by walkie-talkie. Landscape gardeners often plan a new vista for every turn of the garden path, a new focal point. Highways and buildings can be designed in the same fashion.

As the designer looks at his maps and plans, he envisions a safe and well engineered structure in harmony with the nature of the landscape and within costs. Designers can make a building or highway more exciting visually with judicious forethought. One method is to construct the highway so that it seems to point to one of the visible and prominent landmarks of that area, man-made or natural. By planning sight lines over intervening buildings and using structures along the road as frame for the view we can get an imposing view with little extra cost. Sketch a view of the road approaching Washington Monument. Sketch a view of a highway coming over a hill outside a small town, showing only the church spire and trees about the town. Show successive views of the church from a highway going into the town, then from a highway swinging around to bypass the town. Sketch a view of the spire as seen from a car going through the town on a depressed roadway. Assuming the spire is 100 feet tall, where will the highway be located to give the motorists a view of the spire?

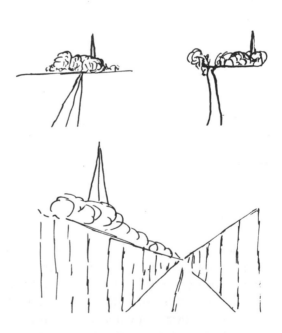

Fig. 53   Church steeple seen from various highway angles.

Other problems could be two structures along a highway, one a spherical gas tank and the other a rectangular building twice as high as the tank and the same width. The highway approaches them so you see the tank lined up with the building, then the highway curves out to the driver's left going around the buildings. Sketch at least five views of the position of each building as seen from the driver's seat. Curve the highway to the right and sketch (Figs. 54 & 55).

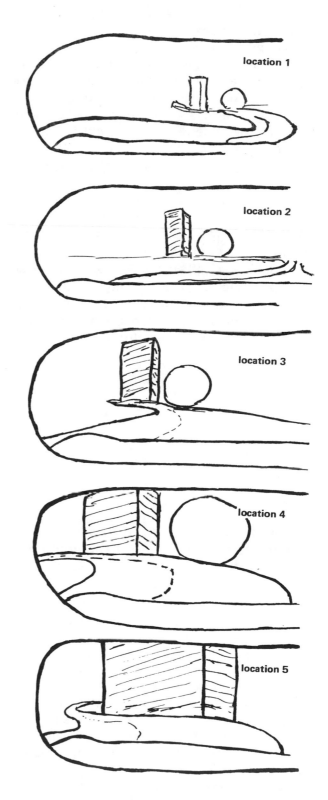

Fig. 55 Structures viewed from each of five station points.

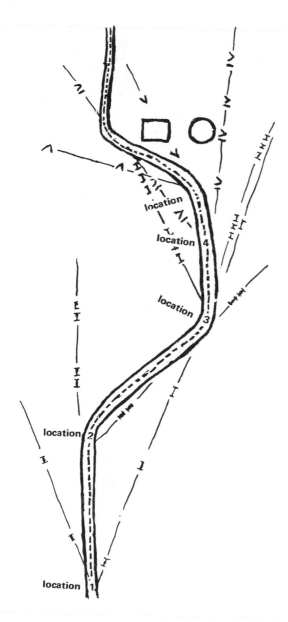

Fig. 54   Map with five station points.

187

Split the highway, one side going around the structures. How much will the structures block out a view of the other road?

Do the same sketch for three buildings, giving each a different shape so that you see each as an individual building. With more skill you would be able to visualize four or more buildings from the driver's seat and be able to tell which would be more pleasing. Some of this skill is just practice in looking, some in sketching.

Bridges that We Drive Over. We have been visualizing bridges seen from the road. Most visualizing of highway bridges is from the driver's seat as he goes over the bridge he is travelling on. Sketch a rather simple approach to an interstate bridge. There is not much to see except guardrails and abutments. Keeping in mind the safety requirements, how could you improve visual comprehension of the bridge?

Fig. 56   Interstate bridge.

On interstates the bridges are often the only break in the monotony. Treat the bridge as a bold structure although you don't see much of it. Keep the guardrails, lampposts and signs from breaking the visual line of the bridge. Sketch solutions for guardrails, then for lampposts and put the sketches over each other to see how both look together. You can also eliminate separate bridges for each lane and have a continuous bridge which looks more pleasing. The use of one unified structure eliminates the center abutment in the fast lane. This poses a problem of whether to treat the median strip with grass or concrete. Sketch both. Some designers have solved this problem by completely separating both lanes, even by a quarter of a mile, so that each driver sees the bridge of the opposite lane.

Bridges Above the Road. Some bridges by their very nature have most of the structure below the level of the road. Others, like suspension bridges, have some structure visible to the driver. Sketch some views of a four-lane suspension bridge as seen head-on by the driver to whom the towers are only a rectangle. Select at least four different proportions for this bridge by varying the height of that tower and see which is the most pleasing rectangle. In each case add bracing at different levels, some at the top and bottom and then at different heights. Look at some existing suspension bridges and sketch some of their solutions. Choose some structure that appeals to you and sketch adaptations of it.

Once you have visualized a suspension bridge from the driver's seat, visualize the bridge from different vantage points along the shore and on the river. You may need orthographic views of the bridge for this sketch. Modern suspension bridges may have the towers far apart where details will not appear and you deal with mass alone. Go over some of your sketches to see if they are pleasing from one mile away *(Fig. 57).*

Fig. 57   Mackinac bridge.

Buildings. You as an engineer will sometimes be the sole designer of the structure of bridges and buildings. Surprisingly, architects don't have much to do with designing buildings, but engineers, bankers, insurance men and developers all do. You as the engineer are often the only professional technical person concerned with the buildings. You can visualize what the building will look like from drawings. Engineers have produced some striking buildings, unlike others, well within cost allowances.

You have been trained to look at the building as a single unit. You can also look at the building in relation to other buildings. Start with the map. First does it fit with the general shape of the land or neighboring buildings. Fiting in doesn't mean identical, in some cases it may be completely different. Where is it in relation to the set-back line, how does it relate in texture, mass and proportion? There may not be a best answer but you can get some idea of its shape and form just by looking at the building and its surroundings and talking to yourself about them.

Start with something simple, a small building about a quarter of a block wide in the middle of a city block and about four stories high. On one side is a four story peaked house converted into office and store and on the other side a three story rectangular shaped building flush with the sidewalk. Sketch several different arrangements of your building and your building's roof, windows and entrances. Sketch from either direction. Make some quick perspective sketches showing different window and wall treatments of the same building. When you have several sketches select one that is pleasing, trace it and retouch it so that it looks even better. Display and defend each solution to your group.

Next try another building, one in a rural area, a new office building for an old company, Start with rolling hills, mountains in the background, a 100 acre property with a hill on which you intend to build. Block out masses first, then go to different shapes and treatments. The building will be a showplace and visible from a main highway. Most places now require park-

ing areas either inside or out so include that and a road. Show views of the building from the highway, from the private road entrance and at a turn in the private road. Design a pleasing sign to be placed on the highway turnoff. Try your hand at a large sign identifying the plant to be visible from the highway. Buildings, like highways, are too bold to be hidden and though visible should fit into the land.

Man Made Structures. Buildings, bridges and highways do occupy a significant piece of our viewing area in America. However, there are other structures which are often visible for miles and are landmarks. Water towers are one. Visualize a town with a hill beyond it. On this hill you are going to put a cylindrical water tower. Sketch several solutions to this including a high thin tower and a short stout one. Also sketch multiple towers, some the same size and some different. Select the most pleasing solution *(Fig. 58)*.

Since water towers are commonly protected, sketch several fences 8 to 10 feet high of different materials. Combine in one drawing the most pleasing water tower and fence. From the distance some of the fence will not show.

Do the same with an antenna tower. Get several pictures of a microwave tower and sketch some aesthetic solutions. Don't be afraid of strong vigorous impressions, think of yourself as making land marks.

The final test of any of your structures will be that it is correct technically and aesthetically.

Fig. 58 Sayreville, N.J. Towers.

Visibility. To open up new vistas when designing highways through scenic country, you must be able to determine what, from a specific spot, will be visible or not visible across the land. Long important in military usage contour maps have been developed and studied for lines of sight and the resulting visibility as practical problems in remaining concealed from or enabled to spy upon the enemy. It is still important enough that all of Europe and America have been re-mapped by computer to find valleys through which planes may fly to escape radar tower surveillance.

Method—By Eye. The most common method is to examine the contour map and imagine that you are standing at one particular spot. From that spot all lower elevations will appear as part of a valley, any higher elevations will be seen as

point may give you a view of the entire hidden part of the valley. With more practice you can determine the location for and height of a tower needed to see the hidden area, or pinpoint a suitable tree for climbing. Any added height from the ground will increase your view but will also increase the number of places from which you can be seen, a major consideration in all military tactics. The same rules of visibility apply to microwave towers.

Method—By Profiles. We have done visibility by eye but it is done more accurately with profiles, drawing only the tops not the entire cross section. The map itself is often used as the drafting paper. Rule in your line of sight from one point to another. Think of this as a base plane in an auxiliary view and from this line draw perpendiculars with scaled lengths, each of the perpendiculars at a spot on the line of sight along which we are interested in finding the visibility. It sounds complicated but by drawing on the map the process goes rather quickly. Of course if you want to save the map you can use tracing paper. This method is easy enough

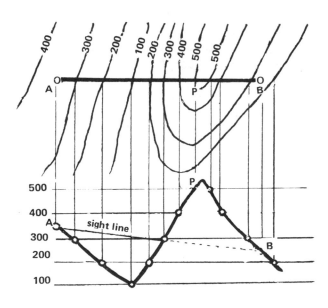

Fig. 59   Visibility by profiles.

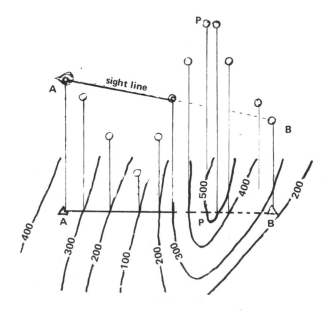

Fig. 60   Visibility by scaled lengths.

hills. These higher elevations *(hills)* will interrupt your line of sight and hide whatever lies beyond of a lesser elevation *(Fig.59)*. The ground behind it can be imagined shaded or hidden but only for that line of sight. Try other lines of sight tangent to the hills. With very little skill and practice you can quickly build up an image of the hidden areas. Moving to a new vantage

to use in the field. You should exaggerate the vertical scale, which won't alter the result, to solve this problem *(Fig. 60)*.

Method—By Similar Triangles. Another method of determining visibility uses similar triangles. On the map *(Fig. 61)* draw a line of sight from **A** to **B**. Find the heights of **A** and **B** and subtract to find the difference between contour heights. By construction draw a line **ba** about two inches away and parallel to **AB**. The line **ba**, arbitrary in length, is scaled to match the units of difference. Connect the ends, **B** to **b**, **A** to **a**, to form similar triangles, **AXB** and **aXb** (**X** being the crossover). To use this diagram pick any point (**P**) along the line **AB**. Draw a line from **P** to **X**, extending the line until it cuts line **ba** at **p**. At **p** read the height which is the height at which the line of sight passes **P**. If the height of the line of sight is greater than the contour height of **P** the line of sight will clear **P** and **P** will not interrupt the visibility. In this figure, **P** is blocking the rest of the line of sight because the height of the line of sight is less than the height of **P** *(Fig. 61)*.

This method while complicated is quick and accurate. It depends upon your judgment in picking **P** for there are many points along the line and you must pick the one which seems to interrupt the line of sight.

All of these methods build up the hidden area line by line. To define an area that is hidden, from your eye point run a set of radial lines, shading this hidden area to give it more meaning.

In all of these problems you must consider that the map may not be correct for visual lines of sight. The contour lines are lines on the ground and no mention is made on the map of trees, buildings, new excavations, which alter what you can see. Sometimes a view of the land itself may be necessary in addition to working from maps.

Computer mapping produces a mass of numbers instead of a map. There are also other methods for determining visibility and undoubtedly new methods will be found to help solve these old engineering problems.

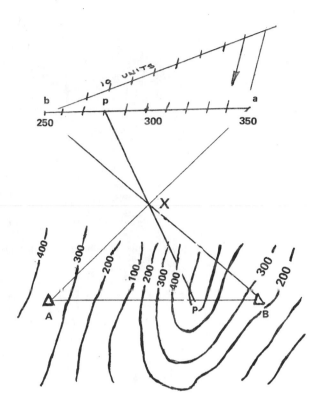

Fig. 61 Visibility by similar triangles.

Fig. 62 Visibility by cutting.

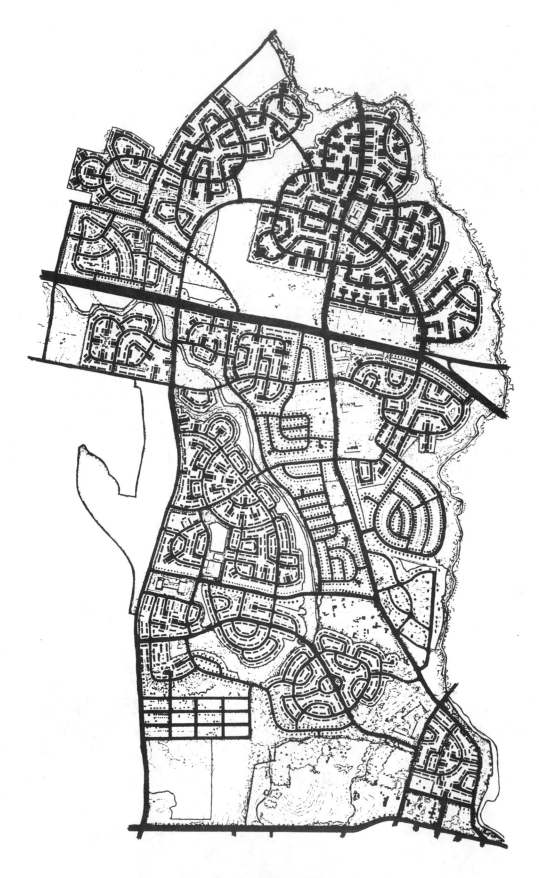

PHILADELPHIA'S MASTER PLAN
(Northeast Area)

SITE PLANNING AND SUBDIVISION LAYOUT 18

Site planning in its narrow sense involves the disposition of space for appropriate uses; the positioning of structures to provide effective relationships; the provision of access to structures in an expeditious, attractive, and safe manner; the design of the services, walks, streets, parking facilities, drainage, and utilities; and the preservation of the natural advantage of the site and its enhancement by landscaping.

Site planning in its larger sense involves consideration of the site in relationship to the physical pattern and economic growth trends of the larger area of which it is a part. An analysis of the area should be based on the following items: population growth, family formation, family size, housing inventory, income levels, schools, taxes and assessments, transportation and traffic patterns, and direction of growth.

An analysis of site development costs should be made in terms of densities, housing types, construction types, topography and grading, and local requirements with regards to zoning, subdivision regulations, and utility services.

PRINCIPLES OF NEIGHBORHOOD PLANNING

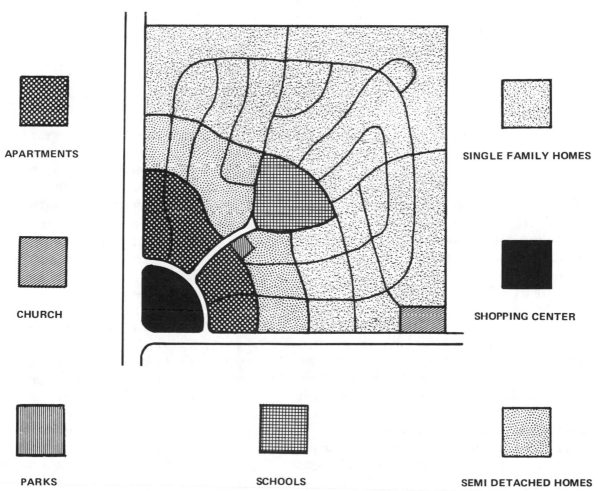

APARTMENTS

CHURCH

PARKS

SINGLE FAMILY HOMES

SHOPPING CENTER

SCHOOLS

SEMI DETACHED HOMES

Fig. 1 Neighborhood Planning.

1. SIZE - A residential unit development should provide housing for that population for which one elementary school is required.

2. BOUNDARIES - The unit should be bounded by arterial streets wide enough to facilitate traffic by-passing the neighborhood instead of passing through it.

3. OPEN SPACES - Small park and recreation space, planned to meet the needs of the particular neighborhood should be provided.

4. INSTITUTION SITES - Sites for schools and other institutions having service spheres coinciding with the limits of the unit should be grouped around a central point, usually combined with the neighborhood recreation area.

5. LOCAL SHOPPING CENTER - Local convenience shopping facility should be located at the edge of an arterial traffic junction and adjacent to similar commercial districts of other adjoining neighborhoods.

6. INTERNAL STREET SYSTEM - The unit should have a special street system, each highway being proportioned to its probable traffic load, and the street not as a whole being designed to facilitate circulation within the unit with good access to main arteries, and discourage through traffic.

HOUSING TYPES

Sites of fewer than 100 houses - range of types should be restricted.

As site size diminishes so should cost of house. Large sites may have single-family rental housing of high rise or garden types may be included where zoning permits. Apartments and town houses often provide a very satisfactory transition between the commercial area and the less dense residential area.

1. SINGLE FAMILY HOUSING - 60 ft. is considered minimum width, 70 to 80 ft. is more common.

Patios, courts and fenced-in areas are used to provide privacy when the lot sizes are small.

2. ROW HOUSE (TOWN HOUSES) Economical use of land and low site development costs. Often 8 to 10 units in a group located around a court, cul-de-sac, or loop street.

Lots should be 20 to 25 ft. wide and lots at the end should be wider with side yards. Garages should be provided within the house structure itself or as a one story attached structure, often as a carport.

3. RENTAL HOUSING - For more attractive appearance is now built at lower densities with emphasis on open space. Often includes club-like features as swimming pools and tennis courts. Densities of 15 to 25 families per acre. Coverage of land 15% to 25% of area. Garden apartments are usually 2 stories high and not over 3 stories. High-rise elevator apartments should restrict land coverage to 10% to 15%.

LOT SIZES AND DEVELOPMENT COSTS

In order to keep the cost of the developed lot from rising to prohibitive levels, site planners have resorted to the "super-block". Lots are 600 to 800 ft. long by 200-250 ft. wide which reduces the number of cross streets and eliminates the need for utilities in them. Typical lots are thus likely to be 1 1/2 to 2 times as deep as they are wide. Deep superblocks, penetrated by culs-de-sac or loop streets, are also used.

STREETS

A subdivision plan must conform with the master street plan for that city, but this usually only applies to major streets. At the boundaries, however, major streets may be an asset if they provide good access to other areas in the community. It is undesirable to have major streets traverse a residential area. Fire protection should be considered in determining the street pattern. Problems to consider are hydrant locations, culs-de-sac turnarounds, access to buildings in multi-family projects and commercial areas, radius of curvature of curbs at intersections, etc.

Streets are necessary evils in a neighborhood or smaller sub-division: They are primarily to provide access to and circulation with the area. Streets serving other purposes (arterial streets) should bound rather than penetrate the area. Collector streets *(Right of way 60 ft.)* are those streets carrying traffic from minor streets to arterial streets - 36 ft. wide of two moving lanes and two parking lanes. Minor streets (Right of way 50 ft.), depending on off-street parking, are 26 ft. wide for single family, 32 ft.

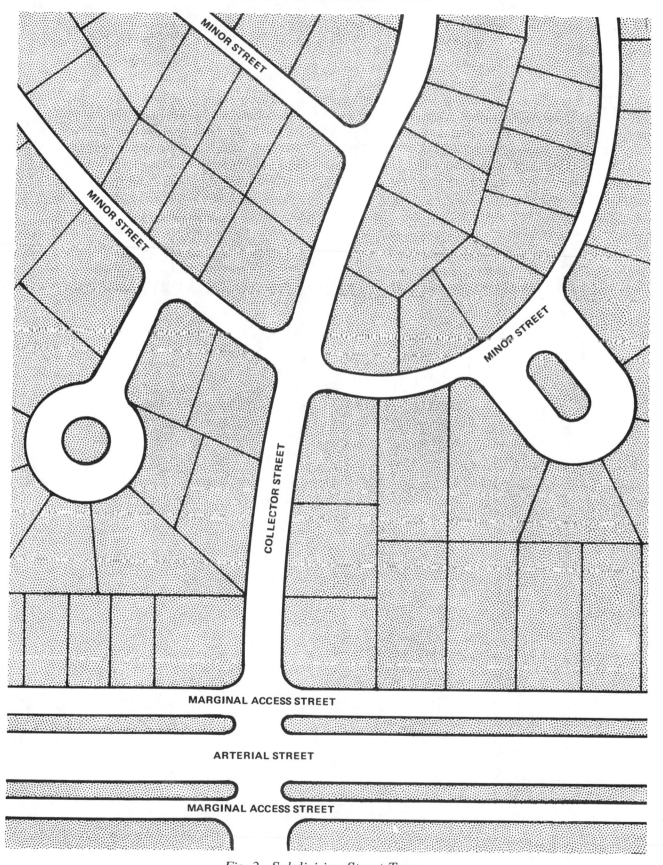

Fig. 2 Subdivision Street Types.

195

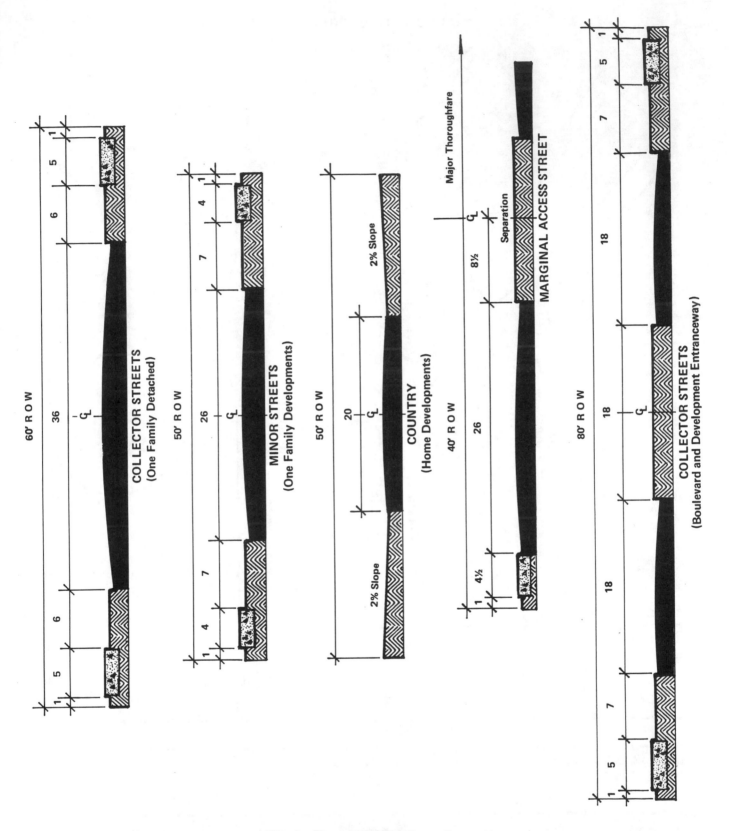

Fig. 3 Typical Street Cross Sections.

196

for row housing and apartments. Short access streets are culs-de-sac or loop streets with a minimum width of 20 ft., and should terminate in a turning circle not less than 80 ft. in diameter between curbs. Should not be over 500 ft. in length. The use of the "T" intersection of minor streets with collector streets are fine if 125 ft. between intersections are maintained. Keep driveways off the main highways. Instead, lots should back up to the highways with heavy planting along rear of lots. Or a local access road parallel to highway and screened from it by planting

SIDEWALKS

High density areas *(more than 5 families per acre)* and streets carrying more than local traffic usually require sidewalks on both sides of street. Four ft. is standard design width for sidewalks. When sidewalks are separated from curb by a planting strip, the strip should be at least 3 ft. wide to provide for snow removal; if trees are included it should be 7 ft. minimum.

CURBS

The rolled curb is more economical than the straight curb and does not require cutting at driveways. A 15 ft. radius for curbs at right angle intersections discourages speeding and use of minor intersections. Cuts in straight curbs for driveways should provide 3 to 5 ft. radiuses and a 9 or 10 ft. wide driveways.

LOT LAYOUT

The layout of the lots in a subdivision can make the difference between an attractive and an unattractive development, also the difference between an economical and an uneconomical project.

Recreation areas are essential and should represent at least 5% of the residential area and more where the lots are small.

LOT SIZE AND DWELLING DENSITIES

DWELLING UNIT TYPE	LOT DIMENSIONS PER DWELLING UNIT IN FEET	*NET DENSITY DWELLING UNITS/ACRE
Detached Houses	100 x 200	2.0
	80 x 160	3.5
	70 x 140	3.3
	60 x 125	4.3
	50 x 100	6.5
Semi-Detached Houses	30 x 125	8.7
	26 x 125	10.0
Row Houses (Two-Story)	20 x 100	16.3
	16 x 100	20.4
Garden Apartments (Two Story)		15-25
Garden Apartments (Three Story)		25-35
Apartments, Multiple Story to Twelve Stories		50-85

*NET DENSITY - Number of dwellings units per acre of land within site, after deducting 25% of the site for allocation of streets, parks and recreation areas.

GROSS DENSITY - Computed on the basis of net land area plus area devoted to streets and other nonresidential uses and one-half bounding streets and one-quarter of bounding street intersections. (From Community Builders Handbook, *Urban Land Institute*)

LOT AREA AND DWELLING DENSITIES

DWELLING UNIT TYPE	D.U.'s PER NET ACRE	ASSUMED AVERAGE SQ. FT. OF LOT PER D. U.
Single-Family	1	40,000
Single-Family	2	20,000
Single-Family	3	12,500
Single-Family	4	10,000
Two-Family	6	6,000
Row House	15	2,600
Garden Apartment	25	1,600
Multi-Story Apartments	50	800

SUBDIVISION REGULATIONS

Streets: location, types, rights-of-way, widths, pavement, widths and specifications, grades, intersections, curvatures, alignments, curbs, gutters and sidewalks.

Blocks: length, width, crosswalks, utility easements.

Lots: size, shape, minimum dimensions.

Open Spaces: size, type.

Utilities: storm and sanitary sewers, culverts, bridges, water service, monuments.

Names: of area and streets and street numbers.

STREET AND BLOCK PATTERNS

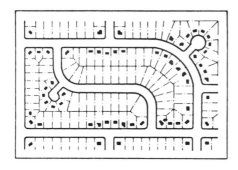

Fig. 4   Good block pattern design showing variety, long blocks eliminating unnecessary cross streets and giving more front selling feet; control of traffic flow.

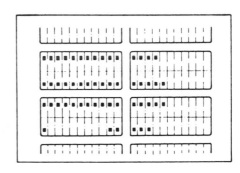

Fig. 5   Poor block pattern design showing lack of individuality, all streets potentially "through" arteries and constructed accordingly, at very high cost.

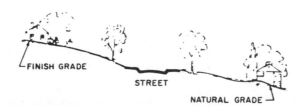

Fig. 6 If side hills are unavoidable, finish grade must control drainage around the buildings.

198

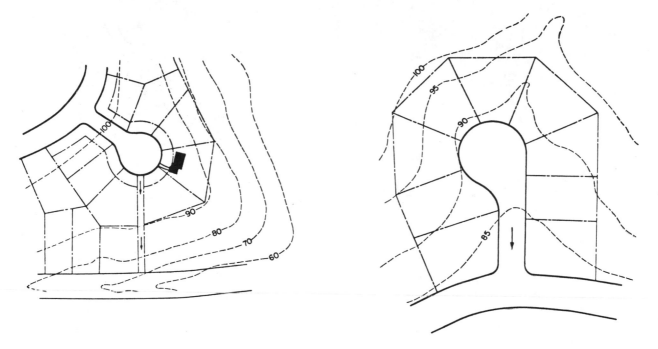

Fig. 7 *The above figures show effective design for the cul-de-sac as used (left) in a ridge site, and (right) valley site.*

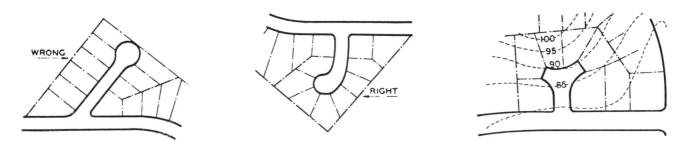

Fig. 8 *Culs-de-sac should not be over 500 feet in length and should have a minimum turnaround of not less than 40 feet radii from the center of the circle to the outside curb. Entire turnaround should be paved. Cul-de-sac should never be brought to property boundary line (left). The Y or T "back-around" (right) is useful on short cul-de-sac and on a steep slope.*

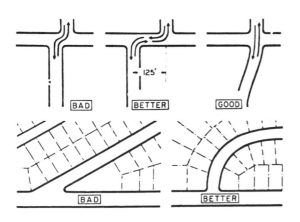

Fig. 9 *Streets should intersect at nearly right angles, avoid jogs whenever possible.*

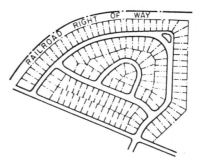

Fig. 10 *Avoid streets which deadend against a railroad right-of-way, open country or some other barrier. They may result in blight for the lots involved. A cul-de-sac is the solution to the problem.*

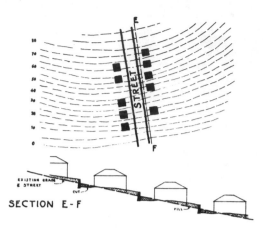

SECTION E-F

Fig. 11 When a street is built directly up a steep slope, excessive grades are created and retaining walls are necessary along the side lot lines.

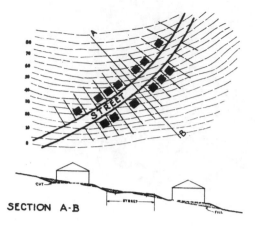

SECTION A-B

Fig. 12 When grades are steep, best practice is to cut diagonally across the contour lines. This avoids excessive grading and retaining walls.

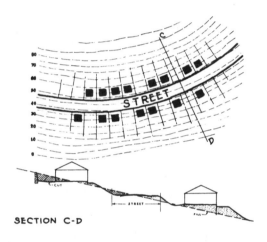

SECTION C-D

Fig. 13 Streets parallel with contour lines involve costly retaining walls. Houses on both sides of the street have no relation to each other as to grade.

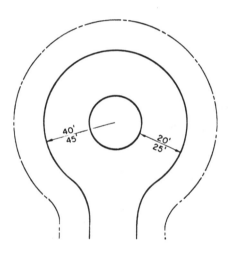

Fig. 14 Minimum cul-de-sac dimensions.

200

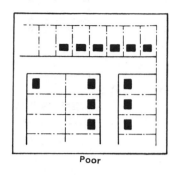
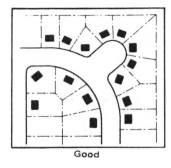

Fig. 15   Try to eliminate future street extensions at corners of property.

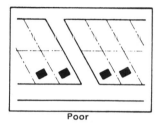
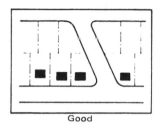
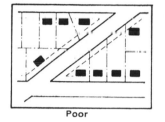
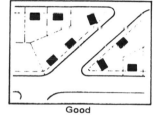

Fig. 16   Proper treatment of lotting where diagonal streets are necessary.

Fig. 17   Proper treatment of lotting where acute angle intersections are unavoidable.

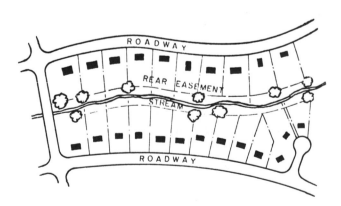
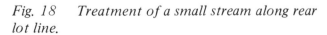
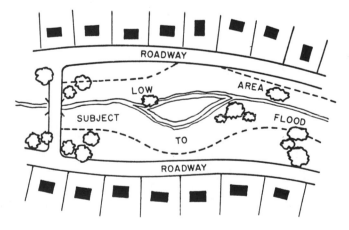

Fig. 18   Treatment of a small stream along rear lot line.

Fig. 19   Make a small stream into a community asset.

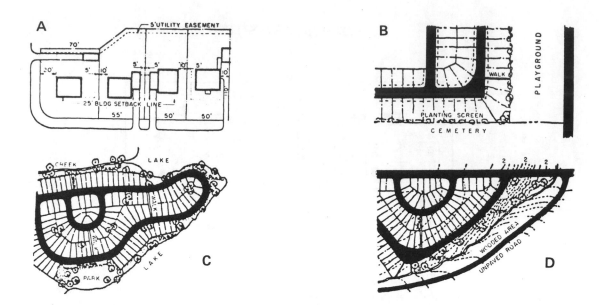

Fig. 20 Desirable conditions: (A) Placement of each house should be controlled to create pleasing variety yet avoid disorderly effect. (B) Lots protected by planting screen from inharmonious adjacent uses. (C) Natural features preserved for their amenity value. (D) Rough wooded strip turned into a neighborhood park can enhance value of all lots.

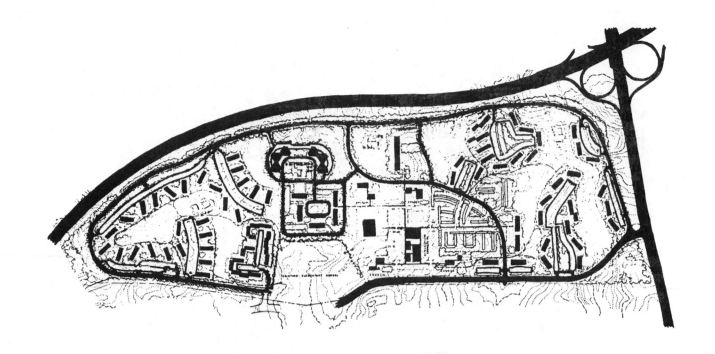

Fig. 21   Plan of Americana Fairfax capitalizes on hilliness of tract.

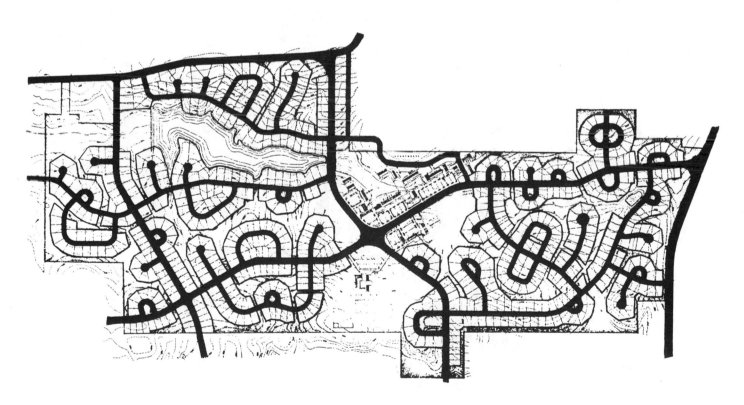

Fig. 22   Parkwood gives each lot access to common open space.

203

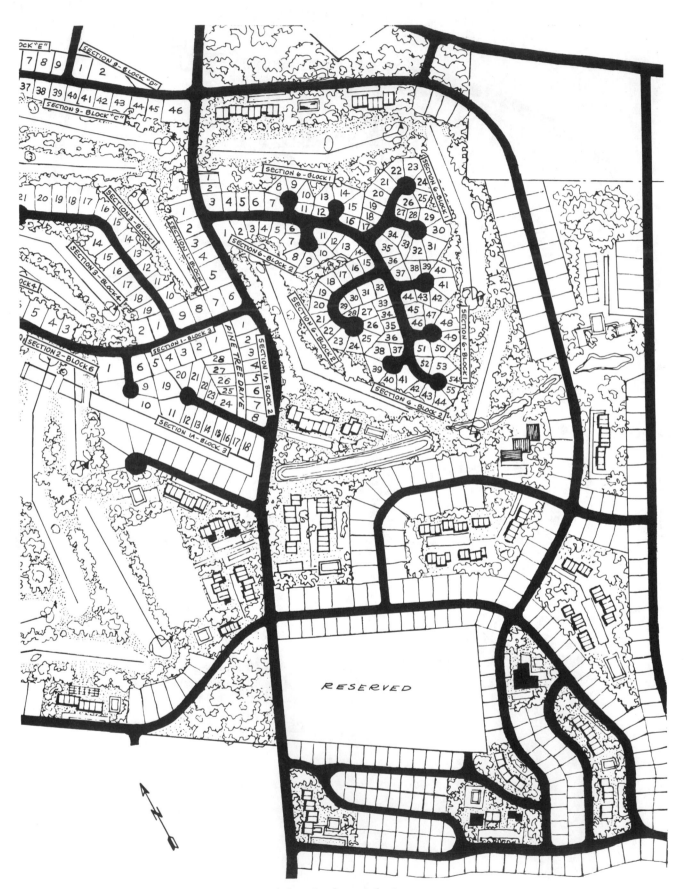

Atlantis cluster design

CLUSTER DEVELOPMENT

CLUS · TER (klus' ter) n. A number of persons or things close together; group. - v.t. & v.i. To grow or to form into a cluster or clusters.

INTRODUCTION

Cluster zoning establishes a maximum density for an area, usually in terms of dwelling units per acre, and grants leeway to subdividers to reduce the lot area for each house as long as the density for the whole subdivision does not exceed the maximum set for the zone. One portion of a tract may be developed at high density and the remainder at very low density, or all development may occur at relatively high density with the remaining open space dedicated for use of persons in the subdivision or for all residents of the community. Depending on the language and intent of the density zoning ordinance, the open space preserved may be retained in public or private ownership.

Cluster zoning permits economies in building and provision of services: only the land best suited to building need be used; less street mileage is needed than in conventional development; utility lines are shorter and therefore more economical; children may be closer to schools; and snow plowing, mail delivery, and garbage pickup are all more economical because the routes are shorter. Cluster zoning also permits preservation of open space at no initial cost to the community. Careful planning in cooperation with the developers can make it possible to create greenbelts by linking open space in one subdivision to that in another.

OPEN SPACE

An important decision to be made by local governments before adoption of cluster zoning is how the resulting open space will be preserved and maintained. If permanent preservation is desired, there must be covenants or restrictions attached to the land so that there can be no subsequent change of zoning to allow develop-

ment. The local government must decide whether it wants open space to be privately owned and maintained, either by individuals or a property owner's association, or dedicated to the local government for public use, or whether subdividers should have an option between these possibilities. Opponents of the cluster concept point to problems of supervision and operation of the common open space. But the problems can be resolved:

1. By setting up a non-profit corporation consisting of home owners. Each home owner should automatically become a member of such organization. Each lot is automatically subject to a charge for a proportionate share of the expenses of home owners association activities, such as maintenance of common open space. Experience has shown the home owners association to be a sound solution where it has been properly established.

2. By setting up a special government district to correspond with the extent of the project's open space. Only a few states have enabling legislation for this special district.

3. By deeding the open space to the local government. This method generally works least well. It would be unreasonable to expect public maintenance of a common area that is largely enclosed and intimately related to the homes it serves and, therefore, unavailable to the general public. Also, the developer and then the buyers have paid for these areas. On the other hand, public maintenance of common properties readily accessible to the general public may encourage heavy public use which can adversely affect the residents of the development. Public maintenance would undercut one of the principle attractions of the cluster and open space concept, the use and enjoyment by the residents of the project.

Just as developers should not make too much of a good thing of cluster, neither should communities look at cluster as a cut rate substitute for buying park land. The best solution as to the problems of supervision and operation of the common open space is a combination of 1 and 3 of the above.

DESIGN

The cluster method requires more skill in design than standard and ordinary methods of land subdivision. Its successful application is largely dependent upon such skill being locally available. This factor is one of several responsible for limited progress to date. The land planner's knowledge of topography, zoning, land use, and land design requires coordination with the ingenuity of the architect in site planning, grouping of structures, street pattern, utility design, and other elements of the plan. Unskilled planning or exploitation of the cluster method might easily generate ugly bunching of dwellings. The competent guidance of a qualified planner, landscape architect or architect will not only benefit developer and community but may spell success for the employment of the cluster concept.

ECONOMICS OF CLUSTER

On economic grounds alone, cluster development makes sense not only for the developer and the homeowner, but for the community itself. Savings over a conventional subdivision are found in the following areas:

1. Lots - Under conventional subdivision plans, the developer might build many homes on less desirable portions of the tract. Under the cluster concept, the developer can work within a set density thus allowing the same number of homes as the conventional plan, but all of the homes could be placed on the choicest part of the tract, leaving wetlands and marginal land in open space. If the lot size reduction is severe, the municipality may also find it necessary to reduce the minimum required building size so that the building and lot are compatible.

2. Sewerage - Since the homes are clustered, the sewer pipe lines have shorter runs and thus reduce the total length of sewer line needed for the development.

3. Building - The developer can build one cluster of the development at a time; thus con-

centrating all his materials and equipment in one place with a considerable saving in man hours and convenience. As soon as one cluster is finished, the materials can be moved to the next cluster site.

4. Roads - Clustering of homes on cul-de-sacs, etc. reduces the need for long stretches of roads and curbing. Up to fifty percent of the lineal street footage can be saved by the use of clustering.

5. Water and Runoff - Conventional development with its many miles of street surface, lays down an impervious surface on a great amount of land; this catches a greater amount of rainfall over the total area and makes necessary more linear feet of storm sewers, curbs and gutters. Cluster development concentrates the building where the drainage problem can be most efficiently handled and leaves the bulk of the natural drainage system alone. A free-flowing stream is an excellent storm sewer and looks better than a concrete channel.

6. Maintenance - Savings in many areas of maintaining the site can be realized such as: garbage collection, since the stops for picking up points are closer together; time of police patrol can be reduced because of the clustering of the homes; and road maintenance costs can be reduced such as snow plowing since the road lengths are shorter than conventional subdivisions.

CONCLUSIONS

County Planning Boards feel that the use of cluster zoning offers the following benefits:

1. Provides opportunities for reserving rapidly disappearing open land without penalizing the land developer.

2. Permits development of project area on whatever size lot and with whatever type of dwelling desired, provided that the number of lots and general quality is in accordance with the intent of the basic zoning.

3. Open spaces created offer opportunity for park and play area.

4. Offers possibility to preserve rough, wooded land usually cleared and re-graded under conventional development practices.

5. Relief from the monotony of the

usual "sterile" rows of dwellings with standard setbacks.

6. Economical and practical method of providing access and service.

7. Freedom from through traffic.

8. Reduces the size of the lot to a more usable and more easily maintained area.

9. Permits the development of land without encroaching on the natural streams and their flood plains.

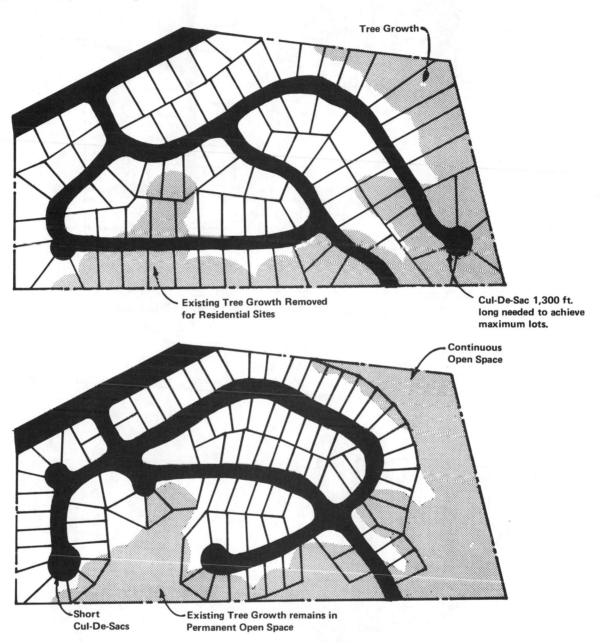

AN EXAMPLE OF DENSITY ZONING CONTROL

Density control zoning applied to large lots and rugged land having existing tree growth is worthy of preservation. Upper plan shows tract of land containing 37 acres zoned 15,000 sq. ft. residential lots. Maximum use yields 86 lots. Lower plan shows same tract with each lot having a minimum area of 10,000 sq. ft. Re-platting yields 86 lots and the remaining wooded area is placed in permanent open space. No lots are lost and there is less street to pave and maintain.

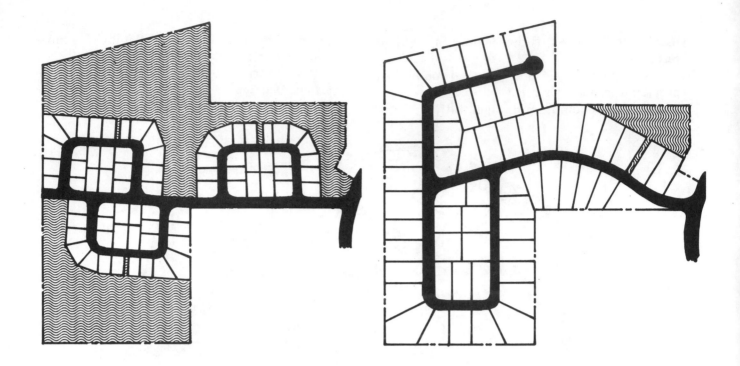

The illustration on the right shows the original subdivision of 79 acres in Hillsborough, New Jersey. The developer plotted it for 62 one acre lots. The illustration on the left shows the subdivision, as built in the early 1960's, with the houses clustered in three groups totaling 35 acres and 72 lots. Under the cluster plan 40 acres were left for open space. Because of savings in water and sewer line length, the land development costs were shaved from $6,500 per lot for the conventional plan to $5,500 for the cluster plan. In addition there was less roadway, less grading and the trees were saved from the bulldozer.

CURVILINEAR 94 lots 11,600 ft. streets

RECTILINEAR 94 lots 12,000 ft. streets

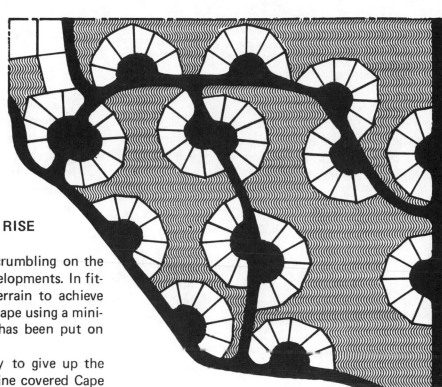

CLUSTER HOUSING ON THE RISE

Cookie cutter architecture is crumbling on the drawing boards of housing developments. In fitting clusters of houses into terrain to achieve maximum beauty of the landscape using a minimum of land, more emphasis has been put on variety.

Many people aren't ready to give up the American dream house -- the vine covered Cape Cod cottage with a picket fence. Then too, many people do not understand cluster housing -- a development of houses built together, sometimes with a common breezeway, garage or walls, but with land that is shared by everyone. You own your own house and pay your own mortgage. It isn't really a new idea. The Romans used it in a similar housing principle in the 6th century.

The new housing style accommodates not only environmental problems, but the saving of land investment provides more houses for less money, and a real bonus for the moderate-income family may be the country-club atmosphere.

Cluster housing has been popular in England for hundreds of years, but it wasn't really accepted in the United States. In protecting the environment and creating more open space, it can enhance the countryside and be developed at prices people can afford.

Although there are millions of acres of undeveloped land in the United States, much cannot be utilized for housing because people must live near their work. Little land is available in urban and suburban areas where it is needed, and what can be obtained is so expensive that it is no longer possible for people to build the little dream house or even a reasonable facsimile of it. It is not even profitable for builders to build

single family homes because of the high cost of land and its development -- sewer systems, water and streets.

In cluster housing people have advantages in groups they might not be able to afford individually as single family home owners. A country club atmosphere can provide tennis, golf, swimming pools, saunas, picnic areas, baseball diamonds and even child day care centers utilizing large acreage set aside for the purpose. Then too, some moderate price bracket ($35,000-$50,000) houses, even have interiors that normally are found only in expensive homes: beamed cathedral ceilings, balconies, fireplace pits, bathrooms with carpets, marble top vanities, fluorescent lighting, windows that go to countertops in the kitchens to accommodate the viewing by mothers who must supervise children.

Fifteen years ago, an engineer would cut up the land into little lots, plop houses on them and put up a "For Sale" sign, now it is all team work -- architects, landscapers, engineers, builders, interior designers, working together to get the best design for that land.

LOCATIONS AND DESIGN OF DEVELOPMENT

1. Should be in harmony with major street plan of community.
2. Should be accessible to main highway -- but access controlled.
3. Practical minimum distance between intersections on main highways -- 800 feet.
4. Assuming not over 40 vehicles per 100 family units move during the peak hours, a roadway with one lane in each direction will provide for 750 family units.

5. A minimum number of cross streets is desirable, consistent with circulation needs.

These standards for building traffic safety into residential development are from the National Committee for Traffic Safety. They closely conform to principles approved by the Community Builders Council of the United Urban Land Institute and the Land Planning Committee of the National Association of Home Builders.

DESIGN OF LOCAL RESIDENTIAL STREETS

Speed: Based on maximum of 25 m.p.h. in accord with Uniform Vehicle Code recommendations. Recommendation will be reasonably satisfactory even if some speeds exceed 25 m.p.h.

	Single-family	Multi-family
Street width:	50 feet	60 feet
Pavement width:	26 feet	32 feet
Curbs:	Straight curb	Straight curb
Sidewalks:		
Width:	4 feet minimum	same
Set back:	3 feet minimum if no trees	same
	7 feet minimum with trees	same
Horizontal Alignment:	200 feet min. sight distance	same
Vertical Alignment:	6-8% maximum grade desirable	
	3-4% per 100 feet maximum rate of change.	same
Cul-de-sac:	400-500 feet maximum length	same
Turn-arounds:	40 feet min. curb radius without parking	same
	50 feet min. curb radius with parking	same
Pavement Surface	Non-skid with strength to carry traffic load	same

DESIGN OF FEEDER STREETS

Street width:	60 feet
Pavement width:	36 feet
Curbs:	Straight curb recommended
Sidewalks:	
Width:	4 feet min.
Set-back:	3 feet min. with trees.
Horizontal Alignment:	Same as for local residential streets
Vertical Alignment:	Same as for local residential streets
Pavement Surface:	Same as for local residential streets

INTERSECTION DESIGN

Sight Distance: Such that each vehicle is visible to the other driver when each is 75 feet from the intersection, for 25 m.p.h. max. speed.
No building or other sight obstruction within sight triangle.

Vertical Alignment: Flat grade within intersection.
Flat section preferred from 50 feet to 100 feet each way from intersection, but in no case over 3-5% grade.
6% maximum between 100 and 150 feet of intersection.

Horizontal Alignment: 90 degree intersections are preferred; less than 60 degrees usually hazarddous.
Curb radius for local and feeder streets - 12 feet.
Curb radius for feeder street intersecting main highway - 50 feet.

Sidewalks:
  Placement: Set-back should be minimum of 7 feet where trees are planted between curb and sidewalk; minimum of 3 feet if no trees.
  Width: 4 feet minimum (4½ - 5 feet minimum near shopping centers.)

PARKING IN RESIDENTIAL AREAS

1.   Ample off-street facilities should be provided.

2.   Private garage or space, with private driveway, should be provided for single and multi-semidetached dwellings.

3.   Parking bays, not physically divided from roadway, may be used on strictly local streets with little traffic. Requires 180 or 210 square feet per car.

4.   Parking bays physically divided from roadway preferred on streets carrying more than local traffic, such as feeder streets. Requires approximately 360 square feet per car, including service aisles and divider.

5.   Parking lot is more desirable off-street facility. Requires 275-300 square feet per car, including aisles.

ALLEYS

1.   Not considered necessary or desirable in single family developments.

2.   May be necessary in group, row house or apartment developments.

3.   If provided should be 20 feet wide and paved.

CURB CUTS FOR DRIVEWAYS

Curb return with radius of 3 to 5 ft. is desired. A 7 ft. radius is desired for entrances.

SI UNIT PREFIXES

Multiplication Factor		Prefix	Symbol	Pronunciation (USA)*	Means
1 000 000 000 000	= 10^{12}	tera	T	as in terrace	One trillion times †
1 000 000 000	= 10^9	giga	G	jig' a (a as in about)	One billion times ‡
1 000 000	= 10^6	mega	M	as in megaphone	One million times
1 000	= 10^3	kilo	k	as in kilowatt	One thousand times
100	= 10^2	hecto	h §	heck' toe	One hundred times
10	= 10	deka	da §	deck' a (a as in about)	Ten times
0.1	= 10^{-1}	deci	d §	as in decimal	One tenth of
0.01	= 10^{-2}	centi	c §	as in centipede	One hundredth of
0.001	= 10^{-3}	milli	m	as in military	One thousandth of
0.000 001	= 10^{-6}	micro	μ	as in microphone	One millionth of
0.000 000 001	= 10^{-9}	nano	n	nan' oh (an as in ant)	One billionth of ‡
0.000 000 000 001	= 10^{-12}	pico	p	peek' oh	One trillionth of †
0.000 000 000 000 001	= 10^{-15}	femto	f	fem' toe (fem as in feminine)	One quadrillionth of **
0.000 000 000 000 000 001	= 10^{-18}	atto	a	as in anatomy	One quintillionth of ††

*The first syllable of every prefix is accented to assure that the prefix will retain its identity. Therefore, the preferred pronunciation of kilometer places the accent on the first syllable, not the second.

†Because trillion means a million million in the United States but a million million million in most other countries, its use should be avoided in technical writing.

‡Because a billion means a thousand million in the United States but a million million in most other countries, its use should be avoided in technical writing.

§While hecto, deka, deci, and centi are SI prefixes, their use should generally be avoided except for measurement of area and volume and non-technical use of centimeter, as for body and clothing measurements.

**One thousand billionth in most countries other than USA. Avoid in technical writing.

††One trillionth in most countries other than USA. Avoid in technical writing.

MODERNIZED METRIC SYSTEM

ENGLISH SYSTEM

The English System which we use has a long, complicated history of gradual growth for over 3000 years. It finally became a refined and well-defined system of measurement in the late 1800's, largely under the influence of the National Bureau of Standards in the United States and the National Physical Laboratory in England. There are awkward complexities to the system, but it is properly useable for science and engineering, and the inch and pound are the heart of the greatest industrial system in the world.

METRIC SYSTEM

About 300 years ago, scientists began seeking a universal coherent system of measurement suitable for international use. This resulted in the establishment of the metric system in France in 1791 and her invitation for the world to join her in its use. The United States and British Commonwealth nations refused, but Germany, France, Italy and others proceeded to develop their industries and industrial standards around the metric system. Many variations in the system have developed, however, because no controls were set up to unify use, and the common metric system is as awkward and illogical as the English system.

INTERNATIONAL SYSTEM OF UNITS

In the late 19th century these variations of units of measure, particularly the minor differences which had grown up between countries using the metric systerm were an obstacle to the rapidly increasing sophistication of science and industry. In 1875 the major nations of the world joined in "The Treaty of the Meter" which established an International Bureau of Weights and Measures near Paris, and set up the General Conference on Weights and Measures, of which the United States is a part, to develop a good international system.

By the year 1900, measurements in the metric system began to be based on meter-kilogram-second units (MKS). Later, Professor Giorgi of Italy recommended that the units of mechanics should be linked with electro-magnetic units, and the ampere was added to create the MKSA (Giorgi) units.

It was not until many years later that the rapid growth of worldwide science and industry led to the requirement for units for the measurement of other physical qualities. When these new units of measure were established, they were often defined in terms of metric system units due to the relative exactness of the definition of the basic metric units for weight, length and volume. These new units, however, were sometimes established by different scientific methods which often resulted in more than one metric unit for measuring the same physical quality.

The Tenth General Conference, held in 1954, adopted a rationalized system of units based on the four MKSA units plus the kelvin as the unit of temperature and the candela as the unit of luminous intensity. The Eleventh General Conference of Weights and Measures, in 1960, formally gave the new system its full title 'Systeme International d'Unites,' for which the universal abbreviation is "SI."

In 1960, the metric system and its units were redefined in an effort to correct some deficiencies that had developed over the years. When the metric system began, the most pressing need of the time was to standardize units of measure to expedite the fair exchange of goods and services. Primary attention was therefore given to standardizing the relatively more simple concepts of length, area, volume and weight.

Obviously, since it is international, the system has names in many languages, but it has agreed to abbreviate its name "SI" *from the French Le Syste'me International d'Unite's.*

SI is the modernized metric system. It is officially recognized by all industrial nations, has been referenced by SAE, ASTM, ASME, and many other societies, is the preferred system of ISO, and is the official basis of our United States units *(the inch and pound are defined in terms of the metre and kilogram).*

There is much about the system that is old and familiar, however, there is also much that is new. The entire system is based on seven fundamentals -- and all necessary units can be derived from these seven:

BASIC UNITS

Quantity	Unit	SI Symbol
length	metre	m
mass	kilogram	kg
time	second	s
electric current	ampere	A
thermodynamic temperature	kelvin	K
amount of substance	mole	mol
luminous intensity	candela	cd

Authorized translations of the original French definitions of the seven base units of the International System (SI) are given in the following paragraphs:

metre - The metre is the length equal to 1 650 763.73 wave lengths in vacuum of the radiation corresponding to the transition between the levels $2p_{10}$ and $5d5$ of the krypton-86 atom.

kilogram - The kilogram is the unit of mass; it is equal to the mass of the international prototype of the kilogram.

second - The second is the duration of 9 192 631 770 periods of the radiation corresponding to the transition between the two hyperfine levels of the ground state of the cesium - 133 atom.

ampere - The ampere is that constant current which, if maintained in two straight parallel conductors of infinite length, of negligible circular cross section, and placed one metre apart in vacuum, would produce between these conductors a force equal to 2 X 10-7 newton per metre of length.

kelvin - The kelvin, unit of thermodynamic temperature, is the fraction 1/273.16 of the thermodynamic temperature of the triple point of water.

mole - The mole is the amount of substance of a system which contains as many elementary entities as there are atoms in 0.012 kilograms of carbon 12.

candela - The candela is the luminous intensity, in the perpendicular direction of a surface of 1/600 000 square metre of a blackbody at the temperature of freez-platinum under a pressure of 101 325 newtons per square metre.

SUPPLEMENTARY UNITS

Quantity	Unit	SI Symbol
plane angle	radian	rad
solid angle	steradian	sr

Authorized translations of the original French definitions of the two supplementary units of the International System are given in the following paragraphs:

radian - The unit of measure of a plane angle with its vertex at the center of a circle and subtended by an arc equal in length to the radius.

steradian - The unit of measure of a solid angle with its vertex at the center of a sphere and enclosing an area of the spherical surface equal to that of a square with sides equal in length to the radius.

In addition to the seven basic units, SI includes derived units which make it a more complete and coherent system, suitable for measurements in physical sciences and engineering.

SOME DERIVED UNITS OF THE INTERNATIONAL SYSTEM
(having special names)

Quantity	Unit	SI Symbol	Formula
electric capacitance	farad	F	$A \cdot s/V$
electric inductance	henry	H	$V \cdot s/A$
electric potential difference	volt	V	W/A
electric resistance	ohm	Ω	V/A
energy	joule	J	$N \cdot m$
force	newton	N	$kg \cdot m/s^2$
frequency	hertz	Hz	(cycle) /s
illuminance	lux	lx	lm/m^2
luminous flux	lumen	lm	$cd \cdot sr$
magnetic flux	weber	Wb	$V \cdot s$
magnetic flux density	tesla	T	Wb/m^2
power	watt	W	J/s
pressure or stress	pascal	Pa	N/m^2
quantity of electricity	coulomb	C	$A \cdot s$

farad - The farad is the capacitance of a capacitor between the plates of which appears a difference of potential of one volt when it is charged by a quantity of electricity equal to one coulomb.

siemens - The siemens is the electrical conductance of a conductor in which a current of one ampere is produced by an electric potential difference of one volt.

henry - The henry is the inductance of a closed circuit in which an electromotive force of one volt is produced when the electric current in the circuit varies uniformly at a rate of one ampere per second.

volt - The volt (unit of electric potential difference and electromotive force) is the difference of electric potential between two points of a conductor carrying a constant current of one ampere, when the power dissipated between these points is equal to one watt.

ohm - The ohm is the electric resistance between two points of a conductor when a constant difference of potential of one volt, applied between these two points, produces in this conductor a current of one ampere, this conductor not being the source of any electromotive force.

joule - The joule is the work done when the point of application of a force of one newton is displaced a distance of one metre in the direction of the force.

newton - The newton is that force which, when applied to a body having a mass of one kilogram gives it an acceration of one metre per second per second.

hertz - The hertz is a frequency of one cycle per second.

lux - The lux is the illuminance produced by a luminous flux of one lumen uniformly distributed over a surface of one square metre.

lumen - The lumen is the luminous flux emitted in a solid angle of one steradian by a point source having a uniform intensity of one candela.

weber - The weber is the magnetic flux which, linking a circuit of one turn, produces in it an electromotive force of one volt as it is reduced to zero at a uniform rate in one second.

telsa - The telsa is the magnetic flux density given by a magnetic flux of one weber per square metre.

watt - The watt is the power which gives rise to the production of energy at the rate of one joule per second.

pascal - The pascal is the pressure or stress of one newton per square metre.

columb - The coulomb is the quantity of electricity transported in one second by a current of one ampere.

Other derived units carry no special names and must always be expressed in terms of units from which they were derived.

SOME DERIVED UNITS OF THE INTERNATIONAL SYSTEM
(without special names)

Quantity	Unit	Formula
acceleration	metre per second squared	m/s^2
angular acceleration	radian per second squared	rad/s^2
angular velocity	radian per second	rad/s
area	square	m^2
dynamic viscosity	newton-second per square metre	$N{\cdot}s/m^2$
electric field strength	volt per metre	V/m
kinematic viscosity	square metre per second	m^2/s
luminance	candela per square metre	cd/m^2
magnetic field strength	ampere per metre	A/m
magnetomotive force	ampere	A
mass density	kilogram per cubic metre	kg/m^3
radiant intensity	watt per steradian	W/sr
radiance	watt per square metre steradian	$W{\cdot}m^{-2}{\cdot}sr^{-1}$
speed, velocity	metre per second	m/s
volume	cubic metre	m^3

METRIC/U.S. CUSTOMARY UNIT EQUIVALENTS

Multiply:	by:	to get:		by:	to get:
LINEAR					
inches	X 25.4	= millimetres (mm)	X 0.03937	= inches	
feet	X 0.3048	= metres (m)	X 3.281	= feet	
yards	X 0.9144	= metres (m)	X 1.0936	= yards	
miles	X 1.6093	= kilometres (km)	X 0.6214	= miles	
inches	X 2.54	= centimetres (cm)	X 0.3937	= inches	
microinches	X 0.0254	= micrometres (μm)	X 39.37	= microinches	
AREA					
inches^2	X 645.16	= millimetres^2 (mm^2)	X 0.00155	= inches^2	
inches^2	X 6.452	= centimetres^2 (cm^2)	X 0.155	= inches^2	
feet^2	X 0.0929	= metres^2 (m^2)	X 10.764	= feet^2	
yards^2	X 0.8361	= metres^2 (m^2)	X 1.196	= yards^2	
acres	X 0.4047	= hectares (10^{4}m^2) (ha)	X 2.471	= acres	
miles^2	X 2.590	= kilometres^2 (km^2)	X 0.3861	= miles^2	
VOLUME					
inches^3	X 16387	= millimetres^3 (mm^3)	X 0.000061	= inches^3	
inches^3	X 16.387	= centimetres^3 (cm^3)	X 0.06102	= inches^3	
inches^3	X 0.01639	= litres (l)	X 61.024	= inches^3	
quarts	X 0.94635	= litres (l)	X 1.0567	= quarts	
gallons	X 3.7854	= litres (l)	X 0.2642	= gallons	
feet^3	X 28.317	= litres (l)	X 0.03531	= feet^3	
feet^3	X 0.02832	= metres^3 (m^3)	X 35.315	= feet^3	
fluid oz	X 29.57	= millilitres (ml)	X 0.03381	= fluid oz	
yards^3	X 0.7646	= metres^3 (m^3)	X 1.3080	= yards^3	
teaspoons	X 4.929	= millilitres (ml)	X 0.2029	= teaspoons	
cups	X 0.2366	= litres (l)	X 4.227	= cups	
MASS					
ounces (av)	X 28.35	= grams (g)	X 0.03527	= ounces (av)	
pounds (av)	X 0.4536	= kilograms (kg)	X 2.2046	= pounds (av)	
tons (2000 lb)	X 907.18	= kilograms (kg)	X 0.001102	= tons (2000 lb)	
tons (2000 lb)	X 0.90718	= metric tons (t)	X 1.1023	= tons (2000 lb)	
FORCE					
ounces — f (av)	X 0.278	= newtons (N)	X 3.597	= ounces — f (av)	
pounds — f (av)	X 4.448	= newtons (N)	X 0.2248	= pounds — f (av)	
kilograms — f	X 9.807	= newtons (N)	X 0.10197	= kilograms — f	

TEMPERATURE

°F	-40	0	32	40	80	98.6 120	160	200	212 240	280	320	°F
°C	-40	-20	0	20	40	60	80	100	120	140	160	°C

°Celsius = 0.556 (°F — 32)   °F = (1.8°C) + 32

Multiply:	by:	to get:		by:	to get:
ACCELERATION					
feet / sec^2	X 0.3048	= metres / sec^2 (m/s^2)	X 3.281	= feet / sec^2	
inches / sec^2	X 0.0254	= metres / sec^2 (m/s^2)	X 39.37	= inches / sec^2	
ENERGY OR WORK (watt−second = joule = newton−metre)					
foot−pounds	X 1.3558	= joules (J)	X 0.7376	= foot−pounds	
calories	X 4.187	= joules (J)	X 0.2388	= calories	
Btu	X 1055	= joules (J)	X 0.000948	= Btu	
watt−hours	X 3600	= joules (J)	X 0.0002778	= watt−hours	
kilowatt − hrs	X 3.600	= megajoules (MJ)	X 0.2778	= kilowatt − hrs	
FUEL ECONOMY AND FUEL CONSUMPTION					
miles / gal	X 0.42514	= kilometres / litre (km/l)	X 2.3522	= miles / gal	

Note:
235.2 / (mi / gal) = litres / 100km
235.2 / (litres / 100 km) = mi / gal

Multiply:	by:	to get:		by:	to get:
LIGHT					
footcandles	X 10.76	= lumens / metre^2 (lm/m^2)	X 0.0929	= footcandles	
PRESSURE OR STRESS (newton / sq metre = pascal)					
inches Hg (60°F)	X 3.377	= kilopascals (kPa)	X 0.2961	= inches Hg	
pounds / sq in	X 6.895	= kilopascals (kPa)	X 0.145	= pounds / sq in	
inches H$_2$O (60°F)	X 0.2488	= kilopascals (kPa)	X 4.0193	= inches H$_2$O	
bars	X 100	= kilopascals (kPa)	X 0.01	= bars	
pounds / sq ft	X 47.88	= pascals (Pa)	X 0.02088	= pounds / sq ft	
POWER					
horsepower	X 0.746	= kilowatts (kW)	X 1.34	= horsepower	
ft−lbf / min	X 0.0226	= watts (W)	X 44.25	= ft−lbf / min	
TORQUE					
pound−inches	X 0.11298	= newton−metres (N·m)	X 8.851	= pound−inches	
pound−feet	X 1.3558	= newton−metres (N·m)	X 0.7376	= pound−feet	
VELOCITY					
miles / hour	X 1.6093	= kilometres / hour (km/h)	X 0.6214	= miles / hour	
feet / sec	X 0.3048	= metres / sec (m/s)	X 3.281	= feet / sec	
kilometres / hr	X 0.27778	= metres / sec (m/s)	X 3.600	= kilometres / hr	
miles / hour	X 0.4470	= metres / sec (m/s)	X 2.237	= miles / hour	

COMMON METRIC PREFIXES

mega	(M)	= 1 000 000 or 10^6	centi	(c)	= 0.01	or	10^{-2}
kilo	(k)	= 1 000 or 10^3	milli	(m)	= 0.001	or	10^{-3}
hecto	(h)	= 100 or 10^2	micro	(μ)	= 0.000 001	or	10^{-6}

APPENDIX

contents

TABLE 1   THE METRIC SYSTEM

LENGTH—Basic unit is meter (m)

Metric Unit	Meters	Inches	Feet	Yards	Miles
Millimeter (mm)	.001	—	—	—	—
Centimeter (cm)	.01	.3937	—	—	—
Decimeter (dm)	.1	3.937	.3281	.1094	—
Meter (m)	1	39.37	3.281	1.094	—
Decameter (dkm)	10	393.7	32.81	10.94	—
Hectometer (hm)	100	3937	328.1	109.4	—
Kilometer (km)	1000	—	3281	1094	.6214

To convert

In. to Millimeters—multiply by 25.4
Millimeters to In.—multiply by .03937
Feet to Meters—multiply by .3048
Meters to Feet—multiply by 3.281

Yards to Meters—multiply by .9144
Meters to Yards—multiply by 1.094
Miles to Kilometers—multiply by 1.609
Kilometers to Miles—multiply by .6214

AREA—Basic unit is centare (ca) which is 1 square meter

Metric Unit	Centares	Square Inches	Square Feet	Square Yards	Acres
Sq. Millimeter (sq. mm)	.000001	—	—	—	—
Sq. Centimeter (sq. cm)	.0001	.1550	—	—	—
Sq. Decimeter (sq. dm)	.01	15.50	.1076	—	—
Centare/Sq. Meter (ca/sq m)	1	1550	10.76	1.196	—
Are (a)	100	—	1076	119.6	—
Hectare (ha)	10,000	—	—	—	2.471
Sq. Kilometer (sq. km)	1,000,000	—	—	—	247.1

To convert

Sq. In. to Sq. cm—multiply by 6.452
Sq. cm to Sq. In.—multiply by .1550
Sq. Ft. to Sq. m.—multiply by .0929
Sq. m. to Sq. Ft.—multiply by 10.76
Sq. Yds. to Sq. m.—multiply by .8361
Sq. m. to Sq. Yds.—multiply by 1.196

Acres to Hectares—multiply by .4047
Hectares to Acres—multiply by 2.471
Acres to Sq. km.—multiply by .004047
Sq. km. to Acres—multiply by 247.1
Sq. Miles to Sq. km.—multiply by 2.590
Sq. km. to Sq. Miles—multiply by .3861

VOLUME—Basic unit is stere (s) which is 1 cubic meter

Metric Unit	Steres	Cubic Inch	Cubic Foot	Cubic Yards
Cu Millimeter (cu mm)	.000000001	—	—	—
Cu Centimeter (cu cm)	.000001	.06102	—	—
Cu Decimeter (cu dm)	.001	61.023	—	—
Desistere (ds)	.1	6102.3	3.531	.1308
Stere/Cu Meter (s/cu m)	1	61023	35.31	1.308
Decastere (dks)	10	—	353.1	13.08

To convert

Cu. In. to Cu mm—multiply by 1639
Cu. mm to Cu. In.—multiply by .000061
Cu. In. to Cu cm—multiply by 16.39
Cu cm to Cu In.—multiply by .06102

Cu. Ft. to Cu. m—multiply by .0283
Cu. m to Cu. Ft.—multiply by 35.31
Cu. Yds. to Cu. m—multiply by .7646
Cu. m to Cu. Yds.—multiply by 1.308

WEIGHT—Basic unit is gram (g)

Metric Unit	Grams	Grains	Ounces	Pounds
Milligram (mg)	.001	.01543	—	—
Centigram (cg)	.01	.1543	—	—
Decigram (dg)	.1	1.543	—	—
Gram	1	15.43	.03527	—
Decagram (dkg)	10	154.3	.3527	—
Hectogram (hg)	100	1543	3.527	.22046
Kilogram (kg)	1000	—	35.27	2.2046
Quintal (q)	100,000	—	3527	220.46
Metric Ton (MT)	1,000,000	—	—	2204.6

To convert

Grains to Centigrams—multiply by 6.48
Centigrams to Grains—multiply by .1543
Ounces to Grams—multiply by 31.103

Grams to Ounces—multiply by .03527
Pounds to Kilograms—multiply by .4536
Kilograms to Pounds—multiply by 2.2046

Tons (2000#) to Metric Tons—multiply by .9078
Metric Tons to Tons (2000#)—multiply by 1.1023

CAPACITY—Basic unit is liter (l)

Metric Unit	Liters	Cubic Capacity		Liquid Capacity			
		Cu. In.	Cu. Ft.	Fl. Ozs.	Pints	Quarts	Gallons
Milliliter (ml)	.001	.06102	—	.03382	—	—	—
Centiliter (cl)	.01	.61023	—	.33815	—	—	—
Deciliter (dl)	.1	6.1023	—	3.3815	.2113	.1057	—
Liter (l)	1	61.023	.0353	33.815	2.113	1.057	.264
Decaliter (dkl)	10	610.23	.3531	338.15	21.13	10.57	2.64
Hectoliter (hl)	100	6102.3	3.531	3381.5	211.3	105.7	26.4
Kiloliter (kl)	1000	61023	35.31	33815	2113	1057	264.

To convert

Cu. In. to Centiliter—multiply by 1.639
Centiliter to Cu. In.—multiply by .61023
Cu. Ft. to Liter—multiply by 28.32
Liter to Cu. Ft.—multiply by .0353
Fl. oz. to Centiliter—multiply by 2.957
Centiliter to Fl. Oz.—multiply by .33815

Pints to Liters—multiply by .4732
Liters to Pints—multiply by 2.113
Quarts to Liters—multiply by .9463
Liters to Quarts—multiply by 1.057
Gallons to Liters—multiply by 3.785
Liters to Gallons—multiply by .2642

TABLE 2 MEASUREMENTS AND TABLES

CUBIC OR SOLID MEASURE
United States and British

1 cubic inch = .0005787 cubic foot = .000021433 cubic yard.
1 cubic foot = 1728 cubic inches = .03703704 cubic yard.
1 cubic yard = 27 cubic feet = 46656 cubic inches.
1 cord of wood = 128 cubic feet = 4 feet by 4 feet by 8 feet.

AVOIRDUPOIS WEIGHT
United States and British

Grains	Drams	Ounces	Pounds	Hundred-weight	Gross Tons
1.	.03657	.002286	.000143	.00000128	.000000064
27.34375	1.	.0625	.003906	.00003488	.000001744
437.5	16.	1.	.0625	.00055803	.00002790
7000.	256.	16.	1.	.0089286	.0004464
784000.	28672.	1792.	112.	1.	.05
15680000.	573440.	35840.	2240.	20.	1.

1 pound avoirdupois = 1.215278 pounds troy.
1 net ton = 2000 pounds = .892857 gross ton.

LINEAR MEASURE
United States and British

Inches	Feet	Yards	Rods	Furlongs	Miles
1	.08333	.02778	.0050505	.00012625	.00001577
12	1.	.33333	.0606061	.00151515	.00018939
36	3.	1.	.1818182	.00454545	.00056818
198	16.5	5.5	1.	.025	.003125
7920	660.	220.	40.	1.	.125
63360	5280.	1760.	320.	8.	1.

SQUARE OR LAND MEASURE
United States and British

Square Inches	Square Feet	Square Yards	Square Rods	Acres	Square Miles
1	.006944	.0007716	....	....	....
144	1.	.111111	....	....	....
1296	9.0	1.	.03306	.0002066	....
39204	272.25	30.25	1.	.00625	.00000977
6272640	43560.	4840.	160.	1.	.0015625
	27878400.	3097600.	102400.	640.	1.

1 square rood = 40 square rods.
1 acre = 4 square roods.
1 square acre = 208.71 feet square.

DRY MEASURE
United States Only

Pints	Quarts	Gallons	Pecks	Bushels	Cubic Inches
1	.50	.125	.0625	.015625	33.6003125
2	1.	.25	.125	.03125	67.200625
8	4.	1.	.50	.125	268.8025
16	8.	2.	1.	.25	537.605
64	32.	8.	4.	1.	2150.42

1 heaped bushel = 1.25 struck bushel, and the cone must be not less than 6 inches high.

LIQUID MEASURE
United States Only

Gills	Pints	Quarts	Gallons	Barrels	Cubic Inches
1	.25	.125	.03125	.000992	7.21875
4	1.	.5	.125	.003968	28.875
8	2.	1.	.25	.007937	57.75
32	8.	4.	1.	.031746	231.
1008	252.	126.	31.5	1.	7276.5

The British imperial gallon = 277.410 cubic inches or 10 pounds avoirdupois of pure water at 62 degrees Fahrenheit and barometer at 30 inches.
The British imperial gallon = 1.20091 United States gallons.
1 fluid drachm = 60 minims = .125 fluid ounce = .0078125 pint.
1 fluid ounce = 480 minims = 8 drachms = .0625 pint.

TABLE 3 CONCRETE FOOTINGS, WALLS, SLABS AND TRENCHES

FOOTINGS

SIZE	MATERIAL		
	Cubic Feet Concrete Per Linear Foot	Cubic Feet Concrete Per 100 Lin. Feet	Cubic Yards Concrete Per 100 Lin. Feet
6 x 12	0.50	50.00	1.9
8 x 12	0.67	66.67	2.5
8 x 16	0.89	88.89	3.3
8 x 18	1.00	100.00	3.7
10 x 12	0.83	83.33	3.1
10 x 16	1.11	111.11	4.1
10 x 18	1.25	125.00	4.6
12 x 12	1.00	100.00	3.7
12 x 16	1.33	133.33	4.9
12 x 20	1.67	166.67	6.1
12 x 24	2.00	200.00	7.4

SLABS

THICKNESS	MATERIAL	
	PER SQUARE FOOT	
	Cubic Feet of Concrete	Square Feet from One Cubic Yard
2 "	0.167	162
3 "	0.25	108
4 "	0.333	81
5 "	0.417	65
6 "	0.50	54

WALLS

WALL THICKNESS	MATERIAL	
	Per 100 Square Feet Wall	
	Cubic Feet Required	Cubic Yards Required
4 "	33.3	1.24
6 "	50.0	1.85
8 "	66.7	2.47
10 "	83.3	3.09
12 "	100.0	3.70

EXCAVATION FACTORS

Depth	Cubic Yards per Square Foot
2"	.006
4"	.012
6"	.018
8"	.025
10"	.031
1' — 0"	.037
1' — 6"	.056
2' — 0"	.074
2' — 6"	.093
3' — 0"	.111
3' — 6"	.130
4' — 0"	.148
4' — 6"	.167
5' — 0"	1.85
5' — 6"	.204
6' — 0"	.222
6' — 6"	.241
7' — 0"	.259
7' — 6"	.278
8' — 0"	.296
8' — 6"	.314
9' — 0"	.332
9' — 6"	.350
10' — 0"	.369

Example: Assume an excavation 24 ft. x 30 ft. and 6 ft. deep. 24 x 30 = 720. In the table the 6 ft. depth has a factor of .222 (the number of cu. yd. in an excavation 1 ft. square and 6 ft. deep). 720 x .222 = 159.84 Cu. Yds.

TRENCH EXCAVATIONS
CU. YD. CONTENT PER 100 LINEAL FT.

Depth in Inches	Trench Width in Inches						
	12	18	24	30	36	42	48
6	1.9	2.8	3.7	4.6	5.6	6.6	7.4
12	3.7	5.6	7.4	9.3	11.1	13.0	14.8
18	5.6	8.3	11.1	13.9	16.7	19.4	22.3
24	7.4	11.1	14.8	18.5	22.2	26.0	29.6
30	9.3	13.8	18.5	23.2	27.8	32.4	37.0
36	11.1	16.6	22.2	27.8	33.3	38.9	44.5
42	13.0	19.4	25.9	32.4	38.9	45.4	52.0
48	14.8	22.2	29.6	37.0	44.5	52.0	59.2
54	16.7	25.0	33.3	41.6	50.0	58.4	66.7
60	18.6	27.8	37.0	46.3	55.5	64.9	74.1

Number of Square Feet of Concrete Floor of Any Thickness From 1 Cubic Yard of Concrete

Thickness Inches	No. Sq. Ft.	Thickness Inches	No. Sq. Ft.	Thickness Inches	No. Sq. Ft.	Thickness Inches	No. Sq. Ft.
1	324	4	81	7	46	10	32
1¼	259	4¼	76	7¼	44	10¼	31
1½	216	4½	72	7½	43	10½	31
1¾	185	4¾	68	7¾	42	10¾	30
2	162	5	65	8	40	11	29½
2¼	144	5¼	62	8¼	39	11¼	29
2½	130	5½	59	8½	38	11½	28
2¾	118	5¾	56	8¾	37	11¾	27½
3	108	6	54	9	36	12	27
3¼	100	6¼	52	9¼	35	12¼	26½
3½	93	6½	50	9½	34	12½	26
3¾	86	6¾	48	9¾	33	12¾	25½

VOLUME OF CONCRETE IN FOOTINGS PER FOOT OF LENGTH

Width (Ft.)	Depth (Ft.)	Volume Per Foot of Length (Cu. Ft./Ft.)
1'-0"	6"	0.50
1'-2"	6"	0.585
1'-4"	6"	0.665
1'-6"	6"	0.75
1'-0"	8"	0.67
1'-2"	8"	0.784
1'-4"	8"	0.889
1'-6"	8"	1.00
1'-0"	10"	0.833
1'-2"	10"	0.972
1'-4"	10"	1.11
1'-6"	10"	1.25
1'-8"	10"	1.39
1'-10"	10"	1.53
2'-0"	10"	1.67
1'-2"	1'-0"	1.17
1'-4"	1'-0"	1.33
1'-6"	1'-0"	1.5
1'-8"	1'-0"	1.67
1'-10"	1'-0"	1.83
2'-0"	1'-0"	2.00

STANDARD 16" CONCRETE MASONRY

Number of Block Per Course For Solid Walls of Various Sizes

Size In Feet	2	4	6	8	10	12	14	16	18	20	22	24	26	28	30	32	34	36	38	40
2	4	7	10	13	16	19	22	25	28	31	34	37	40	43	46	49	52	55	58	61
4	7	10	13	16	19	22	25	28	3'	34	37	40	43	46	49	52	55	58	61	64
6	10	13	16	19	22	25	28	31	34	37	40	43	46	49	52	55	58	61	64	67
8	13	16	19	22	25	28	31	34	37	40	43	46	49	52	55	58	61	64	67	70
10	16	19	22	25	28	31	34	37	40	43	46	49	52	55	58	61	64	67	70	73
12	19	22	25	28	31	34	37	40	43	46	49	52	55	58	61	64	67	70	73	76
14	22	25	28	31	34	37	40	43	46	49	52	55	58	61	64	67	70	73	76	79
16	25	28	31	34	37	40	43	46	49	52	55	58	61	64	67	70	73	76	79	82
18	28	31	34	37	40	43	46	49	52	55	58	61	64	67	70	73	76	79	82	85
20	31	34	37	40	43	46	49	52	55	58	61	64	67	70	73	76	79	82	35	88
22	34	37	40	43	46	49	52	55	58	61	64	67	70	73	76	79	82	85	88	91
24	37	40	43	46	49	52	55	58	61	64	67	70	73	76	79	82	85	88	91	94
26	40	43	46	49	52	55	58	61	64	67	70	73	76	79	82	85	88	91	94	97
28	43	46	49	52	55	58	61	64	67	70	73	76	79	82	85	88	91	94	97	100
30	46	49	52	55	58	61	64	67	70	73	76	79	82	85	88	91	94	97	100	103
32	49	52	55	58	61	64	67	70	73	76	79	82	85	88	91	94	97	100	103	106
34	52	55	58	61	64	67	70	73	76	79	82	85	88	91	94	97	100	103	106	109
36	55	58	61	64	67	70	73	76	79	82	85	88	91	94	97	100	103	106	109	112
38	58	61	64	67	70	73	76	79	82	85	88	91	94	97	100	103	106	109	112	115
40	61	64	67	70	73	76	79	82	85	88	91	94	97	100	103	106	109	112	115	118
42	64	67	70	73	76	79	82	85	88	91	94	97	100	103	106	109	112	115	118	121
44	67	70	73	76	79	82	85	88	91	94	97	100	103	106	109	112	115	118	121	124
46	70	73	76	79	82	85	88	91	94	97	100	103	106	109	112	115	118	121	124	127
48	73	76	79	82	85	88	91	94	97	100	103	106	109	112	115	118	121	124	127	130
50	76	79	82	85	88	91	94	97	100	103	106	109	112	115	118	121	124	127	130	133
52	79	82	85	88	91	94	97	100	103	106	109	112	115	118	121	124	127	130	133	136
54	82	85	88	91	94	97	100	103	106	109	112	115	118	121	124	127	130	133	136	139
56	85	88	91	94	97	100	103	106	109	112	115	118	121	124	127	130	133	136	139	142
58	88	91	94	97	100	103	106	109	112	115	118	121	124	127	130	133	136	139	142	145
60	91	94	97	100	103	106	109	112	115	118	121	124	127	130	133	136	139	142	145	148

To find the number of block for any wall, always use outside measurements. A basement 22 feet by 32 feet for example would require 79 block for one course all around. Multiply 79 by the number of courses needed. Thus a 10-course basement would require a total of 790 block for the solid wall, from which deductions should be made for windows and doors.

If any dimension is an odd number such as 22 feet by 31 feet see table for nearest smaller size; for example, 22 feet by 30 feet, and add 1/2 block per row.

Materials for 100 Sq. Ft. of Walls, Floors, Sidewalks, or any Slabs

Concrete Base

Slab Thick-ness	1:1¾:2¾			1:2:3			1:2:3½			1:2½:4			1:3:5		
	Cement Sacks	Sand Cu. Yd.	Stone Cu. Yd.	Cement Sacks	Sand Cu. Yd.	Stone Cu. Yd.	Cement Sacks	Sand Cu. Yd.	Stone Cu. Yd.	Cement Sacks	Sand Cu. Yd.	Stone Cu. Yd.	Cement Sacks	Sand Cu. Yd.	Stone Cu. Yd.
2½ in.	5.7	0.36	0.62	5.2	0.40	0.59	4.8	0.37	0.64	4.2	0.40	0.63	3.4	0.39	0.65
3	6.8	0.43	0.74	6.3	0.48	0.71	5.8	0.44	0.76	5.0	0.48	0.75	4.1	0.47	0.78
3½	8.0	0.51	0.86	7.3	0.56	0.83	6.8	0.52	0.90	5.8	0.56	0.88	4.8	0.55	0.92
4	9.1	0.58	0.99	8.4	0.64	0.95	7.7	0.59	1.02	6.6	0.64	1.01	5.5	0.63	1.05
4½	10.3	0.65	1.11	9.4	0.72	1.06	8.7	0.66	1.15	7.5	0.72	1.13	6.1	0.70	1.17
5	11.4	0.73	1.23	10.5	0.80	1.19	9.7	0.74	1.28	8.3	0.80	1.26	6.8	0.79	1.31
5½	12.6	0.80	1.36	11.6	0.88	1.31	10.7	0.82	1.41	9.2	0.88	1.39	7.5	0.87	1.45
6	13.7	0.87	1.48	12.6	0.96	1.42	11.6	0.89	1.54	10.0	0.96	1.52	8.2	0.94	1.57

Wearing or Finish Course

Thickness	1:1½		1:2		1:1:1			1:1:1½			1:1:2		
	Cement Sacks	Sand Cu. Yd.	Cement Sacks	Sand Cu. Yd.	Cement Sacks	Sand Cu. Yd.	Stone Cu. Yd.	Cement Sacks	Sand Cu. Yd.	Stone Cu. Yd.	Cement Sacks	Sand Cu. Yd.	Stone Cu. Yd.
½ in.	2.4	0.13	2.0	0.15	2.1	0.08	0.08	1.8	0.07	0.10	1.6	0.06	0.12
¾	3.6	0.19	2.9	0.22	3.1	0.11	0.11	2.7	0.10	0.15	2.4	0.09	0.18
1	4.8	0.26	3.9	0.29	4.2	0.15	0.15	3.7	0.14	0.20	3.2	0.12	0.24
1¼	6.0	0.33	4.9	0.36	5.2	0.19	0.19	4.6	0.17	0.25	4.1	0.15	0.30
1½	7.2	0.40	5.9	0.43	6.3	0.23	0.23	5.5	0.20	0.30	4.9	0.18	0.36
1¾	8.4	0.46	6.9	0.50	7.3	0.27	0.27	6.4	0.24	0.36	5.7	0.21	0.42
2	9.6	0.53	7.9	0.58	8.3	0.31	0.31	7.3	0.27	0.41	6.5	0.25	0.50

TABLE 4 MINIMUM DESIGN LOADS IN BUILDINGS AND OTHER STRUCTURES

1. UNIFORMLY DISTRIBUTED LOADS

The live loads to be assumed in the design of buildings and other structures shall be the greatest loads that probably will be produced by the intended use or occupancy, but in no case less than the minimum uniformly distributed unit loads required in the following table:

Minimum Uniformly Distributed Live Loads

Occupancy or Use	Live Load, lb. per sq. ft.
Apartments	See Residential
Armories and drill rooms	150
Assembly halls and other places of assembly:	
Fixed seats	60
Movable seats	100
Balcony (exterior)	100
Bowling alleys, poolrooms, and similar recreational areas	75
Corridors:	
First floor	100
Other floors	same as occupancy served except as indicated
Dance halls	100
Dining rooms and restaurants	100
Dwellings	See Residential
Garages for passenger cars	100
(Floors shall be designed to carry 150 per cent of the maximum wheel load anywhere on the floor.)	
Gymnasiums, main floors and balconies	100
Hospitals:	
Operating rooms	60
Private rooms	40
Wards	40
Hotels	See Residential
Libraries:	
Reading rooms	60
Stack rooms	150
Manufacturing	125
Marquees	75
Office buildings:	
Offices	80
Lobbies	100
Residential:	
Multifamily houses:	
Private apartments	40
Public rooms	100
Corridors	60
Dwellings:	
First floor	40
Second floor and habitable attics	30
Uninhabitable attics	20
Hotels:	
Guest rooms	40
Public rooms	100
Corridors serving public rooms	100
Public corridors	60
Private corridors	40
Schools:	
Classrooms	40
Corridors	100
Sidewalks, vehicular driveways, and yards, subject to trucking	250
Skating rinks	100
Stairs, fire escapes, and exitways	100
Storage warehouse, light	125
Storage warehouse, heavy	250
Stores:	
Retail:	
First-floor, rooms	100
Upper floors	75
Wholesale	125
Theaters:	
Aisles, corridors, and lobbies	100
Orchestra floors	60
Balconies	60
Stage floors	150
Yards and terraces, pedestrians	100

Loads Not Specified—Stairway and balcony railings, both exterior and interior, should be designed to resist a horizontal thrust of 50 pounds per linear foot applied at the top of the railing.

Provision for partitions—In office buildings or other buildings where partitions might be subject to erection or rearrangement, provision for partition weight shall be made, whether or not partitions are shown on the plans, unless the specified live load exceeds 80 pounds per square foot.

2. CONCENTRATED LOADS

Floors shall be designed to support safely the uniformly distributed live loads prescribed on the previous page or the concentrated load in pounds given in the table below, whichever produces the greater stresses. Unless otherwise specified, the indicated concentration shall be assumed to occupy an area of 2½ feet square and shall be so located as to produce the maximum stress conditions in the structural members.

Location	Load, pounds
Elevator machine room grating (on area of 4 sq. in.)	300
Finish light floor plate construction (on area of 1 sq. in.)	200
Garages, passenger cars	See table on previous page
Office floors	2000
Scuttles, skylight ribs, and accessible ceilings	200
Sidewalks	8000
Stair treads (on center of tread)	300

3. REDUCTION IN LIVE LOADS

Roof live loads—No reduction shall be applied to the roof live load.

Live loads 100 lbs. per sq. ft. or less—The design live load on any member supporting 150 sq. ft. or more may be reduced at the rate of 0.00% per sq. ft. of area supported by the member, except that no reduction shall be made for areas to be occupied as places of public assembly. The reduction shall exceed neither R as determined by the following formula, nor 60%:

$$R = 100 \times \frac{D + L}{4.33L}$$

R = reduction in per cent
D = dead load per square foot of area supported by the member
L = design live load per square foot of area supported by the member

Live loads exceeding 100 lbs. per sq. ft.—No reduction shall be made, except that the design live loads on columns may be reduced 20%.

4. MINIMUM ROOF LOADS

Flat, pitched, or curved roofs—Ordinary roofs, either flat, pitched, or curved, shall be designed for a load not less than 20 lbs. per sq. ft. of horizontal projection in addition to the dead load, and in addition to either the wind or the earthquake load, whichever produces the greater stresses.

Special Conditions—When the effect of the shape of roof structure as determined by actual test or experience indicates lesser or greater snow-retention value than specified herein, the roof load shall be modified as directed or approved by the building official. When valleys are formed by a multiple series of roofs, special provision shall be made for the increased load at the intersections.

Special purpose roofs—When used for incidental promenade purposes, roofs shall be designed for a minimum live load of 60 lbs. per sq. ft.; and 100 lbs. per sq. ft. when designed for roof-garden or assembly uses. Roofs to be used for other special purposes shall be designed for appropriate loads as directed or approved by the building official.

225

TO CONVERT	MULTIPLY BY	TO OBTAIN	TO CONVERT	MULTIPLY BY	TO OBTAIN
	A		bars	1.020×10^4	kgs./sq. meter
			bars	2.089×10^3	pounds/sq. ft.
abamperes	$1. \times 10^1$	amperes	bars	1.45×10^1	pounds/sq. in.
abcoulombs	2.998×10^{10}	statcoulombs	barye	1.00	dynes/sq. cm.
abfarads	$1. \times 10^9$	farads	bolt (u.s., cloth)	3.6576×10^1	meters
abfarads	$1. \times 10^{15}$	microfarads	btu	1.0409×10^1	liter-atmospheres
abhenries	$1. \times 10^{-9}$	henries	btu	1.0550×10^{10}	ergs
abhenries	$1. \times 10^{-6}$	millihenries	btu	7.7816×10^2	foot-pounds
abohms	$1. \times 10^{-9}$	ohms	btu	2.52×10^2	gram-calories
abohms	$1. \times 10^{-15}$	megohms	btu	3.927×10^{-4}	horsepower-hours
abvolts	$1. \times 10^{-8}$	volts	btu	1.055×10^3	joules
acres	$1. \times 10^1$	sq. chains (gunters)	btu	2.52×10^{-1}	kilogram-calories
acres	1.60×10^2	rods	btu	1.0758×10^2	kilogrammeters
acres	$1. \times 10^5$	sq. links	btu	2.928×10^{-4}	kilowatt-hours
acres	4.047×10^{-1}	hectares or sq. hectometers	btu/hr.	2.162×10^{-1}	ft.-pounds/sec.
			btu/hr.	7.0×10^{-2}	gram-cal./sec.
acres	4.35×10^4	sq. ft.	btu/hr.	3.929×10^{-4}	horsepower
acres	4.047×10^3	sq. meters	btu/hr.	2.931×10^{-1}	watts
acres	1.562×10^{-3}	sq. miles	btu/min.	1.296×10^1	ft.-pounds/sec.
acres	4.840×10^3	sq. yards	btu/min.	2.356×10^{-2}	horsepower
acre-feet	4.356×10^4	cu. feet	btu/min.	1.757×10^{-2}	kilowatts
acre-feet	3.259×10^5	gallons	btu/min.	1.757×10^1	watts
amperes/sq. cm.	6.452	amps/sq. in.	btu/sq. ft./min.	1.22×10^{-1}	watts/sq. in.
amperes/sq. cm.	$1. \times 10^4$	amps/sq. meter	bucket (br. dry)	1.8184×10^4	cubic cm.
amperes/sq. in.	1.550×10^{-1}	amps/sq. cm.	bushels	1.2445	cubic ft.
amperes/sq. in.	1.550×10^3	amps/sq. meter	bushels	2.1504×10^3	cubic in.
amperes/sq. meter	1.0×10^{-4}	amps/sq. cm.	bushels	3.524×10^{-2}	cubic meters
amperes/sq. meter	6.452×10^{-4}	amps/sq. in.	bushels	3.524×10^1	liters
ampere-hours	3.600×10^3	coulombs	bushels	4.0	pecks
ampere-hours	3.731×10^{-2}	faradays	bushels	6.4×10^1	pints (dry)
ampere-turns	1.257	gilberts	bushels	3.2×10^1	quarts (dry)
ampere-turns/cm.	2.540	amp-turns/in.			
ampere-turns/cm.	$1. \times 10^2$	amp-turns/meter		**C**	
ampere-turns/in.	3.937×10^{-1}	amp-turns/cm.			
ampere-turns/in.	3.937×10^1	amp-turns/meter	calories, gram (mean)	3.9685×10^{-3}	btu (mean)
ampere-turns/in.	4.950×10^{-1}	gilberts/cm.	candle/sq. cm.	3.146	lamberts
ampere-turns/meter	$1. \times 10^{-2}$	amp-turns/cm.	candle/sq. in.	4.870×10^{-1}	lamberts
ampere-turns/meter	2.54×10^{-2}	amp-turns/in.	centares	1.0	sq. meters
ampere-turns/meter	1.257×10^{-2}	gilberts/cm.	centigrade(degrees)	$(°C \times 9/5) + 32$	fahrenheit(degrees)
angstrom unit	3.937×10^{-9}	inches	centigrade(degrees)	$°C + 273.18$	kelvin (degrees)
angstrom unit	$1. \times 10^{-10}$	meters	centigrams	$1. \times 10^{-2}$	grams
angstrom unit	$1. \times 10^{-4}$	microns or (mu)	centiliters	3.382×10^{-1}	ounce (fluid) u.s.
ares	2.471×10^{-2}	acres (u.s.)	centiliters	6.103×10^{-1}	cubic in.
ares	1.196×10^2	sq. yards	centiliters	2.705	drams
ares	$1. \times 10^2$	sq. meters	centiliters	1.0×10^{-2}	liters
astronomical unit	1.495×10^8	kilometers	centimeters	3.281×10^{-2}	feet
atmospheres	7.348×10^{-3}	tons/sq. in.	centimeters	3.937×10^{-1}	inches
atmospheres	1.058	tons/sq. foot	centimeters	$1. \times 10^{-5}$	kilometers
atmospheres	7.6×10^1	cms. of mercury (at 0°C.)	centimeters	$1. \times 10^{-2}$	meters
			centimeters	6.214×10^{-6}	miles
atmospheres	3.39×10^1	ft. of water (at 4°C.)	centimeters	$1. \times 10^1$	millimeters
atmospheres	2.992×10^1	in. of mercury (at 0°C.)	centimeters	3.937×10^2	mils
			centimeters	1.094×10^{-2}	yards
atmospheres	7.6×10^{-1}	meters of mercury (at 0°C.)	centimeters	$1. \times 10^4$	microns
			centimeters	$1. \times 10^8$	angstrom units
atmospheres	7.6×10^2	millimeters of mercury (at 0°C.)	centimeter-dynes	1.020×10^{-3}	cn-grams
			centimeter-dynes	1.020×10^{-8}	meter-kgs.
atmospheres	1.0333	kgs./sq. cm.	centimeter-dynes	7.376×10^{-8}	pound-ft.
atmospheres	1.0333×10^4	kgs./sq. meter	centimeter-grams	9.807×10^2	cm.-dynes
atmospheres	1.47×10^1	pounds/sq. in.	centimeter-grams	$1. \times 10^{-5}$	meter-kgs.
			centimeter-grams	7.233×10^{-5}	pound-ft.
	B		centimeters of mercury	1.316×10^{-2}	atmospheres
barrels (u.s., dry)	3.281	bushels	centimeters of mercury	4.461×10^{-1}	ft. of water
barrels (u.s., dry)	7.056×10^3	cu. inches			
barrels (u.s., dry)	1.05×10^2	quarts (dry)	centimeters of mercury	1.36×10^2	kgs./sq. meter
barrels (u.s. liquid)	3.15×10^1	gallons			
barrels (oil)	4.2×10^1	gallons (oil)			
bars	9.869×10^{-1}	atmospheres			
bars	$1. \times 10^6$	dynes/sq. cm.			

TABLE 5 *(continued)* **ENGINEERING CONVERSION TABLES**

TO CONVERT	MULTIPLY BY	TO OBTAIN	TO CONVERT	MULTIPLY BY	TO OBTAIN
centimeters of mercury	2.785×10^1	pounds/sq. ft.	cubic meters	6.1023×10^4	cu. inches
			cubic meters	1.308	cu. yards
centimeters of mercury	1.934×10^{-1}	pounds/sq. in.	cubic meters	2.642×10^2	gallons u.s. liquid)
			cubic meters	1.0×10^3	liters
centimeters/sec.	1.969	feet/min.	cubic meters	2.113×10^3	pints (u.s. liquid)
centimeters/sec.	3.281×10^{-2}	feet/sec.	cubic meters	1.057×10^3	quarts (u.s. liquid)
centimeters/sec.	3.6×10^{-2}	kilometers/hr.	cubic yards	7.646×10^5	cu. cms.
centimeters/sec.	1.943×10^{-2}	knots	cubic yards	2.7×10^1	cu. ft.
centimeters/sec.	6.0×10^1	meters/min.	cubic yards	4.6656×10^4	cu. inches
centimeters/sec.	2.237×10^{-2}	miles/hr.	cubic yards	7.646×10^{-1}	cu. meters
centimeters/sec.	3.728×10^{-4}	miles/min.	cubic yards	2.02×10^2	gallons (u.s. liquid)
centimeters/sec./sec.	3.281×10^{-2}	ft./sec./sec.	cubic yards	7.646×10^2	liters
centimeters/sec./sec.	3.6×10^{-2}	kms./hr./sec.	cubic yards	1.6159×10^3	pints (u.s. liquid)
centimeters/sec./sec.	1.0×10^{-2}	meters/sec./sec.	cubic yards	8.079×10^2	quarts (u.s. liquid)
centimeters/sec./sec.	2.237×10^{-2}	miles/hr./sec.	cubic yards/min.	4.5×10^{-1}	cubic ft./sec.
centipoise	1.0×10^{-2}	gr./cm.-sec.	cubic yards/min.	3.367	gallons/sec.
centipoise	6.72×10^{-4}	pound/ft.-sec.	cubic yards/min.	1.274×10^1	liters/sec.
centipoise	2.4	pound/ft.-hr.			
chains (gunters)	7.92×10^2	inches		**D**	
chains (gunters)	2.012×10^1	meters			
chains (gunters)	2.2×10^1	yards	daltons	1.650×10^{-24}	grams
circular mils	5.067×10^{-6}	sq. cm.	days	8.64×10^4	seconds
circular mils	7.854×10^{-1}	sq. mils	days	1.44×10^3	minutes
circular mils	7.854×10^{-7}	sq. inches	days	2.4×10^1	hours
circumference	6.283	radians	decigrams	1.0×10^{-1}	grams
cords	8.0	cord ft.	deciliters	1.0×10^{-1}	liters
cord ft.	1.6×10^1	cubic ft.	decimeters	1.0×10^{-1}	meters
coulombs	2.998×10^9	statcoulombs	degrees (angle)	1.111×10^{-2}	quadrants
coulombs	1.036×10^{-5}	faradays	degrees (angle)	1.745×10^{-2}	radians
coulombs/sq. cm.	6.452	coulombs/sq. in.	degrees (angle)	3.6×10^3	seconds
coulombs/sq. cm.	1.0×10^4	coulombs/sq. meter	degrees/sec.	1.745×10^{-2}	radians/sec.
coulombs/sq. in.	1.550×10^{-1}	coulombs/sq. cm.	degrees/sec.	1.667×10^{-1}	revolutions/min.
coulombs/sq. in.	1.550×10^3	coulombs/sq. meter	degrees/sec.	2.778×10^{-3}	revolutions/sec.
cuolombs/sq. meter	1.0×10^{-4}	coulomsb/sq. cm.	dekagrams	1.0×10^1	grams
cuolombs/sq. meter	6.452×10^{-4}	coulombs/sq. in.	dekaliters	1.0×10^1	liters
cubic centimeters	3.531×10^{-5}	cubic ft.	dekameters	$10. \times 10^1$	meters
cubic centimeters	6.102×10^{-2}	cubic in.	drams (apoth. or troy)	1.3714×10^{-1}	ounces (avdp.)
cubic centimeters	1.0×10^{-6}	cubic meters	drams (apoth. or troy)	1.25×10^{-1}	ounces (troy)
cubic centimeters	1.308×10^{-6}	cubic yards	drams (u.s. fluid or apoth.)	3.6967	cubic cm.
cubic centimeters	2.642×10^{-4}	gallons (u.s. liquid)			
cubic centimeters	1.0×10^{-3}	liters	drams	1.7718	grams
cubic centimeters	2.113×10^{-3}	pints (u.s. liquid)	drams	2.7344×10^1	grains
cubic centimeters	1.057×10^{-3}	quarts (u.s. liquid)	drams	6.25×10^{-2}	ounces
cubic feet	8.036×10^{-1}	bushels (dry)	dynes/sq. cm.	1.0×10^{-2}	ergs/sq. millimeter
cubic feet	2.8320×10^4	cu. cms.	dynes/sq. cm.	9.869×10^{-7}	atmospheres
cubic feet	1.728×10^3	cu. inches	dynes/sq. cm.	2.953×10^{-5}	in. of mercury (at 0°C.)
cubic feet	2.832×10^{-2}	cu. meters			
cubic feet	3.704×10^{-2}	cu. yards	dynes/sq. cm.	4.015×10^{-4}	in. of water (at 4° C.)
cubic feet	7.48052	gallons (u.s. liquid)	dynes	1.020×10^{-3}	grams
cubic feet	2.832×10^1	liters	dynes	1.0×10^{-7}	joules/cm.
cubic feet	5.984×10^1	pints (u.s. liquid)	dynes	1.0×10^{-5}	joules/meter (newtons)
cubic feet	2.992×10^1	quarts (u.s. liquid)			
cubic feet/min.	4.72×10^2	cu. cms./sec.	dynes	1.020×10^{-6}	kilograms
cubic feet/min.	1.247×10^{-1}	gallons/sec.	dynes	7.233×10^{-5}	poundals
cubic feet/min.	4.720×10^{-1}	liters/sec.	dynes	2.248×10^{-6}	pounds
cubic feet/min.	6.243×10^1	pounds water/min.	dynes/sq. cm.	1.0×10^{-6}	bars
cubic feet/sec.	6.46317×10^{-1}	million gals./day			
cubic feet/sec.	4.48831×10^2	gallons/min.		**E**	
cubic inches	1.639×10^1	cu cms.	ell	1.1430×10^2	cm.
cubic inches	5.787×10^{-4}	cu. ft.	ell	4.5×10^1	inches
cubic inches	1.639×10^{-5}	cu. meters	em, pica	1.67×10^{-1}	inch
cubic inches	2.143×10^{-5}	cu. yards	em, pica	4.233×10^{-1}	cm.
cubic inches	4.329×10^{-3}	gallons	erg/sec.	1.0	dyne-cm./sec.
cubic inches	1.639×10^{-2}	liters	ergs	9.486×10^{-11}	btu
cubic inches	3.463×10^{-2}	pints (u.s. liquid)	ergs	1.0	dyne-centimeters
cubic inches	1.732×10^{-2}	quarts (u.s. liquid)	ergs	7.376×10^{-8}	foot-pounds
cubic meters	2.838×10^1	bushels (dry)	ergs	2.389×10^{-8}	gram-calories
cubic meters	1.0×10^6	cu. cms.	ergs	1.020×10^{-3}	gram-cms.
cubic meters	3.531×10^1	cu. ft.	ergs	3.7250×10^{-14}	horsepower-hrs.

TABLE 5 *(continued)* ENGINEERING CONVERSION TABLES

TO CONVERT	MULTIPLY BY	TO OBTAIN
ergs	1.0×10^7	joules
ergs	2.389×10^{11}	kg.-calories
ergs	1.020×10^8	kg.-meters
ergs	2.773×10^{14}	kilowatt hrs.
ergs	2.773×10^{11}	watt hrs.
ergs/sec.	5.668×10^9	btu/min.
ergs/sec.	4.426×10^6	ft.-lbs./min.
ergs/sec.	7.3756×10^8	ft.-lbs./sec.
ergs/sec.	1.341×10^{10}	horsepower
ergs/sec.	1.433×10^9	kg-calories/min.
ergs/sec.	$1. \times 10^{10}$	kilowatts

F

TO CONVERT	MULTIPLY BY	TO OBTAIN
farads	$1. \times 10^6$	microfarads
faraday/sec.	9.65×10^4	ampere (absolute)
faradays	2.68×10^1	ampere hours
faradays	9.649×10^4	coulombs
fathoms	1.8288	meters
fathoms	6.0	feet
feet	3.048×10^1	centimeters
feet	3.048×10^{-4}	kilometers
feet	3.048×10^{-1}	meters
feet	1.645×10^{-4}	miles (naut.)
feet	1.894×10^{-4}	miles (stat.)
feet	3.048×10^2	millimeters
feet	1.2×10^4	mils
feet of water	2.95×10^{-2}	atmospheres
feet of water	8.826×10^{-1}	in. of mercury
feet of water	3.048×10^{-2}	kgs./sq. cm.
feet of water	3.048×10^2	kgs./sq. meter
feet of water	6.243×10^1	pounds/sq. ft.
feet of water	4.335×10^{-1}	pounds/sq. in.
feet/min.	5.080×10^{-1}	cms./sec.
feet/min.	1.667×10^{-2}	feet/sec.
feet/min.	1.829×10^{-2}	kms./hr.
feet/min.	3.048×10^{-1}	meters/min.
feet/min.	1.136×10^{-2}	miles/hr.
feet/sec.	3.048×10^1	cms./sec.
feet/sec.	1.097	kms./hr.
feet/sec.	5.921×10^{-1}	knots
feet/sec.	1.829×10^1	meters/min.
feet/sec.	6.818×10^{-1}	miles/hr.
feet/sec.	1.136×10^{-2}	miles/min.
feet/sec./sec.	3.048×10^1	cms./sec./sec.
feet/sec./sec.	1.097	kms./hr./sec.
feet/sec./sec.	3.048×10^{-1}	meters/sec./sec.
feet/sec./sec.	6.818×10^{-1}	miles/hr./sec.
feet/100 feet	1.0	per cent grade
foot-candle	1.0764×10^1	lumen/sq. meter
foot-candle	1.0764×10^1	lux
foot-pounds	1.286×10^{-3}	btu
foot-pounds	1.356×10^7	ergs
foot-pounds	3.241×10^{-1}	gram calories
foot-pounds	5.050×10^{-7}	horsepower-hrs.
foot-pounds	1.356	joules
foot-pounds	3.241×10^{-4}	kg.-calories
foot-pounds	1.383×10^{-1}	kg.-meters
foot-pounds	3.766×10^{-7}	kilowatt-hrs.
foot-pounds/min.	1.286×10^{-3}	btu/min.
foot-pounds/min.	1.667×10^{-2}	foot-pounds/sec.
foot-pounds/min.	3.030×10^{-5}	horsepower
foot-pounds/min.	3.241×10^{-4}	kg.-calories/min.
foot-pounds/min.	2.260×10^{-5}	kilowatts
foot-pounds/sec.	4.6263	btu/hr.
foot-pounds/sec.	7.717×10^{-2}	btu/min.
foot-pounds/sec.	1.818×10^{-3}	horsepower
foot-pounds/sec.	1.945×10^{-2}	kg.-calories/min.
foot-pounds/sec.	1.356×10^{-3}	kilowatts

TO CONVERT	MULTIPLY BY	TO OBTAIN
furlongs	1.25×10^{-1}	miles (u.s.)
furlongs	4.0×10^1	rods
furlongs	6.6×10^2	feet
furlongs	2.0117×10^2	meters

G

TO CONVERT	MULTIPLY BY	TO OBTAIN
gallons	3.785×10^3	cu. cms.
gallons	1.337×10^{-1}	cu. feet
gallons	2.31×10^2	cu. inches
gallons	3.785×10^{-3}	cu. meters
gallons	4.951×10^{-3}	cu. yards
gallons	3.785	liters
gallons (liq. br. imp.)	1.20095	gallons (u.s. liquid)
gallons (u.s.)	8.3267×10^{-1}	gallons (imp.)
gallons of water	8.337	pounds of water
gallons/min.	2.228×10^{-3}	cu. feet/sec.
gallons/min.	6.308×10^{-2}	liters/sec.
gallons/min.	8.0208	cu. feet/hr.
gausses	6.452	lines/sq. in.
gausses	1.0×10^{-8}	webers/sq. cm.
gausses	6.452×10^{-8}	webers/sq. in.
gausses	1.0×10^{-4}	webers/sq. meter
gausses	7.958×10^{-1}	amp.-turn/cm.
gausses	1.0	gilbert/cm.
gilberts	7.958×10^{-1}	ampere-turns
gilberts/cm.	7.958×10^{-1}	ampere-turns/cm.
gilberts/cm.	2.021	ampere-turns/in.
gilberts/cm.	7.958×10^1	ampere-turns/ meter
gills (british)	1.4207×10^2	cubic cm.
gills (u.s.)	1.18295×10^2	cubic cm.
gills (u.s.)	1.183×10^{-1}	liters
gills (u.s.)	2.5×10^{-1}	pints (liq.)
grade	1.571×10^{-2}	radian
grains	3.657×10^{-2}	drams (avdp.)
grains (troy)	1.0	grains (avdp.)
grains (troy)	6.48×10^{-2}	grams
grains (troy)	2.0833×10^{-3}	ounces (avdp.)
grains (troy)	4.167×10^{-2}	pennyweight (troy)
grains/u.s. gallon	1.7118×10^1	parts/million
grains/u.s. gallon	1.4286×10^2	pounds/million gallons
grains/imp. gallon	1.4286×10^1	parts/million
grams	9.807×10^2	dynes
grams	1.543×10^1	grains (troy)
grams	9.807×10^{-5}	joules/cm.
grams	9.807×10^{-3}	joules/meter (newtons)
grams	1.0×10^{-3}	kilograms
grams	1.0×10^3	milligrams
grams	3.527×10^{-2}	ounces (avdp.)
grams	3.215×10^{-2}	ounces (troy)
grams	7.093×10^{-2}	poundals
grams	2.205×10^{-3}	pounds
grams/cm.	5.6×10^{-3}	pounds/in.
grams/cu. cm.	6.243×10^1	pounds/cu. ft.
grams/cu. cm.	3.613×10^{-2}	pounds/cu. in.
grams/cu. cm.	3.405×10^{-7}	pounds/mil-foot
grams/liter	5.8417×10^1	grains/gal.
grams/liter	8.345	pounds/1,000 gal.
grams/liter	6.2427×10^{-2}	pounds/cu. ft.
grams/sq. cm.	2.0481	pounds/sq. ft.
gram-calories	3.9683×10^{-3}	btu
gram-calories	4.184×10^7	ergs
gram-calories	3.086	foot-pounds
gram-calories	1.5596×10^{-6}	horsepower-hrs.
gram-calories	1.162×10^{-6}	kilowatt-hrs.
gram-calories	1.162×10^{-3}	watt-hrs.

TABLE 5 *(continued)* **ENGINEERING CONVERSION TABLES**

TO CONVERT	MULTIPLY BY	TO OBTAIN	TO CONVERT	MULTIPLY BY	TO OBTAIN
gram-calories/sec.	1.4286×10^1	btu/hr.	internat'l ampere	9.998×10^{-1}	absolute amp. (u.s.)
gram-centimeters	9.297×10^{-8}	btu	internat'l volt	1.00033	absolute volt (u.s.)
gram-centimeters	9.807×10^2	ergs	internat'l coulomb	9.99835×10^{-1}	absolute coulomb
gram-centimeters	9.807×10^{-5}	joules			
gram-centimeters	2.343×10^{-8}	kg.-calories		**J**	
gram-centimeters	1.0×10^{-5}	kg.-meters	joules	9.486×10^{-4}	btu
			joules	1.0×10^7	ergs
	H		joules	7.736×10^{-1}	foot-pounds
hand	1.016×10^1	cm.	joules	2.389×10^{-4}	kg.-calories
hectares	2.471	acres	joules	1.020×10^{-1}	kg.-meters
hectares	1.076×10^5	sq. feet	joules	2.778×10^{-4}	watt-hrs.
hectograms	1.0×10^2	grams	joules/cm.	1.020×10^4	grams
hectoliters	1.0×10^2	liters	joules/cm.	1.0×10^7	dynes
hectometers	1.0×10^2	meters	joules/cm.	1.0×10^2	joules/meter (newtons)
hectowatts	1.0×10^2	watts			
henries	1.0×10^3	millihenries	joules/cm.	7.233×10^2	poundals
hogsheads (british)	1.0114×10^1	cubic ft.	joules/cm.	2.248×10^1	pounds
hogsheads (u.s.)	8.42184	cubic ft.			
hogsheads (u.s.)	6.3×10^1	gallons (u.s.)		**K**	
horsepower	4.244×10^1	btu/min.	kilograms	9.80665×10^5	dynes
horsepower	3.3×10^4	foot-lbs./min.	kilograms	1.0×10^3	grams
horsepower	5.50×10^2	foot-lbs./sec.	kilograms	9.807×10^{-2}	joules/cm.
horsepower (metric)	9.863×10^{-1}	horsepower	kilograms	9.807	joules/meter (newtons)
horsepower	1.014	horsepower (metric)			
horsepower	1.068×10^1	kg.-calories/min.	kilograms	7.093×10^1	poundals
horsepower	7.457×10^{-1}	kilowatts	kilograms	2.2046	pounds
horsepower	7.457×10^2	watts	kilograms	9.842×10^{-4}	tons (long)
horsepower (boiler)	3.352×10^4	btu/hr.	kilograms	1.102×10^{-3}	tons (short)
horsepower (boiler)	9.803	kilowatts	kilograms	3.5274×10^1	ounces (avdp.)
horsepower-hours	2.547×10^3	btu	kilograms/cu. meter	1.0×10^{-3}	grams/cu. cm.
horsepower-hours	2.6845×10^{13}	ergs	kilograms/cu. meter	6.243×10^{-2}	pounds/cu. ft.
horsepower-hours	1.98×10^6	foot-lbs.	kilograms/cu. meter	3.613×10^{-5}	pounds/cu. in.
horsepower-hours	6.4119×10^5	gram-calories	kilograms/cu. meter	3.405×10^{-10}	pounds/mil-foot
horsepower-hours	2.684×10^6	joules	kilograms/meter	6.72×10^{-1}	pounds/ft.
horsepower-hours	6.417×10^2	kg.-calories	kilograms/sq. cm.	9.80665×10^5	dynes/sq. cm.
horsepower-hours	2.737×10^5	kg.-meters	kilograms/sq. cm.	9.678×10^{-1}	atmospheres
horsepower-hours	7.457×10^{-1}	kilowatt-hrs.	kilograms/sq. cm.	3.281×10^1	feet of water
hours	4.167×10^{-2}	days	kilograms/sq. cm.	2.896×10^1	inches of mercury
hours	5.952×10^{-3}	weeks	kilograms/sq. cm.	2.048×10^3	pounds/sq. ft.
hours	3.6×10^3	seconds	kilograms/sq. cm.	1.422×10^1	pounds/sq. in.
hundredwgts(long)	1.12×10^2	pounds	kilograms/sq. meter	9.678×10^{-5}	atmospheres
hundredwgts(long)	5.0×10^{-2}	tons (long)	kilograms/sq. meter	9.807×10^{-5}	bars
hundredwgts(long)	5.08023×10^1	kilograms	kilograms/sq. meter	3.281×10^{-3}	feet of water
hundredwgts(short)	4.53592×10^{-2}	tons (metric)	kilograms/sq. meter	2.896×10^{-3}	inches of mercury
hundredwgts(short)	4.46429×10^{-2}	tons (long)	kilograms/sq. meter	2.048×10^{-1}	pounds/sq. ft.
hundredwgts(short)	4.53592×10^1	kilograms	kilograms/sq. meter	1.422×10^{-3}	pounds/sq. in.
			kilograms/sq. meter	9.80665×10^1	dynes/sq. cm.
	I		kilograms/sq. mm.	1.0×10^6	kgs./sq. meter
inches	2.540	centimeters	kilogram-calories	3.968	btu
inches	2.540×10^{-2}	meters	kilogram-calories	3.086×10^3	foot-pounds
inches	1.578×10^{-5}	miles	kilogram-calories	1.558×10^{-3}	horsepower-hrs.
inches	2.54×10^1	millimeters	kilogram-calories	4.183×10^3	joules
inches	1.0×10^3	mils	kilogram-calories	4.269×10^2	kg.-meters
inches	2.778×10^{-2}	yards	kilogram-calories	4.186	kilojoules
inches	2.54×10^8	angstrom units	kilogram-calories	1.163×10^{-3}	kilowatt-hrs.
inches	5.0505×10^{-3}	rods	kilogram-calories/min.	5.143×10^1	ft.-lbs./sec.
inches of mercury	3.342×10^{-2}	atmospheres	kilogram-calories/min.	9.351×10^{-2}	horsepower
inches of mercury	1.133	feet of water	kilogram-calories/min.	6.972×10^{-2}	kilowatts
inches of mercury	3.453×10^{-2}	kgs./sq. cm.			
inches of mercury	3.453×10^2	kgs./sq. meter	kilogram-meters	9.296×10^{-3}	btu
inches of mercury	7.073×10^1	pounds/sq. ft.	kilogram-meters	9.807×10^7	ergs
inches of mercury	4.912×10^{-1}	pounds/sq. in.	kilogram-meters	7.233	foot-pounds
in. of water (at 4°C.)	2.458×10^{-3}	atmospheres	kilogram-meters	9.807	joules
in. of water (at 4°C.)	7.355×10^{-2}	inches of mercury	kilogram-meters	2.342×10^{-3}	kg.-calories
in. of water (at 4°C.)	2.54×10^{-3}	kgs./sq. cm.	kilogram-meters	2.723×10^{-6}	kilowatt-hrs.
in. of water (at 4°C.)	5.781×10^{-1}	ounces/sq. in.	kilolines	1.0×10^3	maxwells
in. of water (at 4°C.)	5.204	pounds/sq. ft.			
in. of water (at 4°C.)	3.613×10^{-2}	pounds/sq. in.			

TABLE 5 *(continued)* ENGINEERING CONVERSION TABLES

TO CONVERT	MULTIPLY BY	TO OBTAIN	TO CONVERT	MULTIPLY BY	TO OBTAIN
kiloliters	1.0×10^3	liters	liters	1.308×10^{-3}	cu. yards
kiloliters	1.308	cubic yards	liters	2.642×10^{-1}	gallons (u.s. liquid)
kiloliters	3.5316×10^1	cubic feet	liters	2.113	pints (u.s. liquid)
kiloliters	2.6418×10^2	gallons (u.s. liquid)	liters	1.057	quarts (u.s. liquid)
kilometers	1.0×10^5	centimeters	liters/min.	5.886×10^{-4}	cu. ft./sec.
kilometers	3.281×10^3	feet	liters/min.	4.403×10^{-3}	gals./sec.
kilometers	3.937×10^4	inches	$\log_{10} n$	2.303	ln n
kilometers	1.0×10^3	meters	ln n	4.343×10^{-1}	$\log_{10} n$
kilometers	6.214×10^{-1}	miles (statute)	lumen	7.958×10^{-2}	spherical candle power
kilometers	5.396×10^{-1}	miles (nautical)			
kilometers	1.0×10^6	millimeters	lumen/sq. ft.	1.0	foot-candles
kilometers	1.0936×10^3	yards	lumen/sq. ft.	1.076×10^1	lumen-sq. meter
kilometers/hr.	2.778×10^1	cms./sec.	lux	9.29×10^{-2}	foot-candles
kilometers/hr.	5.468×10^1	feet/min.			
kilometers/hr.	9.113×10^{-1}	feet/sec.		**M**	
kilometers/hr.	5.396×10^{-1}	knots			
kilometers/hr.	1.667×10^1	meters/min.	maxwells	1.0×10^{-3}	kilolines
kilometers/hr.	6.214×10^{-1}	miles/hr.	maxwells	1.0×10^{-8}	webers
kilometers/hr./sec.	2.778×10^1	cms./sec./sec.	megalines	1.0×10^4	maxwells
kilometers/hr./sec.	9.113×10^{-1}	ft./sec./sec.	megohms	1.0×10^{12}	microhms
kilometers/hr./sec.	2.778×10^{-1}	meters/sec./sec.	megohms	1.0×10^6	ohms
kilometers/hr./sec.	6.214×10^{-1}	miles/hr./sec.	megmhos/cubic cm.	1.0×10^{-3}	abmhos/cubic cm.
kilowatts	5.692×10^1	btu/min.	megmhos/cubic cm.	2.54	megmhos/cubic in.
kilowatts	4.426×10^4	foot-lbs./min.	megmhos/cubic cm.	1.662×10^{-1}	mhos/mil. ft.
kilowatts	7.376×10^2	foot-lbs./sec.	megmhos/in. cube	3.937×10^{-1}	megmhos/cubic cm.
kilowatts	1.341	horsepower	meters	1.0×10^{10}	angstrom units
kilowatts	1.434×10^1	kg.-calories/min.	meters	1.0×10^2	centimeters
kilowatts	1.0×10^3	watts	meters	5.4681×10^{-1}	fathoms
kilowatt-hrs.	3.413×10^3	btu	meters	3.281	feet
kilowatt-hrs.	3.6×10^{13}	ergs	meters	3.937×10^1	inches
kilowatt-hrs.	2.655×10^6	foot-lbs.	meters	1.0×10^{-3}	kilometers
kilowatt-hrs.	8.5985×10^5	gram calories	meters	5.396×10^{-4}	miles (nautical)
kilowatt-hrs.	1.341	horsepower-hours	meters	6.214×10^{-4}	miles (statute)
kilowatt-hrs.	3.6×10^6	joules	meters	1.0×10^3	millimeters
kilowatt-hrs.	8.605×10^2	kg.-calories	meters	1.094	yards
kilowatt-hrs.	3.671×10^5	kg.-meters	meters/min.	1.667	cms./sec.
kilowatt-hrs.	3.53	pounds of water evaporated from and at 212°F.	meters/min.	3.281	feet/min.
			meters/min.	5.468×10^{-2}	feet/sec.
			meters/min.	6.0×10^{-2}	kms./hr.
			meters/min.	3.238×10^{-2}	knots
kilowatt-hrs.	2.275×10^1	pounds of water raised from 62° to 212°F.	meters/min.	3.728×10^{-2}	miles/hr.
			meters/sec.	1.968×10^2	feet/min.
knots	6.080×10^3	feet/hr.	meters/sec.	3.281	feet/sec.
knots	1.8532	kilometers/hr.	meters/sec.	3.6	kilometers/hr.
knots	1.0	nautical miles/hr.	meters/sec.	6.0×10^{-2}	kilometers/min.
knots	1.151	statute miles/hr.	meters/sec.	2.237	miles/hr.
knots	2.027×10^3	yards/hr.	meters/sec.	3.728×10^{-2}	miles/min.
knots	1.689	feet/sec.	meters/sec./sec.	1.0×10^2	cms./sec./sec.
knots	5.148×10^1	cm./sec.	meters/sec./sec.	3.281	ft./sec./sec.
			meters/sec./sec.	3.6	kms./hr./sec.
	L		meters/sec./sec.	2.237	miles/hr./sec.
			meter-kilograms	9.807×10^7	cm.-dynes
lambert	3.183×10^{-1}	candle/sq. cm.	meter-kilograms	1.0×10^5	cm.-grams
lambert	2.054	candle/sq. in.	meter-kilograms	7.233	pound-feet
league	3.0	miles (approx.)	microfarads	1.0×10^{-15}	abfarads
light year	5.9×10^{12}	miles	microfarads	1.0×10^{-6}	farads
light year	9.46091×10^{12}	kilometers	microfarads	9.0×10^5	statfarads
lines/sq. cm.	1.0	gausses	micrograms	1.0×10^{-6}	grams
lines/sq. in.	1.55×10^{-1}	gausses	microhms	1.0×10^3	abohms
lines/sq. in.	1.55×10^{-9}	webers/sq. cm.	microhms	1.0×10^{-12}	megohms
lines/sq. in.	1.0×10^8	webers/sq. in.	microhms	1.0×10^{-6}	ohms
lines/sq. in.	1.55×10^{-5}	webers/sq. meter	microliters	1.0×10^{-6}	liters
links (engineers)	1.2×10^1	inches	micromicrons	1.0×10^{-12}	meters
links (surveyors)	7.92	inches	microns	1.0×10^{-6}	meters
liters	2.838×10^{-2}	bushels (u.s. dry)	miles (nautical)	6.076×10^3	feet
liters	1.0×10^3	cu. cm.	miles (nautical)	1.853	kilometers
liters	3.531×10^{-2}	cu. ft.	miles (nautical)	1.853×10^3	meters
liters	6.102×10^1	cu. inches	miles (nautical)	1.1516	miles (statute)
liters	1.0×10^{-3}	cu. meters	miles (nautical)	2.0254×10^3	yards

TABLE 5 *(continued)* **ENGINEERING CONVERSION TABLES**

TO CONVERT	MULTIPLY BY	TO OBTAIN	TO CONVERT	MULTIPLY BY	TO OBTAIN
miles (statute)	1.609×10^5	centimeters	ohms	1.0×10^6	microhms
miles (statute)	5.280×10^3	feet	ounces	8.0	drams
miles (statute)	6.336×10^4	inches	ounces	4.375×10^2	grains
miles (statute)	1.609	kilometers	ounces	2.8349×10^1	grams
miles (statute)	1.609×10^3	meters	ounces	6.25×10^{-2}	pounds
miles (statute)	8.684×10^{-1}	miles (nautical)	ounces	9.115×10^{-1}	ounces (troy)
miles (statute)	1.760×10^3	yards	ounces	2.790×10^{-5}	tons (long)
miles (statute)	1.69×10^{-13}	light years	ounces	3.125×10^{-5}	tons (short)
miles/hr.	4.470×10^1	cms./sec.	ounces (fluid)	1.805	cu. inches
miles/hr.	8.8×10^1	ft./min.	ounces (fluid)	2.957×10^{-2}	liters
miles/hr.	1.467	ft./sec.	ounces (troy)	4.80×10^2	grains
miles/hr.	1.6093	kms./hr.	ounces (troy)	3.1103×10^1	grams
miles/hr.	2.682×10^{-2}	kms./min.	ounces (troy)	1.097	ounces (avdp.)
miles/hr.	8.684×10^{-1}	knots	ounces (troy)	2.0×10^1	pennyweights (troy)
miles/hr.	2.682×10^1	meters/min.	ounces (troy)	8.333×10^{-2}	pounds (troy)
miles/hr.	1.667×10^{-2}	miles/min.	ounce/sq. in.	4.309×10^3	dynes/sq. cm.
miles/hr./sec.	4.47×10^1	cms./sec./sec.	ounce/sq. in.	6.25×10^{-2}	pounds/sq. in.
miles/hr./sec.	1.467	ft./sec./sec.			
miles/hr./sec.	1.6093	kms./hr./sec.		**P**	
miles/hr./sec.	4.47×10^{-1}	meters/sec./sec.	pace	3.0×10^1	inches
miles/min.	2.682×10^3	cms./sec.	parsec	1.9×10^{13}	miles
miles/min.	8.8×10^1	feet/sec.	parsec	3.084×10^{13}	kilometers
miles/min.	1.6093	kms./min.	parts/million	5.84×10^{-2}	grains/u.s. gal.
miles/min.	8.684×10^{-1}	knots/min.	parts/million	7.016×10^{-1}	grains/imp. gal.
miles/min.	6.0×10^1	miles/hr	parts/million	8.345	pounds/million gal.
milliers	1.0×10^8	kilograms	pecks (british)	5.546×10^2	cubic inches
millimicrons	1.0×10^{-9}	meters	pecks (british)	9.0919	liters
milligrams	1.5432×10^{-2}	grains	pecks (u.s.)	2.5×10^{-1}	bushels
milligrams	1.0×10^{-3}	grams	pecks (u.s.)	5.376×10^2	cubic inches
milligrams/liter	1.0	parts/million	pecks (u.s.)	8.8096	liters
millihenries	1.0×10^{-3}	henries	pecks (u.s.)	8	quarts (dry)
milliliters	1.0×10^{-3}	liters	pennyweights (troy)	2.4×10^1	grains
millimeters	1.0×10^{-1}	centimeters	pennyweights (troy)	5.0×10^{-2}	ounces (troy)
millimeters	3.281×10^{-3}	feet	pennyweights (troy)	1.555	grams
millimeters	3.937×10^{-2}	inches	pennyweights (troy)	4.1667×10^{-3}	pounds (troy)
millimeters	1.0×10^{-6}	kilometers	pints (dry)	3.36×10^1	cubic inches
millimeters	1.0×10^{-3}	meters	pints (dry)	1.5625×10^{-2}	bushels
millimeters	6.214×10^{-7}	miles	pints (dry)	5.0×10^{-1}	quarts
millimeters	3.937×10^1	mils	pints (dry)	5.5059×10^{-1}	liters
millimeters	1.094×10^{-3}	yards	pints (liquid)	4.732×10^2	cubic cms.
million gals./day	1.54723	cu. ft./sec.	pints (liquid)	1.671×10^{-2}	cubic ft.
mils	2.54×10^{-3}	centimeters	pints (liquid)	2.887×10^1	cubic inches
mils	8.333×10^{-5}	feet	pints (liquid)	4.732×10^{-4}	cubic meters
mils	1.0×10^{-3}	inches	pints (liquid)	6.189×10^{-4}	cubic yards
mils	2.54×10^{-8}	kilometers	pints (liquid)	1.25×10^{-1}	gallons
mils	2.778×10^{-5}	yards	pints (liquid)	4.732×10^{-1}	liters
miner's inches	1.5	cu. ft./min.	pints (liquid)	5.0×10^{-1}	quarts (liquid)
minims (british)	5.9192×10^{-2}	cubic cm.	planck's quantum	6.624×10^{-27}	erg-seconds
minims (u.s. fluid)	6.1612×10^{-2}	cubic cm.	poise	1.0	gram/cm.-sec.
minutes (angles)	1.667×10^{-2}	degrees	pounds (avdp.)	1.4583×10^1	ounces (troy)
minutes (angles)	1.852×10^{-4}	quadrants	poundals	1.3826×10^4	dynes
minutes (angles)	2.909×10^{-4}	radians	poundals	1.41×10^1	grams
minutes (angles)	6.0×10^1	seconds	poundals	1.383×10^{-3}	joules/cm.
minutes (time)	9.9206×10^{-5}	weeks	poundals	1.383×10^{-1}	joules/meter (newtons)
minutes (time)	6.944×10^{-4}	days			
minutes (time)	1.667×10^{-2}	hours	poundals	1.41×10^{-2}	kilograms
minutes (time)	6.0×10^1	seconds	poundals	3.108×10^{-2}	pounds
myriagrams	1.0×10^1	kilograms	pounds	2.56×10^2	drams
myriameters	1.0×10^1	kilometers	pounds	4.448×10^5	dynes
myriawatts	1.0×10^1	kilowatts	pounds	7.0×10^3	grains
			pounds	4.5359×10^2	grams
	N		pounds	4.448×10^{-2}	joules/cm.
nails	2.25	inches	pounds	4.448	joules/meter (newtons)
newtons	1.0×10^5	dynes			
			pounds	4.536×10^{-1}	kilograms
	O		pounds	1.6×10^1	ounces
ohm (international)	1.0005	ohm (absolute)	pounds	1.458×10^1	ounces (troy)
ohms	1.0×10^{-6}	megohms	pounds	3.217×10^1	poundals

TABLE 5 *(continued)* ENGINEERING CONVERSION TABLES

TO CONVERT	MULTIPLY BY	TO OBTAIN	TO CONVERT	MULTIPLY BY	TO OBTAIN
pounds	1.21528	pounds (troy)	revolutions	3.60×10^2	degrees
pounds	5.0×10^{-4}	tons (short)	revolutions	4.0	quadrants
pounds (troy)	5.760×10^3	grains	revolutions	6.283	radians
pounds (troy)	3.7324×10^2	grams	revolutions/min.	6.0	degrees/sec.
pounds (troy)	1.3166×10^1	ounces (avdp.)	revolutions/min.	1.047×10^{-1}	radians/sec.
pounds (troy)	1.2×10^1	ounces (troy)	revolutions/min.	1.667×10^{-2}	revs./sec.
pounds (troy)	2.4×10^2	pennyweights (troy)	revs./min./min.	1.745×10^{-3}	radians/sec./sec.
pounds (troy)	8.2286×10^{-1}	pounds (avdp.)	revs./min./min.	1.667×10^{-2}	revs./min./sec.
pounds (troy)	3.6735×10^{-4}	tons (long)	revs./min./min.	2.778×10^{-4}	revs./sec./sec.
pounds (troy)	3.7324×10^{-4}	tons (metric)	revolutions/sec.	3.6×10^2	degrees/sec.
pounds (troy)	4.1143×10^{-4}	tons (short)	revolutions/sec.	6.283	radians/sec.
pounds of water	1.602×10^{-2}	cu. ft.	revolutions/sec.	6.0×10^1	revs./min.
pounds of water	2.768×10^1	cu. inches	revs./sec./sec.	6.283	radians/sec./sec.
pounds of water	1.198×10^{-1}	gallons	revs./sec./sec.	3.6×10^3	revs./min./min.
pounds of water/min.	2.670×10^{-4}	cu. ft./sec.	revs./sec./sec.	6.0×10^1	revs./min./sec.
pound-feet	1.356×10^7	cm.-dynes	rods	2.5×10^{-1}	chains (gunters)
pound-feet	1.3825×10^4	cm.-grams	rods	5.029	meters
pound-feet	1.383×10^{-1}	meter kgs.	rods (surveyors' meas.)	5.5	yards
pounds/cu. ft.	1.602×10^{-2}	grams/cu. cm.			
pounds/cu. ft.	1.602×10^1	kgs./cu. meter	rods	1.65×10^1	feet
pounds/cu. ft.	5.787×10^{-4}	pounds/cu. inches	rods	1.98×10^2	inches
pounds/cu. ft.	5.456×10^{-9}	pounds/mil-foot	rods	3.125×10^{-3}	miles
pounds/cu. in.	2.768×10^1	grams/cu.cm.	rope	2.0×10^1	feet
pounds/cu. in.	2.768×10^4	kgs./cu. meter			
pounds/cu. in.	1.728×10^3	pounds/cu. ft.		**S**	
pounds/cu. in.	9.425×10^{-6}	pounds/mil-foot	scruples	2.0×10^1	grains
pounds/ft.	1.488	kgs./meter	seconds (angle)	2.778×10^{-4}	degrees
pounds/in.	1.786×10^2	grams/cm.	seconds (angle)	1.667×10^{-2}	minutes
pounds/mil-foot	2.306×10^6	grams/cu. cm.	seconds (angle)	3.087×10^{-6}	quadrants
pounds/sq. ft.	4.725×10^{-4}	atmospheres	seconds (angle)	4.848×10^{-6}	radians
pounds/sq. ft.	1.602×10^{-2}	feet of water	slugs	1.459×10^1	kilograms
pounds/sq. ft.	1.414×10^{-2}	inches of mercury	slugs	3.217×10^1	pounds
pounds/sq. ft.	4.882	kgs./sq. meter	sphere (solid angle)	1.257×10^1	steradians
pounds/sq. ft.	6.944×10^{-3}	pounds/sq. inch	square centimeters	1.973×10^5	circular mils
pounds/sq. in.	6.804×10^{-2}	atmospheres	square centimeters	1.076×10^{-3}	sq. feet
pounds/sq. in.	2.307	feet of water	square centimeters	1.550×10^{-1}	sq. inches
pounds/sq. in.	2.036	inches of mercury	square centimeters	1.0×10^{-4}	sq. meters
pounds/sq. in.	7.031×10^2	kgs./sq. meter	square centimeters	3.861×10^{-11}	sq. miles
pounds/sq. in.	1.44×10^2	pounds/sq. ft.	square centimeters	1.0×10^2	sq. millimeters
pounds/sq. in.	7.2×10^{-2}	short tons/sq. ft.	square centimeters	1.196×10^{-4}	sq. yards
pounds/sq. in.	7.03×10^{-2}	kgs./sq. cm.	square degrees	3.0462×10^{-4}	steradians
			square feet	2.296×10^{-5}	acres
	Q		square feet	1.833×10^8	circular mils
quadrants (angle)	9.0×10^1	degrees	square feet	9.29×10^2	sq. cms.
quadrants (angle)	5.4×10^3	minutes	square feet	1.44×10^2	sq. inches
quadrants (angle)	1.571	radians	square feet	9.29×10^{-2}	sq. meters
quadrants (angle)	3.24×10^5	seconds	square feet	3.587×10^{-8}	sq. miles
quarts (dry)	6.72×10^1	cu. inches	square feet	9.29×10^4	sq. millimeters
quarts (liquid)	9.464×10^2	cu. cms.	square feet	1.111×10^{-1}	sq. yards
quarts (liquid)	3.342×10^{-2}	cu. ft.	square inches	1.273×10^6	circular mils
quarts (liquid)	5.775×10^1	cu. inches	square inches	6.452	sq. cms.
quarts (liquid)	9.464×10^{-4}	cu. meters	square inches	6.944×10^{-3}	sq. ft.
quarts (liquid)	1.238×10^{-3}	cu. yards	square inches	6.452×10^2	sq. millimeters
quarts (liquid)	2.5×10^{-1}	gallons	square inches	1.0×10^6	sq. mils
quarts (liquid)	9.463×10^{-1}	liters	square inches	7.716×10^{-4}	sq. yards
			square kilometers	2.471×10^2	acres
	R		square kilometers	1.0×10^{10}	sq. cms.
radians	5.7296×10^1	degrees	square kilometers	1.076×10^7	sq. ft.
radians	3.438×10^3	minutes	square kilometers	1.550×10^9	sq. inches
radians	6.366×10^{-1}	quadrants	square kilometers	1.0×10^6	sq. meters
radians	2.063×10^5	seconds	square kilometers	3.861×10^{-1}	sq. miles
radians/sec.	5.7296×10^1	degrees/sec.	square kilometers	1.196×10^6	sq. yards
radians/sec.	9.549	revolutions/min.	square meters	2.471×10^{-4}	acres
radians/sec.	1.592×10^{-1}	revolution/sec.	square meters	1.0×10^4	sq. cms.
radians/sec./sec.	5.7296×10^2	revs./min./min.	square meters	1.076×10^1	sq. ft.
radians/sec./sec.	9.549	revs./min./sec.	square meters	1.55×10^3	sq. inches
radians/sec./sec.	1.592×10^{-1}	revs./sec./sec.	square meters	3.861×10^{-7}	sq. miles
reams	5.0×10^2	sheets	square meters	1.0×10^6	sq. millimeters

TABLE 5 *(continued)* ENGINEERING CONVERSION TABLES

TO CONVERT	MULTIPLY BY	TO OBTAIN	TO CONVERT	MULTIPLY BY	TO OBTAIN
square meters	1.196	sq. yards		**V**	
square miles	6.40×10^2	acres	volt/inch	3.937×10^7	abvolts/cm.
square miles	2.788×10^7	sq. ft.	volt/inch	3.937×10^{-1}	volt/cm.
square miles	2.590	sq. kms.	volt (absolute)	3.336×10^{-3}	statvolts
square miles	2.590×10^6	sq. meters	volts	1.0×10^8	abvolts
square miles	3.098×10^6	sq. yards			
square millimeters	1.973×10^3	circular mils			
square millimeters	1.0×10^2	sq. cms.		**W**	
square millimeters	1.076×10^{-5}	sq. ft.	watts	3.4129	btu/hr.
square millimeters	1.55×10^{-3}	sq. inches	watts	5.688×10^{-2}	btu/min.
square mils	1.273	circular mils	watts	1.0×10^7	ergs/sec.
square mils	6.452×10^{-6}	sq. cms.	watts	4.427×10^1	ft.-lbs./min.
square mils	1.0×10^{-6}	sq. inches	watts	7.378×10^{-1}	ft.-lbs./sec.
square yards	2.066×10^{-4}	acres	watts	1.341×10^{-3}	horsepower
square yards	8.361×10^3	sq. cms.	watts	1.36×10^{-3}	horsepower (metric)
square yards	9.0	sq. ft.	watts	1.433×10^{-2}	kg.-calories/min.
square yards	1.296×10^3	sq. inches	watts	1.0×10^{-3}	kilowatts
square yards	8.361×10^{-1}	sq. meters	watts (abs.)	1.0	joules/sec.
square yards	3.228×10^{-7}	sq. miles	watt-hours	3.413	btu
square yards	8.361×10^5	sq. millimeters	watt-hours	3.6×10^{10}	ergs
steradians	7.958×10^{-2}	spheres	watt-hours	2.656×10^3	foot-lbs.
steradians	1.592×10^{-1}	hemispheres	watt-hours	8.605×10^2	gram-calories
steradians	6.366×10^{-1}	spherical right angles	watt-hours	1.341×10^{-3}	horsepower-hours
			watt-hours	8.605×10^{-1}	kilogram-calories
steradians	3.283×10^3	square degrees	watt-hours	3.672×10^2	kilogram-meters
steres	9.99973×10^2	liters	watt-hours	1.0×10^{-3}	kilowatt-hours
			watt (international)	1.000165	watt (absolute)
	T		webers	1.0×10^8	maxwells
temperature (°C.) +273	1.0	absolute temperature (°K.)	webers	1.0×10^5	kilolines
			webers/sq. in.	1.55×10^7	gausses
temperature (°C.) +17.78	1.8	temperature (°F.)	webers/sq. in.	1.0×10^8	lines/sq. in.
			webers/sq. in.	1.55×10^{-1}	webers/sq. cm.
temperature (°F.) +460	1.0	absolute temperature (°R.)	webers/sq. in.	1.55×10^3	webers/sq. meter
			webers/sq. meter	1.0×10^4	gausses
temperature (°F.) −32	5/9	temperature (°C.)	webers/sq. meter	6.452×10^4	lines/sq. in.
tons (long)	1.016×10^3	kilograms	webers/sq. meter	1.0×10^{-4}	webers/sq. cm.
tons (long)	2.24×10^3	pounds	webers/sq. meter	6.452×10^{-4}	webers/sq. in.
tons (long)	1.12	tons (short)	weeks	1.68×10^2	hours
tons (metric)	1.0×10^3	kilograms	weeks	1.008×10^4	minutes
tons (metric)	2.205×10^3	pounds	weeks	6.048×10^5	seconds
tons (short)	9.0718×10^2	kilograms			
tons (short)	3.2×10^4	ounces			
tons (short)	2.9166×10^4	ounces (troy)		**Y**	
tons (short)	2.0×10^3	pounds	yards	9.144×10^1	centimeters
tons (short)	2.43×10^3	pounds (troy)	yards	9.144×10^{-4}	kilometers
tons (short)	8.9287×10^{-1}	tons (long)	yards	9.144×10^{-1}	meters
tons (short)	9.078×10^{-1}	tons (metric)	yards	4.934×10^{-4}	miles (nautical)
tons (short)/sq. ft.	9.765×10^3	kgs./sq. meter	yards	5.682×10^{-4}	miles (statute)
tons (short)/sq. ft.	1.389×10^1	pounds/sq. in.	yards	9.144×10^2	millimeters
tons (short)/sq. in.	1.406×10^6	kgs./sq. meter	years	3.65256×10^2	days (mean solar)
tons (short)/sq. in.	2.0×10^3	pounds/sq. in.	years	8.7661×10^3	hours (mean solar)
tons of water/24 hrs.	8.333×10^1	pounds of water/hr.			
tons of water/24 hrs.	1.6643×10^{-1}	gallons/min.			
tons of water/24 hrs.	1.3349	cu. ft./hr.			

TABLE 6 FRACTION, DECIMAL AND METRIC EQUIVALENTS

Fractional Inch	Dec. Equiv.	Millimeters	Fractional Inch	Dec. Equiv.	Millimeters
1/64	.0156	.397	17/32	.5313	13.494
1/32	.0313	.794	35/64	.5469	13.891
3/64	.0469	1.191	9/16	.5625	14.288
1/16	.0625	1.588	37/64	.5781	14.684
5/64	.0781	1.984	7/12	.5833	14.817
1/12	.0833	2.117	19/32	.5938	15.081
3/32	.0938	2.381	3/5	.6000	15.240
1/10	.1000	2.540	39/64	.6094	15.478
7/64	.1094	2.778	5/8	.6250	15.875
1/8	.1250	3.175	41/64	.6406	16.272
9/64	.1406	3.572	21/32	.6563	16.669
1/6	.1667	4.233	2/3	.6667	16.933
11/64	.1719	4.366	43/64	.6719	17.066
3/16	.1875	4.700	11/16	.6875	17.463
1/5	.2000	5.080	7/10	.7000	17.780
13/64	.2031	5.159	45/64	.7031	17.859
7/32	.2188	5.556	23/32	.7188	18.256
15/64	.2344	5.953	47/64	.7344	18.653
1/4	.2500	6.350	3/4	.7500	19.050
17/64	.2656	6.747	49/64	.7656	19.447
9/32	.2813	7.144	25/32	.7813	19.844
19/64	.2969	7.541	51/64	.7969	20.241
3/10	.3000	7.620	4/5	.8000	20.320
5/16	.3125	7.937	13/16	.8125	20.638
1/3	.3333	8.467	53/64	.8281	21.034
11/32	.3438	8.731	5/6	.8333	21.167
23/64	.3594	9.128	27/32	.8438	21.431
3/8	.3750	9.525	55/64	.8594	21.828
25/64	.3906	9.922	7/8	.8750	22.225
2/5	.4000	10.160	57/64	.8906	22.622
13/32	.4063	10.319	9/10	.9000	22.860
5/12	.4167	10.583	29/32	.9063	23.019
27/64	.4219	10.716	11/12	.9167	23.283
7/16	.4375	11.112	59/64	.9219	23.416
29/64	.4531	11.509	15/16	.9375	23.813
15/32	.4688	11.906	61/64	.9531	24.209
31/64	.4844	12.303	31/32	.9688	24.606
1/2	.5000	12.700	63/64	.9844	25.003
33/64	.5156	13.097	1″	1.0000	25.400

To convert a decimal to percentage, carry the decimal point two places to the right. Thus, 63/64, or .9844, equals 98.44%.

TABLE 7 CONVERTING INCHES INTO DECIMALS OF A FOOT

Inches	Decimal of a Ft.	Inches	Decimal of a Ft.	Inches	Decimal of a Ft.
0″ 1/16	.005208	4″ 1/16	.338542	8″ 1/16	.671875
1/8	.010416	1/8	.343750	1/8	.677083
3/16	.015625	3/16	.348958	3/16	.682292
1/4	.020833	1/4	.354166	1/4	.687500
5/16	.026042	5/16	.359375	5/16	.692708
3/8	.031250	3/8	.364583	3/8	.697916
7/16	.036458	7/16	.369792	7/16	.703125
1/2 (.33333)	.041666	1/2 (.33333)	.375000	1/2 (.66666)	.708333
9/16	.046875	9/16	.380208	9/16	.713542
5/8	.052083	5/8	.385416	5/8	.718750
11/16	.057292	11/16	.390625	11/16	.723958
3/4	.062500	3/4	.395833	3/4	.729166
13/16	.067708	13/16	.401042	13/16	.734375
7/8	.072916	7/8	.406250	7/8	.739583
15/16	.078125	15/16	.411458	15/16	.744792
1″ (.083333) 1/16	.088542	5″ 1/16	.421875	9″ 1/16	.755208
1/8	.093750	1/8	.427083	1/8	.760416
3/16	.098958	3/16	.432292	3/16	.765625
1/4	.104166	1/4	.437500	1/4	.770833
5/16	.109375	5/16	.442708	5/16	.776042
3/8	.114583	3/8	.447916	3/8	.781250
7/16	.119792	7/16	.453125	7/16	.786458
1/2	.125000	1/2 (.416666)	.458333	1/2 (.750)	.791666
9/16	.130208	9/16	.463542	9/16	.796875
5/8	.135416	5/8	.463750	5/8	.802083
11/16	.140625	11/16	.473958	11/16	.807292
3/4	.145833	3/4	.479166	3/4	.812500
13/16	.151042	13/16	.484375	13/16	.817708
7/8	.156250	7/8	.489583	7/8	.822916
15/16	.161458	15/16	.494792	15/16	.828125
2″ (.166666) 1/16	.171875	6″ 1/16	.505208	10″ 1/16	.838542
1/8	.177083	1/8	.510416	1/8	.843750
3/16	.182292	3/16	.515625	3/16	.848958
1/4	.187500	1/4	.520833	1/4	.854166
5/16	.192708	5/16	.526042	5/16	.859375
3/8	.197916	3/8	.531250	3/8	.864583
7/16	.203125	7/16	.536458	7/16	.869792
1/2	.208333	1/2 (.50)	.541666	1/2 (.833333)	.875000
9/16	.213542	9/16	.546875	9/16	.880208
5/8	.218750	5/8	.552083	5/8	.885416
11/16	.223958	11/16	.557292	11/16	.890625
3/4	.229166	3/4	.562500	3/4	.895833
13/16	.234375	13/16	.567708	13/16	.901042
7/8	.239583	7/8	.572916	7/8	.906250
15/16	.244792	15/16	.578125	15/16	.911458
3″ (.250) 1/16	.255208	7″ 1/16	.588542	11″ 1/16	.921875
1/8	.260416	1/8	.593750	1/8	.927083
3/16	.265625	3/16	.598958	3/16	.932292
1/4	.270833	1/4	.604166	1/4	.937500
5/16	.276042	5/16	.609375	5/16	.942708
3/8	.281250	3/8	.614583	3/8	.947916
7/16	.286458	7/16	.619792	7/16	.953125
1/2	.291666	1/2 (.583333)	.625000	1/2 (.916666)	.958333
9/16	.296875	9/16	.630208	9/16	.963542
5/8	.302083	5/8	.635416	5/8	.968750
11/16	.307292	11/16	.640625	11/16	.973958
3/4	.312500	3/4	.645833	3/4	.979166
13/16	.317708	13/16	.651042	13/16	.984375
7/8	.322916	7/8	.656250	7/8	.989583
15/16	.328125	15/16	.661458	15/16	.994792

TABLE 8 PROPERTIES OF VARIOUS CROSS SECTIONS

Area A	Distance from Centroid to Extremity of Section C	Moment of Inertia I	Section Modulus $Z = I/C$	Radius of Gyration $k = \sqrt{I/A}$
b^2	$.5b$	$.0833b^4$	$.167b^3$	$.289b$
b^2	$.7071b$	$.0833b^4$	$.1178b^3$	$.289b$
$b^2-b_1^2$	$.5b$	$.0833(b^4-b_1^4)$	$\dfrac{.167(b^4-b_1^4)}{b}$	$.289\sqrt{b^2+b_1^2}$
$b^2-b_1^2$	$.7071b$	$.0833(b^4-b_1^4)$	$\dfrac{.1178(b^4-b_1^4)}{b}$	$.289\sqrt{b^2+b_1^2}$
bh	$.5h$	(y_1) $.0833bh^3$ (y_2) $.333bh^3$ (y_3) $bh\left(\dfrac{h^2}{12}+d^2\right)$	$.167bh^2$	(y_1) $.289h$
bh	$\dfrac{bh}{\sqrt{b^2+h^2}}$	$.167\dfrac{b^3h^3}{(b^2+h^2)}$	$.167\dfrac{b^2h^2}{\sqrt{b^2+h^2}}$	$.408\dfrac{bh}{\sqrt{b^2+h^2}}$
bh	$.5(h\cos\alpha+b\sin\alpha)$	$.0833bh\,(h^2\cos^2\alpha+b^2\sin^2\alpha)$		$.289\sqrt{h^2\cos^2\alpha+b^2\sin^2\alpha}$
$b(h-h_1)$	$.5h$	$.0833\,b\,(h^3-h_1^3)$	$\dfrac{.167b\,(h^3-h_1^3)}{h}$	$.289\sqrt{\dfrac{h^3-h_1^3}{h-h_1}}$
$.5bh$	$.667h$	$.0277bh^3$	$.0417bh^2$	$.236h$
$.5bh$	$.667h$	$.02083hb^3$	$.0417hb^2$	$.204b$

Area A	Distance from Centroid to Extremity of Section C	Moment of Inertia I	Section Modulus $Z = I/C$	Radius of Gyration $k = \sqrt{I/A}$
$.5h\,(b+b_1)$	$.33h\left(\dfrac{2b+b_1}{b+b_1}\right)$	$.0277h^3\left(\dfrac{b^2+4bb_1+b_1^2}{b+b_1}\right)$	$.0833h^2\left(\dfrac{b^2+4bb_1+b_1^2}{2b+b_1}\right)$	$.236h\dfrac{\sqrt{b^2+4bb_1+b_1^2}}{b+b_1}$
$2.598b^2$	b	$.5413b^4$	$.625b^3$	$.456b$
$2.598b^2$	b	$.5413b^4$	$.5413b^3$	$.456b$
$.8284a^2$	$.541a$	$.0547a^4$	$.1095a^3$	$.257a$
$3.1416r^2$	r	$.7854r^4$	$.7854r^3$	
$.7854d^2$	$.5d$	$.04908d^4$	$.09816d^3$	$.25d$
$.7854\,(d_0^2-d_i^2)$	$.5d_0$	$.04908\,(d_0^4-d_i^4)$	$\dfrac{.09816\,(d_0^4-d_i^4)}{d_0}$	$.25\sqrt{d_0^2+d_i^2}$

Half circle

$A = 1.5708r^2$

- $y_1 = .5756r$, $I_1 = .1098r^4$, $Z_1 = .1907r^3$, $k_1 = .2643r$
- $y_2 = .4244r$, $I_2 = .3927r^4$, $Z_2 = .9253r^3$, $k_2 = .5r$

Circular segment

$A = .5r^2(2\alpha - \sin 2\alpha)$ (1)

$$y_1 = r\left(1 - \frac{4\sin^3\alpha}{6\alpha - 3\sin 2\alpha}\right)$$

$$y_2 = r\left(\frac{4\sin^3\alpha}{6\alpha - 3\sin 2\alpha} - \cos\alpha\right) \quad (2)$$

Circular sector

$A = r^2\alpha$ (3)

$$y_1 = r\left(1 - \frac{2\,\sin\alpha}{3\alpha}\right)$$

$$y_2 = 2r\,\frac{\sin\alpha}{3\alpha} \quad (4)$$

Quarter circle

$A = .7854r^2$

- $y_1 = .5756r$, $I_1 = .0549r^4$, $Z_1 = .0954r^3$, $.264r$
- $y_2 = .4244r$, $Z_2 = .1294r^3$

Spandrel

$A = .2146r^2$

- $y_1 = .2234r$, $I = .0075r^4$, $Z_2 = .0097r^3$, $.181r$
- $y_2 = .7766r$

TABLE 8 *(continued)* **PROPERTIES OF VARIOUS CROSS SECTIONS**

	Area A	Distance from Centroid to Extremity of Section C	Moment of Inertia I	Section Modulus $Z=I/C$	Radius of Gyration $k=\sqrt{I/A}$

 $6.2832rt$ — r — $3.14164r^3t$ — $3.1416r^2t$ — $.707r$

$3.1416rt$ — $.6366r$ — $I_1=.2978r^3t$, $I_2=1.5708r^3t$ — $Z_1=.4678r^2t$ — $k_1=.308r$, $k_2=.707r$

$2\alpha rt$

$$I_1=r^3t\left(\alpha+\sin\alpha\,\cos\alpha-\frac{2\sin^2\alpha}{\alpha}\right)$$
$$y_1=r\left(1-\frac{\sin\alpha}{\alpha}\right)\qquad k_1=r\sqrt{\frac{\alpha+\sin\alpha\,\cos\alpha-\frac{2\sin^2\alpha}{\alpha}}{2\alpha}}$$
$$I_2=r^3t(\alpha-\sin\alpha\,\cos\alpha)$$
$$y_2=r\left(\frac{\sin\alpha}{\alpha}-\cos\alpha\right)\qquad k_2=r\sqrt{\frac{\alpha-\sin\alpha\,\cos\alpha}{2\alpha}}$$

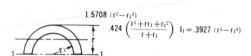 $1.5708\,(r^2-r_1^2)$ — $.424\left(\dfrac{r^2+rr_1+r_1^2}{r+r_1}\right)$ — $I_1=.3927\,(r^4-r_1^4)$

 $.7854\,(r^2-r_1^2)$ — $.424\left(\dfrac{r^2+rr_1+r_1^2}{r+r_1}\right)$ — $I_1=.1963\,(r^4-r_1^4)$

 $.7854bh$ — $.5h$ — $.0491bh^3$ — $.098bh^2$ — $.25h$

 $.7854\,(bh-b_1h_1)$ — $.5h$ — $I_1=.0491\,(bh^3-b_1h_1^3)$ — $\dfrac{.098\,(bh^3-b_1h_1^3)}{h}$ — $k_1=.25\sqrt{\dfrac{bh^3-b_1h_1^3}{bh-b_1h_1}}$

(1) $$I_1=r^4\left[.125\,(2\alpha-\sin 2\alpha)\left(1+\frac{2\sin^3\alpha\,\cos\alpha}{\alpha-\sin\alpha\,\cos\alpha}\right)-.88\frac{\sin^6\alpha}{2\alpha-\sin 2\alpha}\right]$$

$$I_2=r^4\left[.125\,(2\alpha-\sin 2\alpha)-.083\frac{(2\alpha-\sin 2\alpha)\,(\sin^3\alpha\,\cos\alpha)}{\alpha-\sin\alpha\,\cos\alpha}\right]$$

(2) $$k_1=.5r\sqrt{1+\frac{2\sin^3\alpha\,\cos\alpha}{\alpha-\sin\alpha\,\cos\alpha}-7.11\frac{\sin^6\alpha}{(2\alpha-\sin 2\alpha)^2}}$$

$$k_2=.5r\sqrt{1-\frac{2\sin^3\alpha\,\cos\alpha}{3\,(\alpha-\sin\alpha\,\cos\alpha)}}$$

(3) $$I_1=.25r^4\left(\alpha+\sin\alpha\,\cos\alpha-1.77\frac{\sin^2\alpha}{\alpha}\right)$$

$$I_2=.25r^4\,(\alpha-\sin\alpha\,\cos\alpha)$$

(4) $$k_1=.5r\sqrt{1+\frac{\sin\alpha\,\cos\alpha}{\alpha}-1.77\frac{\sin^2\alpha}{\alpha^2}}$$

$$k_2=.5r\sqrt{1-\frac{\sin\alpha\,\cos\alpha}{\alpha}}$$

TABLE 9   FORMULAS

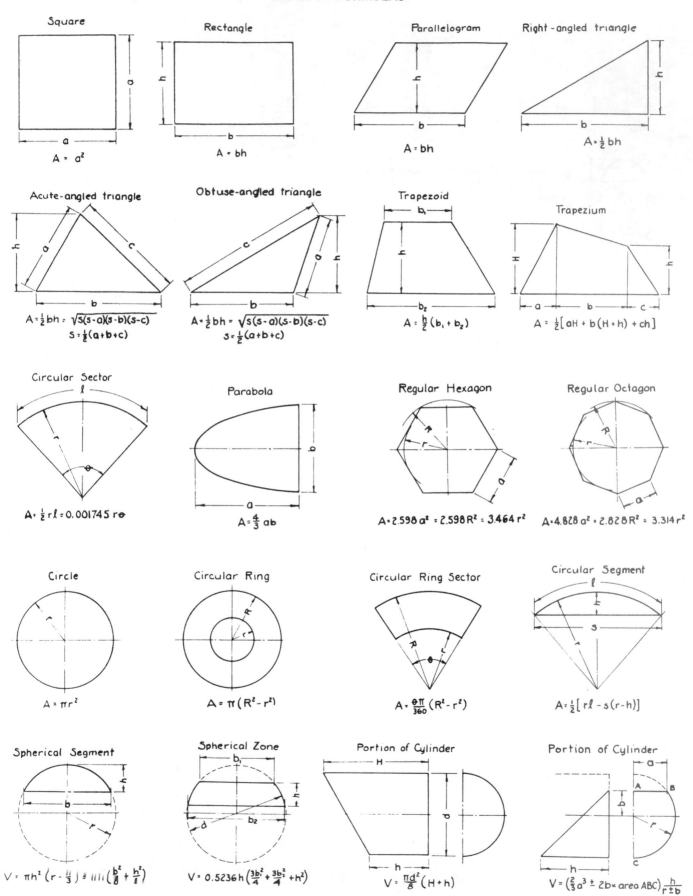

Square

$A = a^2$

Rectangle

$A = bh$

Parallelogram

$A = bh$

Right-angled triangle

$A = \frac{1}{2} bh$

Acute-angled triangle

$A = \frac{1}{2} bh = \sqrt{s(s-a)(s-b)(s-c)}$
$S = \frac{1}{2}(a+b+c)$

Obtuse-angled triangle

$A = \frac{1}{2} bh = \sqrt{s(s-a)(s-b)(s-c)}$
$s = \frac{1}{2}(a+b+c)$

Trapezoid

$A = \frac{h}{2}(b_1 + b_2)$

Trapezium

$A = \frac{1}{2}[aH + b(H+h) + ch]$

Circular Sector

$A = \frac{1}{2} rl = 0.001745 \, r\theta$

Parabola

$A = \frac{4}{3} ab$

Regular Hexagon

$A = 2.598 \, a^2 = 2.598 \, R^2 = 3.464 \, r^2$

Regular Octagon

$A = 4.828 \, a^2 = 2.828 \, R^2 = 3.314 \, r^2$

Circle

$A = \pi r^2$

Circular Ring

$A = \pi(R^2 - r^2)$

Circular Ring Sector

$A = \frac{\theta \pi}{360}(R^2 - r^2)$

Circular Segment

$A = \frac{1}{2}[rl - s(r-h)]$

Spherical Segment

$V = \pi h^2 \left(r - \frac{h}{3}\right) = \pi h \left(\frac{b^2}{8} + \frac{h^2}{1}\right)$

Spherical Zone

$V = 0.5236 \, h \left(\frac{3b_1^2}{4} + \frac{3b_2^2}{4} + h^2\right)$

Portion of Cylinder

$V = \frac{\pi d^2}{8}(H + h)$

Portion of Cylinder

$V = \left(\frac{2}{3} a^3 \pm 2b \times \text{area } ABC\right)\frac{h}{r \pm b}$

238

TABLE 9 *(continued)* **FORMULAS**

Frustum of Cone

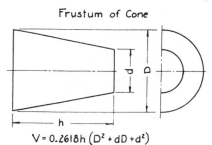

$$V = 0.2618h \left(D^2 + dD + d^2 \right)$$

Torus

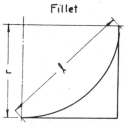

$$V = 2.4674 \, Dd^2$$

Fillet

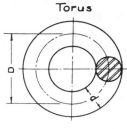

$$A = 0.215 \, r^2 = 0.1075 \, \ell^2$$

Portion of Cylinder

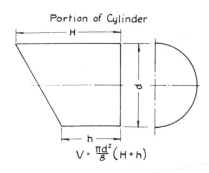

$$V = \frac{\pi d^2}{8} (H + h)$$

Portion of Cylinder

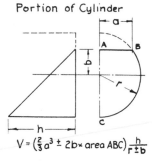

$$V = \left(\frac{2}{3} a^3 \pm 2b \times \text{area ABC} \right) \frac{h}{r \pm b}$$

Frustum of Cone

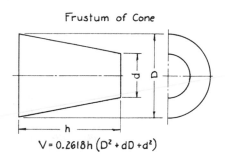

$$V = 0.2618h \left(D^2 + dD + d^2 \right)$$

Circular Segment

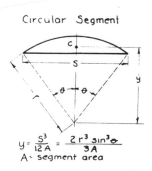

$$y = \frac{S^3}{12A} = \frac{2 r^3 \sin^3 \theta}{3A}$$
A = segment area

Circular Sector

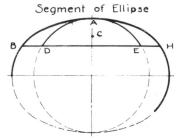

$$y = \frac{2rs}{3\ell} = 38.197 \frac{r \sin \theta}{\theta}$$

Area of Parabola

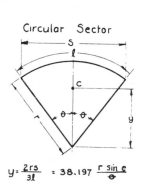

$$x = \frac{3a}{5}$$

Area of Semi-Parabola

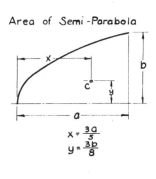

$$x = \frac{3a}{5}$$
$$y = \frac{3b}{8}$$

Segment of Ellipse

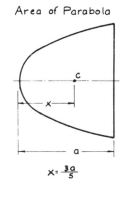

C, for the segment ABH of an ellipse, is at the same point as C for the segment ADE of a circle

Surfaces of Spherical Segments

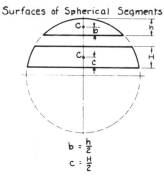

$$b = \frac{h}{2}$$
$$c = \frac{H}{2}$$

Volume of hemisphere

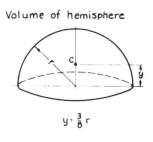

$$y = \frac{3}{8} r$$

Cylindrical Shell

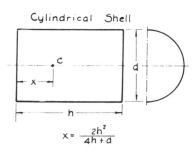

$$x = \frac{2h^2}{4h + d}$$

Cylindrical Solid

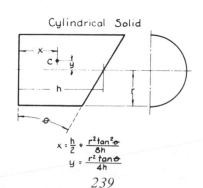

$$x = \frac{h}{2} + \frac{r^2 \tan^2 \theta}{6h}$$
$$y = \frac{r^2 \tan \theta}{4h}$$

Portion of Solid Cylinder

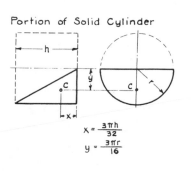

$$x = \frac{3\pi h}{32}$$
$$y = \frac{3\pi r}{16}$$

TABLE 9 *(continued)* **FORMULAS**

Portion of hollow cylinder   Spherical Segment   Center of Gravity of Two Bodies

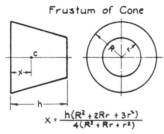

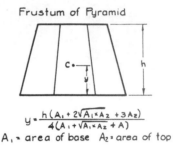

$$y = \frac{3\pi(R^4 - r^4)}{16(R^3 - r^3)}$$

$$x = \frac{3\pi(H^4 - h^4)}{32(H^3 - h^3)}$$

$$y = \frac{3(2r - h)^2}{4(3r - h)}$$

$$a = \frac{h(4r - h)}{4(3r - h)}$$

$$a = \frac{Bd}{A + B} \qquad b = \frac{Ad}{A + B}$$

A and B are weights of bodies

Frustum of Cone   Frustum of Pyramid

$$x = \frac{h(R^2 + 2Rr + 3r^2)}{4(R^2 + Rr + r^2)}$$

$$y = \frac{h(A_1 + 2\sqrt{A_1 \times A_2} + 3A_2)}{4(A_1 + \sqrt{A_1 \times A_2} + A)}$$

A_1 = area of base A_2 = area of top

Area of a square = length x breadth or height.

Area of a rectangle = length x breadth or height.

Area of a triangle = base x 1/2 altitude.

Area of parallelogram = base x altitude.

Area of trapezoid = altitude x 1/2 the sum of parallel sides.

Area of trapezium = divide into two triangles, total their areas.

Circumference of circle = diameter x 3.1416.

Circumference of circle = radius x 6.283185.

Diameter of circle = circumference x .3183.

Diameter of circle = square root of area x 1.12838.

Radius of a circle = circumference x .159155.

Area of a circle = half diameter x half circumference.

Area of a circle = square of diameter x .7854.

Area of a circle = square of circumference x .07958.

Area of a sector of circle = length of arc x 1/2 radius.

Area of a segment of circle = area of sector of equal radius — area of a triangle, when the segment is less, and plus area of triangle, when segment is greater than the semi-circle.

Area of circular ring = sum of the diameter of the two circles x difference of the diameter of the two circles and that product x .7854.

Side of square that shall equal area of circle = diameter x .8862.

Side of square that shall equal area of circle = circumference x .2821.

Diameter of circle that shall contain area of a given square = side of square x 1.1284.

Side of inscribed equilateral triangle = diameter x .86

Side of inscribed square = diameter x .7071.

Side of inscribed square = circumference x .225.

Area of ellipse = product of the two diameters x .7854.

Area of a parabola = base x 2/3 of altitude.

Area of a regular polygon = sum of its sides x perpendicular from its center to one of its sides divided by 2.

Surface of cylinder or prism = area of both ends plus length and x circumference.

Surface of sphere = diameter x circumference.

Solidity of sphere = surface x 1/6 diameter.

Solidity of sphere = cube of diameter x .5236.

Solidity of sphere = cube of radius x 4.1888.

Solidity of sphere = cube of circumference x .016887.

Diameter of sphere = cube root of solidity x 1.2407.

Diameter of sphere = square root of surface x .56419.

Circumference of sphere = square root of surface x 1.772454.

Circumference of sphere = cube root of solidity x 3.8978.

Contents of segment of sphere = (height squared plus three times the square of radius of base) x (height x .5236).

Contents of a sphere = diameter x .5236.

Side of inscribed cube of sphere = radius x 1.1547.

Side of inscribed cube of sphere = square root of diameter.

Surface of pyramid or cone = circumference of base x 1/2 of the slant height plus area of base.

Contents of pyramid or cone = area of base x 1/3 altitude.

Contents of frustum of pyramid or cone = sum of circumference at both ends x 1/2 slant height plus area of both ends.

Contents of frustum of pyramid or cone = multiply areas of two ends together and extract square root. Add to this root the two areas and x 1/3 altitude.

Contents of a wedge = area of base x 1/2 altitude.

TABLE 10 STRUCTURAL DIMENSIONS FOR DETAILING W SHAPES

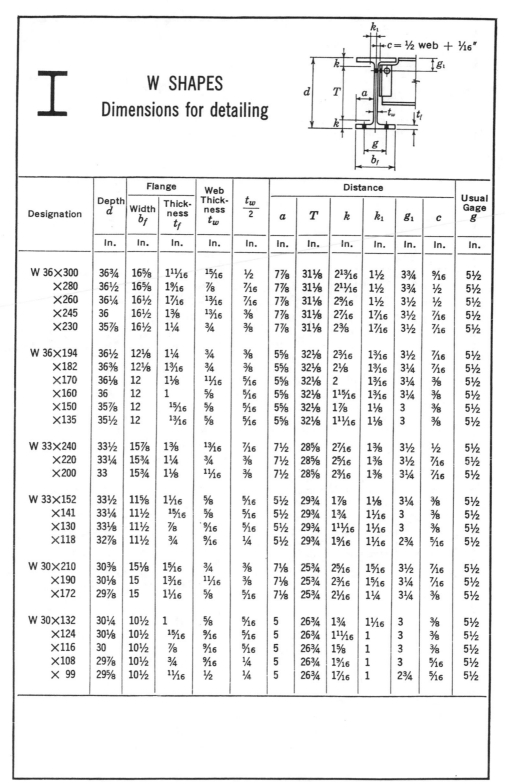

W SHAPES
Dimensions for detailing

$c = \frac{1}{2}$ web $+ \frac{1}{16}''$

Designation	Depth d	Flange Width b_f	Flange Thickness t_f	Web Thickness t_w	$\frac{t_w}{2}$	a	T	k	k_1	g_1	c	Usual Gage g
	In.	In.	In.	In.	In.	In.	In.	In.	In.	In.	In.	In.
W 36×300	36¾	16⅝	1¹¹⁄₁₆	¹⁵⁄₁₆	½	7⅞	31⅛	2¹³⁄₁₆	1½	3¾	⁹⁄₁₆	5½
×280	36½	16⅝	1⁹⁄₁₆	⅞	⁷⁄₁₆	7⅞	31⅛	2¹¹⁄₁₆	1½	3¾	½	5½
×260	36¼	16½	1⁷⁄₁₆	¹³⁄₁₆	⁷⁄₁₆	7⅞	31⅛	2⁹⁄₁₆	1½	3½	½	5½
×245	36	16½	1⅜	¹³⁄₁₆	⅜	7⅞	31⅛	2⁷⁄₁₆	1⁷⁄₁₆	3½	⁷⁄₁₆	5½
×230	35⅞	16½	1¼	¾	⅜	7⅞	31⅛	2⅜	1⁷⁄₁₆	3½	⁷⁄₁₆	5½
W 36×194	36½	12⅛	1¼	¾	⅜	5⅝	32⅛	2³⁄₁₆	1³⁄₁₆	3½	⁷⁄₁₆	5½
×182	36⅜	12⅛	1³⁄₁₆	¾	⅜	5⅝	32⅛	2⅛	1³⁄₁₆	3¼	⁷⁄₁₆	5½
×170	36⅛	12	1⅛	¹¹⁄₁₆	⁵⁄₁₆	5⅝	32⅛	2	1³⁄₁₆	3¼	⅜	5½
×160	36	12	1	⅝	⁵⁄₁₆	5⅝	32⅛	1¹⁵⁄₁₆	1³⁄₁₆	3¼	⅜	5½
×150	35⅞	12	¹⁵⁄₁₆	⅝	⁵⁄₁₆	5⅝	32⅛	1⅞	1⅛	3	⅜	5½
×135	35½	12	¹³⁄₁₆	⅝	⁵⁄₁₆	5⅝	32⅛	1¹¹⁄₁₆	1⅛	3	⅜	5½
W 33×240	33½	15⅞	1⅜	¹³⁄₁₆	⁷⁄₁₆	7½	28⅝	2⁷⁄₁₆	1⅜	3½	½	5½
×220	33¼	15¾	1¼	¾	⅜	7½	28⅝	2⁵⁄₁₆	1⅜	3½	⁷⁄₁₆	5½
×200	33	15¾	1⅛	¹¹⁄₁₆	⅜	7½	28⅝	2³⁄₁₆	1⅜	3¼	⁷⁄₁₆	5½
W 33×152	33½	11⅝	1¹⁄₁₆	⅝	⁵⁄₁₆	5½	29¾	1⅞	1⅛	3¼	⅜	5½
×141	33¼	11½	¹⁵⁄₁₆	⅝	⁵⁄₁₆	5½	29¾	1¾	1¹⁄₁₆	3	⅜	5½
×130	33⅛	11½	⅞	⁹⁄₁₆	⁵⁄₁₆	5½	29¾	1¹¹⁄₁₆	1¹⁄₁₆	3	⅜	5½
×118	32⅞	11½	¾	⁹⁄₁₆	¼	5½	29¾	1⁹⁄₁₆	1¹⁄₁₆	2¾	⁵⁄₁₆	5½
W 30×210	30⅜	15⅛	1⁵⁄₁₆	¾	⅜	7⅛	25¾	2⁵⁄₁₆	1⁵⁄₁₆	3½	⁷⁄₁₆	5½
×190	30⅛	15	1³⁄₁₆	¹¹⁄₁₆	⅜	7⅛	25¾	2³⁄₁₆	1⁵⁄₁₆	3¼	⁷⁄₁₆	5½
×172	29⅞	15	1¹⁄₁₆	⅝	⁵⁄₁₆	7⅛	25¾	2¹⁄₁₆	1¼	3¼	⅜	5½
W 30×132	30¼	10½	1	⅝	⁵⁄₁₆	5	26¾	1¾	1¹⁄₁₆	3	⅜	5½
×124	30⅛	10½	¹⁵⁄₁₆	⁹⁄₁₆	⁵⁄₁₆	5	26¾	1¹¹⁄₁₆	1	3	⅜	5½
×116	30	10½	⅞	⁹⁄₁₆	⁵⁄₁₆	5	26¾	1⅝	1	3	⅜	5½
×108	29⅞	10½	¾	⁹⁄₁₆	¼	5	26¾	1⁹⁄₁₆	1	3	⁵⁄₁₆	5½
× 99	29⅝	10½	¹¹⁄₁₆	½	¼	5	26¾	1⁷⁄₁₆	1	2¾	⁵⁄₁₆	5½

AMERICAN INSTITUTE OF STEEL CONSTRUCTION

TABLE 10 *(continued)* STRUCTURAL DIMENSIONS FOR DETAILING W SHAPES

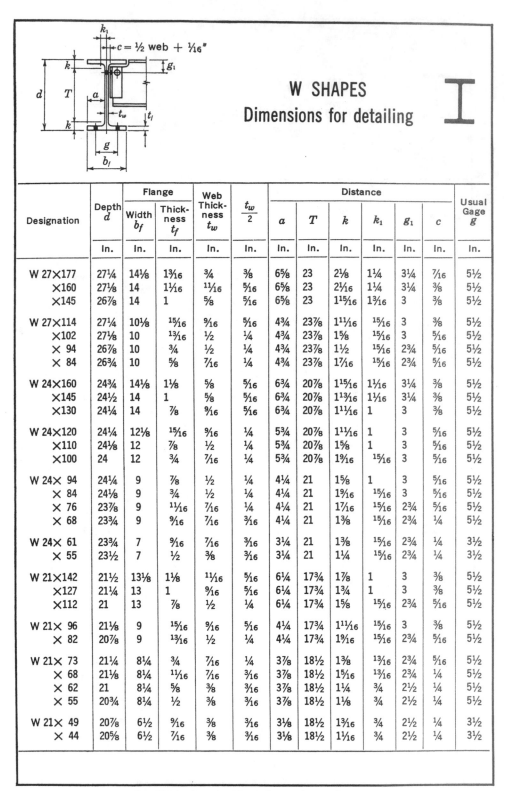

W SHAPES
Dimensions for detailing

Designation	Depth d	Flange Width b_f	Flange Thickness t_f	Web Thickness t_w	$\frac{t_w}{2}$	a	T	k	k_1	g_1	c	Usual Gage g
	In.	In.	In.	In.	In.	In.	In.	In.	In.	In.	In.	In.
W 27×177	27¼	14⅛	1³⁄₁₆	¾	⅜	6⅝	23	2⅛	1¼	3¼	⁷⁄₁₆	5½
×160	27⅛	14	1¹⁄₁₆	¹¹⁄₁₆	⁵⁄₁₆	6⅝	23	2¹⁄₁₆	1¼	3¼	⅜	5½
×145	26⅞	14	1	⅝	⁵⁄₁₆	6⅝	23	1¹⁵⁄₁₆	1³⁄₁₆	3	⅜	5½
W 27×114	27¼	10⅛	¹⁵⁄₁₆	⁹⁄₁₆	⁵⁄₁₆	4¾	23⅞	1¹¹⁄₁₆	¹⁵⁄₁₆	3	⅜	5½
×102	27⅛	10	¹³⁄₁₆	½	¼	4¾	23⅞	1⅝	¹⁵⁄₁₆	3	⁵⁄₁₆	5½
× 94	26⅞	10	¾	½	¼	4¾	23⅞	1½	¹⁵⁄₁₆	2¾	⁵⁄₁₆	5½
× 84	26¾	10	⅝	⁷⁄₁₆	¼	4¾	23⅞	1⁷⁄₁₆	¹⁵⁄₁₆	2¾	⁵⁄₁₆	5½
W 24×160	24¾	14⅛	1⅛	⅝	⁵⁄₁₆	6¾	20⅞	1¹⁵⁄₁₆	1¹⁄₁₆	3¼	⅜	5½
×145	24½	14	1	⅝	⁵⁄₁₆	6¾	20⅞	1¹³⁄₁₆	1¹⁄₁₆	3¼	⅜	5½
×130	24¼	14	⅞	⁹⁄₁₆	⁵⁄₁₆	6¾	20⅞	1¹¹⁄₁₆	1	3	⅜	5½
W 24×120	24¼	12⅛	¹⁵⁄₁₆	⁹⁄₁₆	¼	5¾	20⅞	1¹¹⁄₁₆	1	3	⁵⁄₁₆	5½
×110	24⅛	12	⅞	½	¼	5¾	20⅞	1⅝	1	3	⁵⁄₁₆	5½
×100	24	12	¾	⁷⁄₁₆	¼	5¾	20⅞	1⁹⁄₁₆	¹⁵⁄₁₆	3	⁵⁄₁₆	5½
W 24× 94	24¼	9	⅞	½	¼	4¼	21	1⅝	1	3	⁵⁄₁₆	5½
× 84	24⅛	9	¾	½	¼	4¼	21	1⁹⁄₁₆	¹⁵⁄₁₆	3	⁵⁄₁₆	5½
× 76	23⅞	9	¹¹⁄₁₆	⁷⁄₁₆	¼	4¼	21	1⁷⁄₁₆	¹⁵⁄₁₆	2¾	⁵⁄₁₆	5½
× 68	23¾	9	⁹⁄₁₆	⁷⁄₁₆	³⁄₁₆	4¼	21	1⅜	¹⁵⁄₁₆	2¾	¼	5½
W 24× 61	23¾	7	⁹⁄₁₆	⁷⁄₁₆	³⁄₁₆	3¼	21	1⅜	¹⁵⁄₁₆	2¾	¼	3½
× 55	23½	7	½	⅜	³⁄₁₆	3¼	21	1¼	¹⁵⁄₁₆	2¾	¼	3½
W 21×142	21½	13⅛	1⅛	¹¹⁄₁₆	⁵⁄₁₆	6¼	17¾	1⅞	1	3	⅜	5½
×127	21¼	13	1	⁹⁄₁₆	⁵⁄₁₆	6¼	17¾	1¾	1	3	⅜	5½
×112	21	13	⅞	½	¼	6¼	17¾	1⅝	¹⁵⁄₁₆	2¾	⁵⁄₁₆	5½
W 21× 96	21⅛	9	¹⁵⁄₁₆	⁹⁄₁₆	⁵⁄₁₆	4¼	17¾	1¹¹⁄₁₆	¹⁵⁄₁₆	3	⅜	5½
× 82	20⅞	9	¹³⁄₁₆	½	¼	4¼	17¾	1⁹⁄₁₆	¹⁵⁄₁₆	2¾	⁵⁄₁₆	5½
W 21× 73	21¼	8¼	¾	⁷⁄₁₆	¼	3⅞	18½	1⅜	¹³⁄₁₆	2¾	⁵⁄₁₆	5½
× 68	21⅛	8¼	¹¹⁄₁₆	⁷⁄₁₆	³⁄₁₆	3⅞	18½	1⁵⁄₁₆	¹³⁄₁₆	2¾	¼	5½
× 62	21	8¼	⅝	⅜	³⁄₁₆	3⅞	18½	1¼	¾	2½	¼	5½
× 55	20¾	8¼	½	⅜	³⁄₁₆	3⅞	18½	1⅛	¾	2½	¼	5½
W 21× 49	20⅞	6½	⁹⁄₁₆	⅜	³⁄₁₆	3⅛	18½	1³⁄₁₆	¾	2½	¼	3½
× 44	20⅝	6½	⁷⁄₁₆	⅜	³⁄₁₆	3⅛	18½	1¹⁄₁₆	¾	2½	¼	3½

TABLE 10 *(continued)* **STRUCTURAL DIMENSIONS FOR DETAILING W SHAPES**

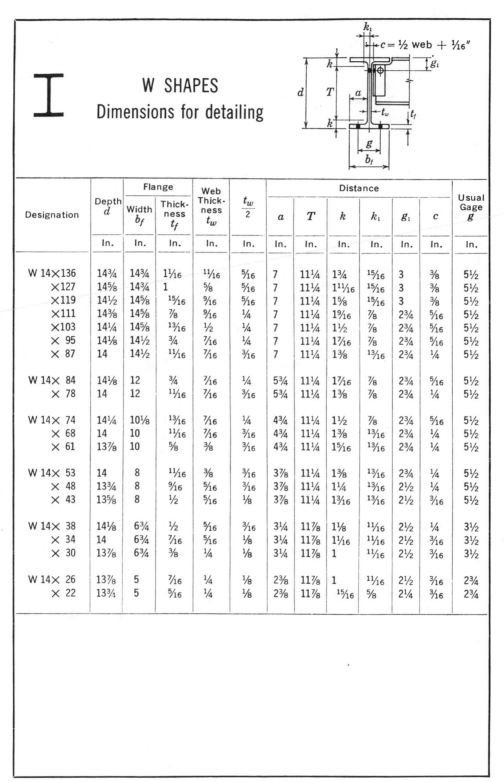

W SHAPES
Dimensions for detailing

Designation	Depth d	Flange Width b_f	Flange Thickness t_f	Web Thickness t_w	$\dfrac{t_w}{2}$	a	T	k	k_1	g_1	c	Usual Gage g
	In.	In.	In.	In.	In.	In.	In.	In.	In.	In.	In.	In.
W 14×136	14¾	14¾	1 1/16	11/16	5/16	7	11¼	1¾	15/16	3	⅜	5½
×127	14⅝	14¾	1	⅝	5/16	7	11¼	1 11/16	15/16	3	⅜	5½
×119	14½	14⅝	15/16	9/16	5/16	7	11¼	1⅝	15/16	3	⅜	5½
×111	14⅜	14⅝	⅞	9/16	¼	7	11¼	1 9/16	⅞	2¾	5/16	5½
×103	14¼	14⅝	13/16	½	¼	7	11¼	1½	⅞	2¾	5/16	5½
× 95	14⅛	14½	¾	7/16	¼	7	11¼	1 7/16	⅞	2¾	5/16	5½
× 87	14	14½	11/16	7/16	3/16	7	11¼	1⅜	13/16	2¾	¼	5½
W 14× 84	14⅛	12	¾	7/16	¼	5¾	11¼	1 7/16	⅞	2¾	5/16	5½
× 78	14	12	11/16	7/16	3/16	5¾	11¼	1⅜	⅞	2¾	¼	5½
W 14× 74	14¼	10⅛	13/16	7/16	¼	4¾	11¼	1½	⅞	2¾	5/16	5½
× 68	14	10	11/16	7/16	3/16	4¾	11¼	1⅜	13/16	2¾	¼	5½
× 61	13⅞	10	⅝	⅜	3/16	4¾	11¼	15/16	13/16	2¾	¼	5½
W 14× 53	14	8	11/16	⅜	3/16	3⅞	11¼	1⅜	13/16	2¾	¼	5½
× 48	13¾	8	9/16	5/16	3/16	3⅞	11¼	1¼	13/16	2½	¼	5½
× 43	13⅝	8	½	5/16	⅛	3⅞	11¼	1 3/16	13/16	2½	3/16	5½
W 14× 38	14⅛	6¾	½	5/16	3/16	3¼	11⅞	1⅛	11/16	2½	¼	3½
× 34	14	6¾	7/16	5/16	⅛	3¼	11⅞	1 1/16	11/16	2½	3/16	3½
× 30	13⅞	6¾	⅜	¼	⅛	3¼	11⅞	1	11/16	2½	3/16	3½
W 14× 26	13⅞	5	7/16	¼	⅛	2⅜	11⅞	1	11/16	2½	3/16	2¾
× 22	13¾	5	5/16	¼	⅛	2⅜	11⅞	15/16	⅝	2¼	3/16	2¾

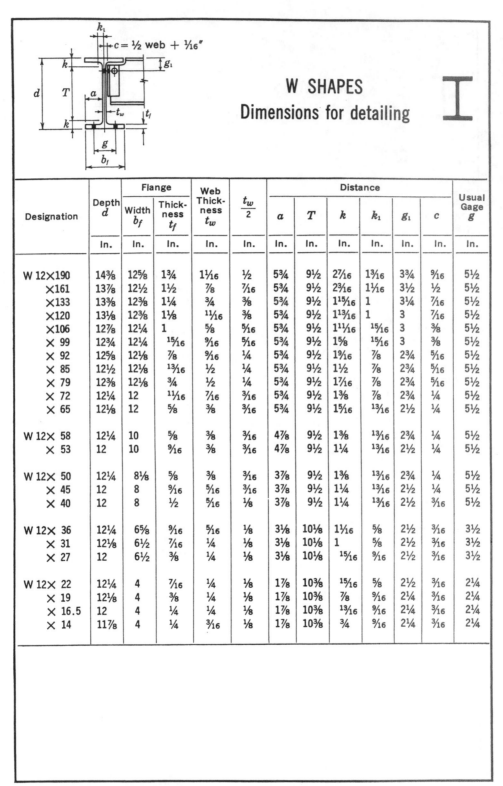

W SHAPES
Dimensions for detailing

Designation	Depth d	Flange Width b_f	Flange Thickness t_f	Web Thickness t_w	$\frac{t_w}{2}$	a	T	k	k_1	g_1	c	Usual Gage g
	In.	In.	In.	In.	In.	In.	In.	In.	In.	In.	In.	In.
W 12×190	14⅜	12⅝	1¾	1¹⁄₁₆	½	5¾	9½	2⁷⁄₁₆	1³⁄₁₆	3¾	⁹⁄₁₆	5½
×161	13⅞	12½	1½	⅞	⁷⁄₁₆	5¾	9½	2³⁄₁₆	1¹⁄₁₆	3½	½	5½
×133	13⅜	12⅜	1¼	¾	⅜	5¾	9½	1¹⁵⁄₁₆	1	3¼	⁷⁄₁₆	5½
×120	13⅛	12⅜	1⅛	¹¹⁄₁₆	⅜	5¾	9½	1¹³⁄₁₆	1	3	⁷⁄₁₆	5½
×106	12⅞	12¼	1	⅝	⁵⁄₁₆	5¾	9½	1¹¹⁄₁₆	¹⁵⁄₁₆	3	⅜	5½
× 99	12¾	12¼	¹⁵⁄₁₆	⁹⁄₁₆	⁵⁄₁₆	5¾	9½	1⅝	¹⁵⁄₁₆	3	⅜	5½
× 92	12⅝	12⅛	⅞	⁹⁄₁₆	¼	5¾	9½	1⁹⁄₁₆	⅞	2¾	⁵⁄₁₆	5½
× 85	12½	12⅛	¹³⁄₁₆	½	¼	5¾	9½	1½	⅞	2¾	⁵⁄₁₆	5½
× 79	12⅜	12⅛	¾	½	¼	5¾	9½	1⁷⁄₁₆	⅞	2¾	⁵⁄₁₆	5½
× 72	12¼	12	¹¹⁄₁₆	⁷⁄₁₆	³⁄₁₆	5¾	9½	1⅜	⅞	2¾	¼	5½
× 65	12⅛	12	⅝	⅜	³⁄₁₆	5¾	9½	1⁵⁄₁₆	¹³⁄₁₆	2½	¼	5½
W 12× 58	12¼	10	⅝	⅜	³⁄₁₆	4⅞	9½	1⅜	¹³⁄₁₆	2¾	¼	5½
× 53	12	10	⁹⁄₁₆	⅜	³⁄₁₆	4⅞	9½	1¼	¹³⁄₁₆	2½	¼	5½
W 12× 50	12¼	8⅛	⅝	⅜	³⁄₁₆	3⅞	9½	1⅜	¹³⁄₁₆	2¾	¼	5½
× 45	12	8	⁹⁄₁₆	⁵⁄₁₆	³⁄₁₆	3⅞	9½	1¼	¹³⁄₁₆	2½	¼	5½
× 40	12	8	½	⁵⁄₁₆	⅛	3⅞	9½	1¼	¹³⁄₁₆	2½	³⁄₁₆	5½
W 12× 36	12¼	6⅝	⁹⁄₁₆	⁵⁄₁₆	⅛	3⅛	10⅛	1¹⁄₁₆	⅝	2½	³⁄₁₆	3½
× 31	12⅛	6½	⁷⁄₁₆	¼	⅛	3⅛	10⅛	1	⅝	2½	³⁄₁₆	3½
× 27	12	6½	⅜	¼	⅛	3⅛	10⅛	¹⁵⁄₁₆	⁹⁄₁₆	2½	³⁄₁₆	3½
W 12× 22	12¼	4	⁷⁄₁₆	¼	⅛	1⅞	10⅜	¹⁵⁄₁₆	⅝	2½	³⁄₁₆	2¼
× 19	12⅛	4	⅜	¼	⅛	1⅞	10⅜	⅞	⁹⁄₁₆	2¼	³⁄₁₆	2¼
× 16.5	12	4	¼	¼	⅛	1⅞	10⅜	¹³⁄₁₆	⁹⁄₁₆	2¼	³⁄₁₆	2¼
× 14	11⅞	4	¼	³⁄₁₆	⅛	1⅞	10⅜	¾	⁹⁄₁₆	2¼	³⁄₁₆	2¼

TABLE 11 STRUCTURAL DIMENSIONS FOR DETAILING M SHAPES

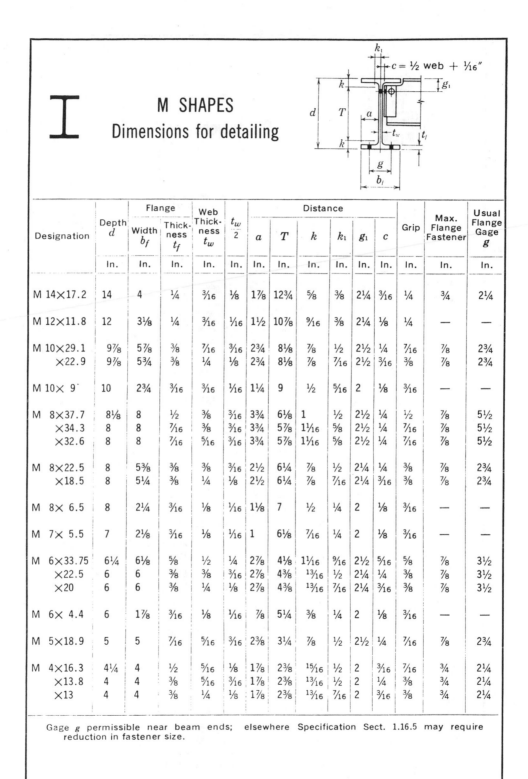

M SHAPES
Dimensions for detailing

Designation	Depth d	Flange Width b_f	Flange Thickness t_f	Web Thickness t_w	$\frac{t_w}{2}$	a	T	k	k_1	g_1	c	Grip	Max. Flange Fastener	Usual Flange Gage g
	In.	In.	In.	In.	In.	In.	In.	In.	In.	In.	In.	In.	In.	In.
M 14×17.2	14	4	¼	3/16	⅛	1⅞	12¾	⅝	⅜	2¼	3/16	¼	¾	2¼
M 12×11.8	12	3⅛	¼	3/16	1/16	1½	10⅞	9/16	⅜	2¼	⅛	¼	—	—
M 10×29.1	9⅞	5⅞	⅜	7/16	3/16	2¾	8⅛	⅞	½	2½	¼	7/16	⅞	2¾
×22.9	9⅞	5¾	⅜	¼	⅛	2¾	8⅛	⅞	7/16	2½	3/16	⅜	⅞	2¾
M 10× 9	10	2¾	3/16	3/16	1/16	1¼	9	½	5/16	2	⅛	3/16	—	—
M 8×37.7	8⅛	8	½	⅜	3/16	3¾	6⅛	1	½	2½	¼	½	⅞	5½
×34.3	8	8	7/16	⅜	3/16	3¾	5⅞	1 1/16	⅝	2½	¼	7/16	⅞	5½
×32.6	8	8	7/16	5/16	3/16	3¾	5⅞	1 1/16	⅝	2½	¼	7/16	⅞	5½
M 8×22.5	8	5⅜	⅜	⅜	3/16	2½	6¼	⅞	½	2¼	¼	⅜	⅞	2¾
×18.5	8	5¼	⅜	¼	⅛	2½	6¼	⅞	7/16	2¼	3/16	⅜	⅞	2¾
M 8× 6.5	8	2¼	3/16	⅛	1/16	1⅛	7	½	¼	2	⅛	3/16	—	—
M 7× 5.5	7	2⅛	3/16	⅛	1/16	1	6⅛	7/16	¼	2	⅛	3/16	—	—
M 6×33.75	6¼	6⅛	⅝	½	¼	2⅞	4⅛	1 1/16	9/16	2½	5/16	⅝	⅞	3½
×22.5	6	6	⅜	⅜	3/16	2⅞	4⅜	13/16	½	2¼	¼	⅜	⅞	3½
×20	6	6	⅜	¼	⅛	2⅞	4⅜	13/16	7/16	2¼	3/16	⅜	⅞	3½
M 6× 4.4	6	1⅞	3/16	⅛	1/16	⅞	5¼	⅜	¼	2	⅛	3/16	—	—
M 5×18.9	5	5	7/16	5/16	3/16	2⅜	3¼	⅞	½	2½	¼	7/16	⅞	2¾
M 4×16.3	4¼	4	½	5/16	⅛	1⅞	2⅜	15/16	½	2	3/16	7/16	¾	2¼
×13.8	4	4	⅜	5/16	3/16	1⅞	2⅜	13/16	½	2	¼	⅜	¾	2¼
×13	4	4	⅜	¼	⅛	1⅞	2⅜	13/16	7/16	2	3/16	⅜	¾	2¼

Gage g permissible near beam ends; elsewhere Specification Sect. 1.16.5 may require reduction in fastener size.

TABLE 12 STRUCTURAL DIMENSIONS FOR DETAILING S SHAPES

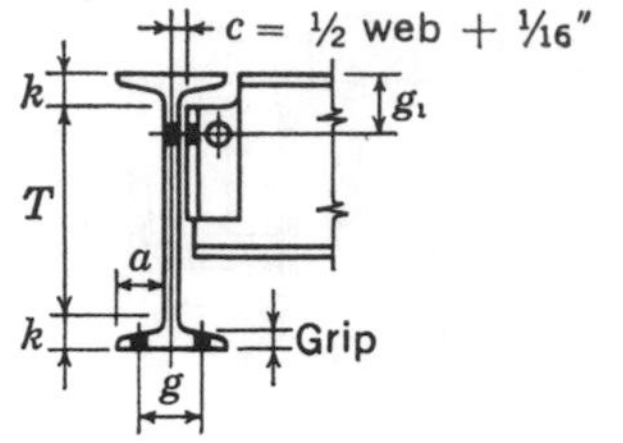

S SHAPES
Dimensions for detailing

Designation	Depth d	Flange		Web Thickness t_w	$\frac{t_w}{2}$	Distance					Grip	Max. Flange Fastener	Usual Flange Gage g
		Width b_f	Thickness t_f			a	T	k	g_1	c			
	In.	In.	In.	In.	In.	In.	In.	In.	In.	In.	In.	In.	In.
S 24×120	24	8	1⅛	13/16	⅜	3⅝	20	2	3¼	7/16	1⅛	1	4
×105.9	24	7⅞	1⅛	⅝	5/16	3⅝	20	2	3¼	⅜	1⅛	1	4
S 24×100	24	7¼	⅞	¾	⅜	3¼	20½	1¾	3	7/16	⅞	1	4
× 90	24	7⅛	⅞	⅝	5/16	3¼	20½	1¾	3	⅜	⅞	1	4
× 79.9	24	7	⅞	½	¼	3¼	20½	1¾	3	5/16	⅞	1	4
S 20× 95	20	7¼	15/16	13/16	⅜	3¼	16¼	1⅞	3	7/16	15/16	1	4
× 85	20	7	15/16	⅝	5/16	3¼	16¼	1⅞	3	⅜	⅞	1	4
S 20× 75	20	6⅜	13/16	⅝	5/16	2⅞	16¾	1⅝	3	⅜	13/16	⅞	3½
× 65.4	20	6¼	13/16	½	¼	2⅞	16¾	1⅝	3	5/16	¾	⅞	3½
S 18× 70	18	6¼	11/16	11/16	⅜	2¾	15	1½	2¾	7/16	11/16	⅞	3½
× 54.7	18	6	11/16	7/16	¼	2¾	15	1½	2¾	5/16	11/16	⅞	3½
S 15× 50	15	5⅝	⅝	9/16	¼	2½	12¼	1⅜	2¾	5/16	9/16	¾	3½
× 42.9	15	5½	⅝	7/16	3/16	2½	12¼	1⅜	2¾	¼	9/16	¾	3½
S 12× 50	12	5½	11/16	11/16	5/16	2⅜	9⅛	1 7/16	2¾	⅜	11/16	¾	3
× 40.8	12	5¼	11/16	7/16	¼	2⅜	9⅛	1 7/16	2¾	5/16	⅝	¾	3
S 12× 35	12	5⅛	9/16	7/16	3/16	2⅜	9⅝	1 3/16	2½	¼	½	¾	3
× 31.8	12	5	9/16	⅜	3/16	2⅜	9⅝	1 3/16	2½	¼	½	¾	3
S 10× 35	10	5	½	⅝	5/16	2⅛	7¾	1⅛	2½	⅜	½	¾	2¾
× 25.4	10	4⅝	½	5/16	⅛	2⅛	7¾	1⅛	2½	3/16	½	¾	2¾
S 8× 23	8	4⅛	7/16	7/16	¼	1⅞	6	1	2½	5/16	7/16	¾	2¼
× 18.4	8	4	7/16	¼	⅛	1⅞	6	1	2½	3/16	7/16	¾	2¼
S 7× 20	7	3⅞	⅜	7/16	¼	1¾	5¼	⅞	2½	5/16	⅜	⅝	2¼
× 15.3	7	3⅝	⅜	¼	⅛	1¾	5¼	⅞	2½	3/16	⅜	⅝	2¼
S 6× 17.25	6	3⅝	⅜	7/16	¼	1½	4⅜	13/16	2¼	5/16	⅜	⅝	2
× 12.5	6	3⅜	⅜	¼	⅛	1½	4⅜	13/16	2¼	3/16	5/16	—	—
S 5× 14.75	5	3¼	5/16	½	¼	1⅜	3½	¾	2¼	5/16	5/16	—	—
× 10	5	3	5/16	3/16	⅛	1⅜	3½	¾	2¼	3/16	5/16	—	—
S 4× 9.5	4	2¾	5/16	5/16	3/16	1¼	2⅝	11/16	2	¼	5/16	—	—
× 7.7	4	2⅝	5/16	3/16	⅛	1¼	2⅝	11/16	2	3/16	5/16	—	—
S 3× 7.5	3	2½	¼	⅜	3/16	1⅛	1¾	⅝	—	¼	¼	—	—
× 5.7	3	2⅜	¼	3/16	1/16	1⅛	1¾	⅝	—	⅛	¼	—	—

Gage g permissible near beam ends; elsewhere Specification Sect. 1.16.5 may require reduction in fastener size.

AMERICAN INSTITUTE OF STEEL CONSTRUCTION

TABLE 13 STRUCTURAL DIMENSIONS FOR DETAILING HP SHAPES

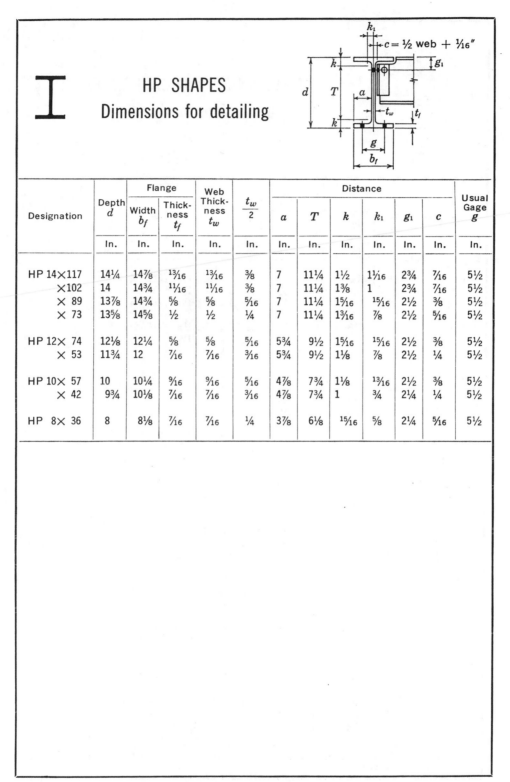

HP SHAPES
Dimensions for detailing

$c = \frac{1}{2}$ web $+ \frac{1}{16}''$

Designation	Depth d	Flange Width b_f	Flange Thickness t_f	Web Thickness t_w	$\frac{t_w}{2}$	a	T	k	k_1	g_1	c	Usual Gage g
	In.	In.	In.	In.	In.	In.	In.	In.	In.	In.	In.	In.
HP 14×117	14¼	14⅞	¹³⁄₁₆	¹³⁄₁₆	⅜	7	11¼	1½	1¹⁄₁₆	2¾	⁷⁄₁₆	5½
×102	14	14¾	¹¹⁄₁₆	¹¹⁄₁₆	⅜	7	11¼	1⅜	1	2¾	⁷⁄₁₆	5½
× 89	13⅞	14¾	⅝	⅝	⁵⁄₁₆	7	11¼	1⁵⁄₁₆	¹⁵⁄₁₆	2½	⅜	5½
× 73	13⅝	14⅝	½	½	¼	7	11¼	1³⁄₁₆	⅞	2½	⁵⁄₁₆	5½
HP 12× 74	12⅛	12¼	⅝	⅝	⁵⁄₁₆	5¾	9½	1⁵⁄₁₆	¹⁵⁄₁₆	2½	⅜	5½
× 53	11¾	12	⁷⁄₁₆	⁷⁄₁₆	³⁄₁₆	5¾	9½	1⅛	⅞	2½	¼	5½
HP 10× 57	10	10¼	⁹⁄₁₆	⁹⁄₁₆	⁵⁄₁₆	4⅞	7¾	1⅛	¹³⁄₁₆	2½	⅜	5½
× 42	9¾	10⅛	⁷⁄₁₆	⁷⁄₁₆	³⁄₁₆	4⅞	7¾	1	¾	2¼	¼	5½
HP 8× 36	8	8⅛	⁷⁄₁₆	⁷⁄₁₆	¼	3⅞	6⅛	¹⁵⁄₁₆	⅝	2¼	⁵⁄₁₆	5½

TABLE 14 STRUCTURAL DIMENSIONS FOR DETAILING C SHAPES

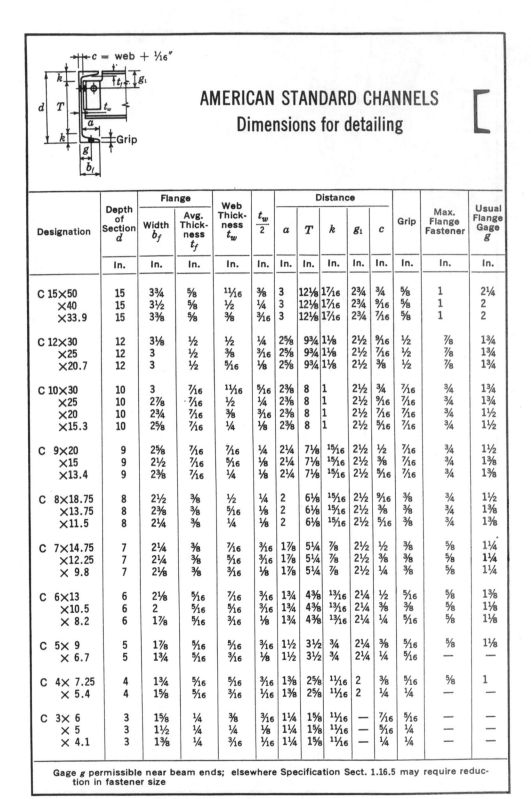

AMERICAN STANDARD CHANNELS
Dimensions for detailing

c = web + $\frac{1}{16}$"

Designation	Depth of Section d	Flange Width b_f	Flange Avg. Thickness t_f	Web Thickness t_w	$\frac{t_w}{2}$	Distance a	T	k	g_1	c	Grip	Max. Flange Fastener	Usual Flange Gage g
	In.	In.	In.	In.	In.	In.	In.	In.	In.	In.	In.	In.	In.
C 15×50	15	3¾	⅝	11/16	⅜	3	12⅛	17/16	2¾	¾	⅝	1	2¼
×40	15	3½	⅝	½	¼	3	12⅛	17/16	2¾	9/16	⅝	1	2
×33.9	15	3⅜	⅝	⅜	3/16	3	12⅛	17/16	2¾	7/16	⅝	1	2
C 12×30	12	3⅛	½	½	¼	2⅝	9¾	1⅛	2½	9/16	½	⅞	1¾
×25	12	3	½	⅜	3/16	2⅝	9¾	1⅛	2½	7/16	½	⅞	1¾
×20.7	12	3	½	5/16	⅛	2⅝	9¾	1⅛	2½	⅜	½	⅞	1¾
C 10×30	10	3	7/16	11/16	5/16	2⅜	8	1	2½	¾	7/16	¾	1¾
×25	10	2⅞	7/16	½	¼	2⅜	8	1	2½	9/16	7/16	¾	1¾
×20	10	2¾	7/16	⅜	3/16	2⅜	8	1	2½	7/16	7/16	¾	1½
×15.3	10	2⅝	7/16	¼	⅛	2⅜	8	1	2½	5/16	7/16	¾	1½
C 9×20	9	2⅝	7/16	7/16	¼	2¼	7⅛	15/16	2½	½	7/16	¾	1½
×15	9	2½	7/16	5/16	⅛	2¼	7⅛	15/16	2½	⅜	7/16	¾	1⅜
×13.4	9	2⅜	7/16	¼	⅛	2¼	7⅛	15/16	2½	5/16	7/16	¾	1⅜
C 8×18.75	8	2½	⅜	½	¼	2	6⅛	15/16	2½	9/16	⅜	¾	1½
×13.75	8	2⅜	⅜	5/16	⅛	2	6⅛	15/16	2½	⅜	⅜	¾	1⅜
×11.5	8	2¼	⅜	¼	⅛	2	6⅛	15/16	2½	5/16	⅜	¾	1⅜
C 7×14.75	7	2¼	⅜	7/16	3/16	1⅞	5¼	⅞	2½	½	⅜	⅝	1¼
×12.25	7	2¼	⅜	5/16	3/16	1⅞	5¼	⅞	2½	⅜	⅜	⅝	1¼
×9.8	7	2⅛	⅜	3/16	⅛	1⅞	5¼	⅞	2½	¼	⅜	⅝	1¼
C 6×13	6	2⅛	5/16	7/16	3/16	1¾	4⅜	13/16	2¼	½	5/16	⅝	1⅜
×10.5	6	2	5/16	5/16	3/16	1¾	4⅜	13/16	2¼	⅜	⅜	⅝	1⅛
×8.2	6	1⅞	5/16	3/16	⅛	1¾	4⅜	13/16	2¼	¼	5/16	⅝	1⅛
C 5×9	5	1⅞	5/16	5/16	3/16	1½	3½	¾	2¼	⅜	5/16	⅝	1⅛
×6.7	5	1¾	5/16	3/16	⅛	1½	3½	¾	2¼	¼	5/16	—	—
C 4×7.25	4	1¾	5/16	5/16	3/16	1⅜	2⅝	11/16	2	⅜	5/16	⅝	1
×5.4	4	1⅝	5/16	3/16	1/16	1⅜	2⅝	11/16	2	¼	¼	—	—
C 3×6	3	1⅝	¼	⅜	3/16	1¼	1⅝	11/16	—	7/16	5/16	—	—
×5	3	1½	¼	¼	⅛	1¼	1⅝	11/16	—	5/16	¼	—	—
×4.1	3	1⅜	¼	3/16	1/16	1¼	1⅝	11/16	—	¼	¼	—	—

Gage g permissible near beam ends; elsewhere Specification Sect. 1.16.5 may require reduction in fastener size

AMERICAN INSTITUTE OF STEEL CONSTRUCTION

248

TABLE 15 STRUCTURAL DIMENSIONS FOR DETAILING MC SHAPES

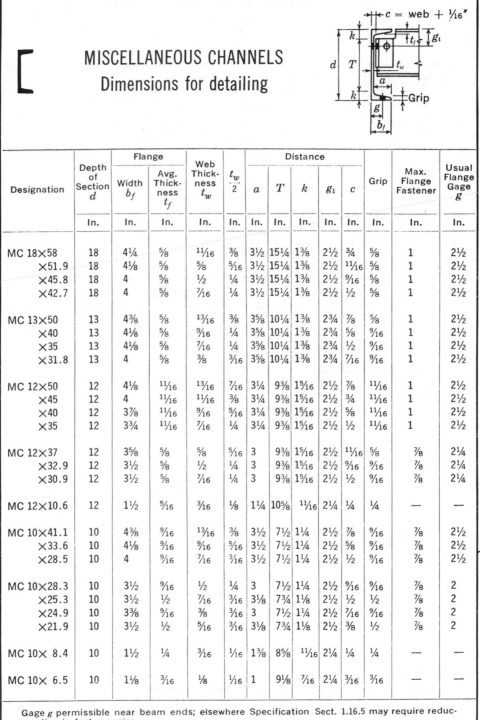

MISCELLANEOUS CHANNELS
Dimensions for detailing

Designation	Depth of Section d	Flange Width b_f	Flange Avg. Thickness t_f	Web Thickness t_w	$\frac{t_w}{2}$	Distance a	Distance T	Distance k	Distance g_1	Distance c	Grip	Max. Flange Fastener	Usual Flange Gage g
	In.	In.	In.	In.	In.	In.	In.	In.	In.	In.	In.	In.	In.
MC 18×58	18	4¼	⅝	¹¹⁄₁₆	⅜	3½	15¼	1⅜	2½	¾	⅝	1	2½
×51.9	18	4⅛	⅝	⅝	⁵⁄₁₆	3½	15¼	1⅜	2½	¹¹⁄₁₆	⅝	1	2½
×45.8	18	4	⅝	½	¼	3½	15¼	1⅜	2½	⁹⁄₁₆	⅝	1	2½
×42.7	18	4	⅝	⁷⁄₁₆	¼	3½	15¼	1⅜	2½	½	⅝	1	2½
MC 13×50	13	4⅜	⅝	¹³⁄₁₆	⅜	3⅝	10¼	1⅜	2¾	⅞	⅝	1	2½
×40	13	4⅛	⅝	⁹⁄₁₆	¼	3⅝	10¼	1⅜	2¾	⅝	⁹⁄₁₆	1	2½
×35	13	4⅛	⅝	⁷⁄₁₆	¼	3⅝	10¼	1⅜	2¾	½	⁹⁄₁₆	1	2½
×31.8	13	4	⅝	⅜	³⁄₁₆	3⅝	10¼	1⅜	2¾	⁷⁄₁₆	⁹⁄₁₆	1	2½
MC 12×50	12	4⅛	¹¹⁄₁₆	¹³⁄₁₆	⁷⁄₁₆	3¼	9⅜	1⁵⁄₁₆	2½	⅞	¹¹⁄₁₆	1	2½
×45	12	4	¹¹⁄₁₆	¹¹⁄₁₆	⅜	3¼	9⅜	1⁵⁄₁₆	2½	¾	¹¹⁄₁₆	1	2½
×40	12	3⅞	¹¹⁄₁₆	⁹⁄₁₆	⁵⁄₁₆	3¼	9⅜	1⁵⁄₁₆	2½	⅝	¹¹⁄₁₆	1	2½
×35	12	3¾	¹¹⁄₁₆	⁷⁄₁₆	¼	3¼	9⅜	1⁵⁄₁₆	2½	½	¹¹⁄₁₆	1	2½
MC 12×37	12	3⅝	⅝	⅝	⁵⁄₁₆	3	9⅜	1⁵⁄₁₆	2½	¹¹⁄₁₆	⅝	⅞	2¼
×32.9	12	3½	⅝	½	¼	3	9⅜	1⁵⁄₁₆	2½	⁹⁄₁₆	⁹⁄₁₆	⅞	2¼
×30.9	12	3½	⅝	⁷⁄₁₆	¼	3	9⅜	1⁵⁄₁₆	2½	½	⁹⁄₁₆	⅞	2¼
MC 12×10.6	12	1½	⁵⁄₁₆	³⁄₁₆	⅛	1¼	10⅝	¹¹⁄₁₆	2¼	¼	¼	—	—
MC 10×41.1	10	4⅜	⁹⁄₁₆	¹³⁄₁₆	⅜	3½	7½	1¼	2½	⅞	⁹⁄₁₆	⅞	2½
×33.6	10	4⅛	⁹⁄₁₆	⁹⁄₁₆	⁵⁄₁₆	3½	7½	1¼	2½	⅝	⁹⁄₁₆	⅞	2½
×28.5	10	4	⁹⁄₁₆	⁷⁄₁₆	³⁄₁₆	3½	7½	1¼	2½	½	⁹⁄₁₆	⅞	2½
MC 10×28.3	10	3½	⁹⁄₁₆	½	¼	3	7½	1¼	2½	⁹⁄₁₆	⁹⁄₁₆	⅞	2
×25.3	10	3½	½	⁷⁄₁₆	³⁄₁₆	3⅛	7¾	1⅛	2½	½	½	⅞	2
×24.9	10	3⅜	⁹⁄₁₆	⅜	³⁄₁₆	3	7½	1¼	2½	⁷⁄₁₆	⁹⁄₁₆	⅞	2
×21.9	10	3½	½	⁵⁄₁₆	³⁄₁₆	3⅛	7¾	1⅛	2½	⅜	½	⅞	2
MC 10× 8.4	10	1½	¼	³⁄₁₆	¹⁄₁₆	1⅜	8⅝	¹¹⁄₁₆	2¼	¼	¼	—	—
MC 10× 6.5	10	1⅛	³⁄₁₆	⅛	¹⁄₁₆	1	9⅛	⁷⁄₁₆	2¼	³⁄₁₆	³⁄₁₆	—	—

Gage g permissible near beam ends; elsewhere Specification Sect. 1.16.5 may require reduction in fastener size.

AMERICAN INSTITUTE OF STEEL CONSTRUCTION

TABLE 16 FRAMED BEAM CONNECTIONS

FRAMED BEAM CONNECTIONS
Bolted or riveted
TABLE I   Allowable loads in kips

6 ROWS

W 36, 33, 30, 27, 24, 21
S 24

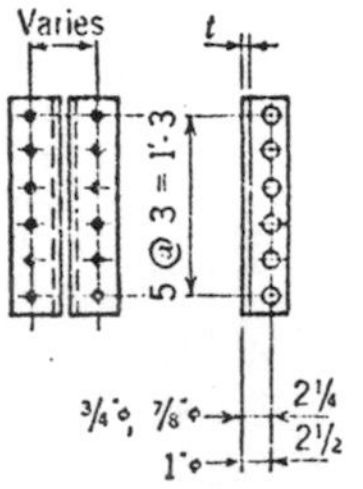

TABLE I-A6   Total Shear, kips

ªFastener Designation	F_v ksi	Fastener Diameter					
		¾		⅞		1	
		Load	t^b	Load	t^b	Load	t^b
A307	10.0	53.0	¼	72.2	¼	94.3	¼
A325-F A325-N A502-1	15.0	79.5	¼	108	¼	141	5⁄16
A490-F A502-2	20.0	106	¼	144	5⁄16	189	⅜
A325-X	22.0	117	5⁄16	159	⅜	207	7⁄16
A490-N	22.5	119	5⁄16	162	⅜	212	7⁄16
A490-X	32.0	170	7⁄16	231	½	302	⅝

TABLE I-B6   Total Bearing,ᶜ kips, 6 fasteners on 1″ thick material

F_y		36	42	45	50	55	60	65	100
Fastener Diameter	¾	219	255	273	304	334	365	395	608
	⅞	255	298	319	354	390	425	461	709
	1	292	340	365	405	446	486	527	810

5 ROWS

W 30, 27, 24, 21, 18
S 24, 20, 18
C 18

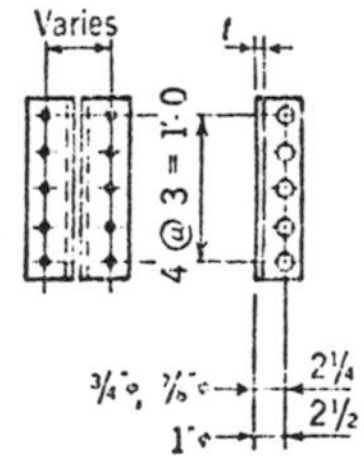

TABLE I-A5   Total Shear, kips

ªFastener Designation	F_v ksi	Fastener Diameter					
		¾		⅞		1	
		Load	t^b	Load	t^b	Load	t^b
A307	10.0	44.2	¼	60.2	¼	78.6	¼
A325-F A325-N A502-1	15.0	66.3	¼	90.2	¼	118	5⁄16
A490-F A502-2	20.0	88.4	¼	120	5⁄16	157	⅜
A325-X	22.0	97.2	5⁄16	132	⅜	173	7⁄16
A490-N	22.5	99.4	5⁄16	135	⅜	177	7⁄16
A490-X	32.0	141	7⁄16	192	½	251	⅝

TABLE I-B5   Total Bearing,ᶜ kips, 5 fasteners on 1″ thick material

F_y		36	42	45	50	55	60	65	100
Fastener Diameter	¾	182	213	228	253	278	304	329	505
	⅞	213	248	266	295	325	354	384	591
	1	243	284	304	338	371	405	439	675

ª For description of fastener designation see page 4-12.
ᵇ Thickness t based on connection angles of $F_y = 36$ ksi material.
ᶜ Use decimal thickness of enclosed web material as multiplying factor for these values.

AMERICAN INSTITUTE OF STEEL CONSTRUCTION

TABLE 16 *(continued)*   **FRAMED BEAM CONNECTIONS**

FRAMED BEAM CONNECTIONS
Bolted or riveted
TABLE I   Allowable loads in kips

4 ROWS

W 24, 21, 18, 16
S 24, 20, 18, 15
C 18, 15

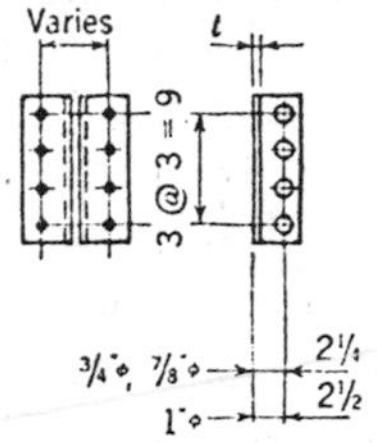

Varies

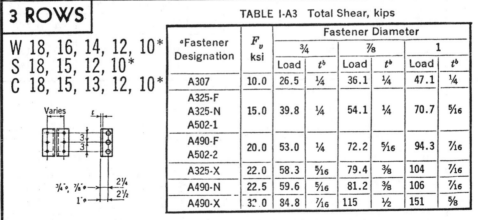

3@3 = 9

¾"ø, ⅞"ø
1"ø

2¼
2½

TABLE I-A4   Total Shear, kips

ᵃFastener Designation	F_v ksi	Fastener Diameter					
		¾		⅞		1	
		Load	t^b	Load	t^b	Load	t^b
A307	10.0	35.4	¼	48.1	¼	62.8	¼
A325-F A325-N A502-1	15.0	53.0	¼	72.2	¼	94.2	⁵⁄₁₆
A490-F A502-2	20.0	70.7	¼	96.2	⁵⁄₁₆	126	⁷⁄₁₆
A325-X	22.0	77.8	⁵⁄₁₆	106	⅜	138	⁷⁄₁₆
A490-N	22.5	79.5	⁵⁄₁₆	108	⅜	141	⁷⁄₁₆
A490-X	32.0	113	⁷⁄₁₆	154	½	201	⅝

TABLE I-B4   Total Bearing,ᶜ ksi, 4 fasteners on 1″ thick material

	F_y	36	42	45	50	55	60	65	100
Fastener Diameter	¾	146	170	182	203	223	243	263	405
	⅞	170	198	213	236	260	284	307	473
	1	194	227	243	270	297	324	351	540

3 ROWS

W 18, 16, 14, 12, 10*
S 18, 15, 12, 10*
C 18, 15, 13, 12, 10*

Varies

3
3

¾"ø, ⅞"ø
1"ø

2¼
2½

TABLE I-A3   Total Shear, kips

ᵃFastener Designation	F_v ksi	Fastener Diameter					
		¾		⅞		1	
		Load	t^b	Load	t^b	Load	t^b
A307	10.0	26.5	¼	36.1	¼	47.1	¼
A325-F A325-N A502-1	15.0	39.8	¼	54.1	¼	70.7	⁵⁄₁₆
A490-F A502-2	20.0	53.0	¼	72.2	⁵⁄₁₆	94.3	⁷⁄₁₆
A325-X	22.0	58.3	⁵⁄₁₆	79.4	⅜	104	⁷⁄₁₆
A490-N	22.5	59.6	⁵⁄₁₆	81.2	⅜	106	⁷⁄₁₆
A490-X	32.0	84.8	⁷⁄₁₆	115	½	151	⅝

TABLE I-B3   Total Bearing,ᶜ kips, 3 fasteners on 1″ thick material

	F_y	36	42	45	50	55	60	65	100
Fastener Diameter	¾	109	128	137	152	167	182	197	304
	⅞	128	149	159	177	195	213	230	354
	1	146	170	182	203	223	243	263	405

ᵃ For description of fastener designation see page 4-12.
ᵇ Thickness t based on connection angles of F_y = 36 ksi material.
ᶜ Use decimal thickness of enclosed web material as multiplying factor for these values.
* Limited to W 10 × 11.5, 15, 17, 19, 21, 25, 29; S 10 × 9; C 10 × 6.5, 8.4.

AMERICAN INSTITUTE OF STEEL CONSTRUCTION

251

RIVETS AND THREADED FASTENERS

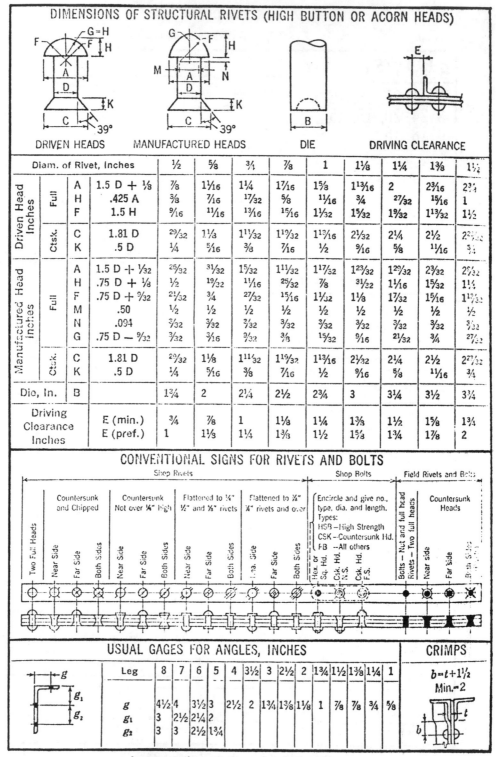

DIMENSIONS OF STRUCTURAL RIVETS (HIGH BUTTON OR ACORN HEADS)

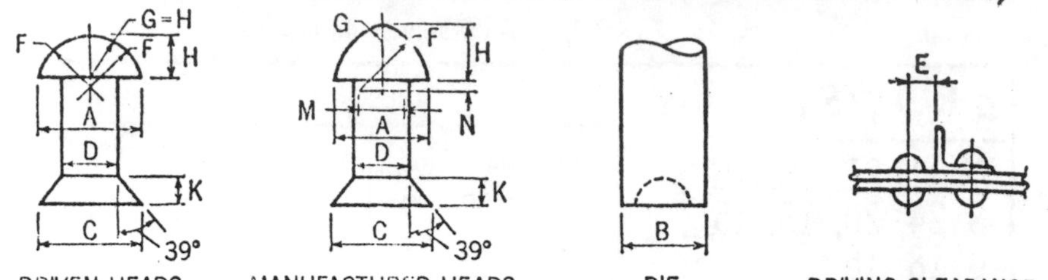
G=H
F
F
H
A
D
K
C
39°
G
F
H
M
N
A
D
K
C
39°
B
E
DRIVEN HEADS
MANUFACTURED HEADS
DIE
DRIVING CLEARANCE

Diam. of Rivet, Inches				½	⅝	¾	⅞	1	1⅛	1¼	1⅜	1½
Driven Head Inches	Full	A	1.5 D + ⅛	⅞	1$\frac{1}{16}$	1¼	1$\frac{7}{16}$	1⅝	1$\frac{13}{16}$	2	2$\frac{3}{16}$	2¾
		H	.425 A	⅜	$\frac{7}{16}$	$\frac{17}{32}$	⅝	$\frac{11}{16}$	¾	$\frac{27}{32}$	$\frac{15}{16}$	1
		F	1.5 H	$\frac{9}{16}$	$\frac{11}{16}$	$\frac{13}{16}$	$\frac{15}{16}$	1$\frac{1}{32}$	1$\frac{5}{32}$	1$\frac{9}{32}$	1$\frac{13}{32}$	1½
	Ctsk.	C	1.81 D	$\frac{29}{32}$	1⅛	1$\frac{11}{32}$	1$\frac{19}{32}$	1$\frac{13}{16}$	2$\frac{1}{32}$	2¼	2½	2$\frac{23}{32}$
		K	.5 D	¼	$\frac{5}{16}$	⅜	$\frac{7}{16}$	½	$\frac{9}{16}$	⅝	$\frac{11}{16}$	¾
Manufactured Head Inches	Full	A	1.5 D + $\frac{1}{32}$	$\frac{25}{32}$	$\frac{31}{32}$	1$\frac{5}{32}$	1$\frac{11}{32}$	1$\frac{17}{32}$	1$\frac{23}{32}$	1$\frac{29}{32}$	2$\frac{3}{32}$	2$\frac{9}{32}$
		H	.75 D + ⅛	½	$\frac{19}{32}$	$\frac{11}{16}$	$\frac{25}{32}$	⅞	$\frac{31}{32}$	1$\frac{1}{16}$	1$\frac{5}{32}$	1¼
		F	.75 D + $\frac{9}{32}$	$\frac{21}{32}$	¾	$\frac{27}{32}$	$\frac{15}{16}$	1$\frac{1}{32}$	1⅛	1$\frac{7}{32}$	1$\frac{5}{16}$	1$\frac{13}{32}$
		M	.50	½	½	½	½	½	½	½	½	½
		N	.094	$\frac{3}{32}$	$\frac{3}{32}$	$\frac{3}{32}$	$\frac{3}{32}$	$\frac{3}{32}$	$\frac{3}{32}$	$\frac{3}{32}$	$\frac{3}{32}$	$\frac{3}{32}$
		G	.75 D − $\frac{9}{32}$	$\frac{3}{32}$	$\frac{3}{16}$	$\frac{9}{32}$	⅜	$\frac{15}{32}$	$\frac{9}{16}$	$\frac{21}{32}$	¾	$\frac{27}{32}$
	Ctsk.	C	1.81 D	$\frac{29}{32}$	1⅛	1$\frac{11}{32}$	1$\frac{19}{32}$	1$\frac{13}{16}$	2$\frac{1}{32}$	2¼	2½	2$\frac{23}{32}$
		K	.5 D	¼	$\frac{5}{16}$	⅜	$\frac{7}{16}$	½	$\frac{9}{16}$	⅝	$\frac{11}{16}$	¾
Die, In.		B		1¾	2	2¼	2½	2¾	3	3¼	3½	3¾
Driving Clearance Inches			E (min.)	¾	⅞	1	1⅛	1¼	1⅜	1½	1⅝	1¾
			E (pref.)	1	1⅛	1¼	1⅜	1½	1⅝	1¾	1⅞	2

CONVENTIONAL SIGNS FOR RIVETS AND BOLTS

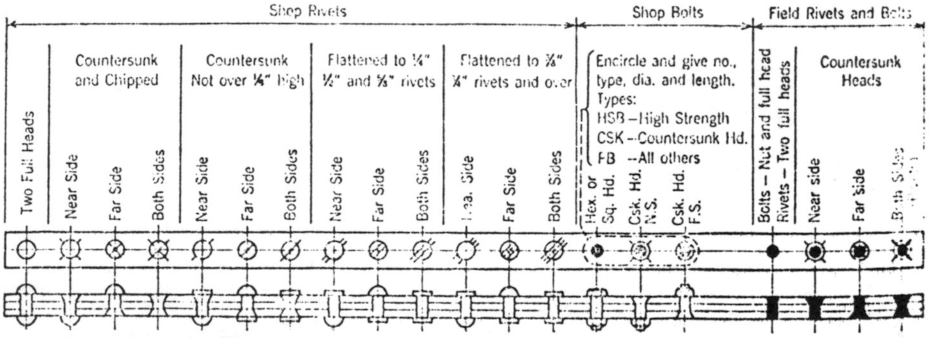
Shop Rivets
Shop Bolts
Field Rivets and Bolts
Two Full Heads
Countersunk and Chipped
Near Side
Far Side
Both Sides
Countersunk Not over ⅛" High
Near Side
Far Side
Both Sides
Flattened to ¼" ½" and ⅝" rivets
Near Side
Far Side
Both Sides
Flattened to ⅜" ¾" rivets and over
Far Side
Both Sides
Encircle and give no., type, dia. and length.
Types:
HSB – High Strength
CSK – Countersunk Hd.
FB – All others
Hex. or Sq. Hd.
Csk. Hd. N.S.
Csk. Hd. F.S.
Bolts – Nut and full head
Rivets – Two full heads
Countersunk Heads
Near side
Far side

USUAL GAGES FOR ANGLES, INCHES

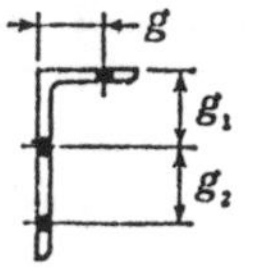
g
g_1
g_2

Leg	8	7	6	5	4	3½	3	2½	2	1¾	1½	1⅜	1¼	1
g	4½	4	3½	3	2½	2	1¾	1⅜	1⅛	1	⅞	⅞	¾	⅝
g_1	3	2½	2¼	2										
g_2	3	3	2½	1¾										

CRIMPS

$b = t + 1\frac{1}{2}$
Min. = 2

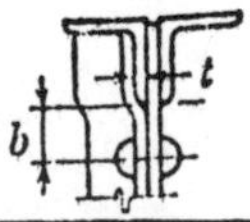
t
b

AMERICAN INSTITUTE OF STEEL CONSTRUCTION

TABLE 17 *(continued)* **STRUCTURAL RIVETS AND THREADED FASTENERS**

RIVETS
Lengths of undriven rivets
In inches, for various grips

FULL HEAD   COUNTERSUNK HEAD

Grip Inches	Diameter of Rivet, Inches							Grip Inches	Diameter of Rivet, Inches						
	1/2	5/8	3/4	7/8	1	1 1/8	1 1/4		1/2	5/8	3/4	7/8	1	1 1/8	1 1/4
1/2	1 5/8	1 7/8	1 7/8	2	2 1/8			1/2	1	1	1 1/8	1 1/4	1 1/4		
5/8	1 3/4	2	2	2 1/8	2 1/4			5/8	1 1/8	1 1/4	1 1/4	1 3/8	1 3/8		
3/4	1 7/8	2 1/8	2 1/8	2 1/4	2 3/8			3/4	1 3/8	1 3/8	1 3/8	1 1/2	1 1/2		
7/8	2	2 1/4	2 1/4	2 3/8	2 1/2			7/8	1 1/2	1 1/2	1 1/2	1 5/8	1 5/8		
1	2 1/4	2 3/8	2 3/8	2 1/2	2 5/8	2 3/4	2 7/8	1	1 5/8	1 5/8	1 5/8	1 3/4	1 3/4	1 7/8	1 7/8
1/8	2 3/8	2 1/2	2 1/2	2 5/8	2 3/4	2 7/8	3	1/8	1 3/4	1 3/4	1 7/8	1 7/8	1 7/8	2	2
1/4	2 1/2	2 5/8	2 5/8	2 3/4	2 7/8	3	3 1/8	1/4	2	2	2	2	2	2 1/8	2 1/8
3/8	2 5/8	2 3/4	2 3/4	2 7/8	3	3 1/8	3 1/4	3/8	2 1/8	2 1/8	2 1/8	2 1/4	2 1/4	2 3/8	2 3/8
1/2	2 7/8	3	3	3 1/8	3 1/4	3 3/8	3 1/2	1/2	2 1/4	2 1/4	2 1/4	2 3/8	2 3/8	2 1/2	2 1/2
5/8	3	3 1/8	3 1/8	3 1/4	3 3/8	3 1/2	3 1/2	5/8	2 3/8	2 3/8	2 3/8	2 1/2	2 1/2	2 5/8	2 5/8
3/4	3 1/8	3 1/4	3 1/4	3 1/2	3 5/8	3 3/4	3 3/4	3/4	2 5/8	2 5/8	2 5/8	2 5/8	2 5/8	2 3/4	2 3/4
7/8	3 1/4	3 3/8	3 3/8	3 5/8	3 3/4	3 7/8	3 7/8	7/8	2 3/4	2 3/4	2 3/4	2 3/4	2 3/4	2 7/8	2 7/8
2	3 1/2	3 1/2	3 5/8	3 3/4	3 7/8	4	4	2	2 7/8	2 7/8	2 7/8	2 7/8	2 7/8	3	3
1/8	3 5/8	3 5/8	3 3/4	3 7/8	4	4 1/8	4 1/8	1/8	3 1/8	3	3	3	3	3 1/8	3 1/8
1/4	3 3/4	3 7/8	3 7/8	4	4 1/8	4 1/4	4 1/4	1/4	3 1/4	3 1/8	3 1/8	3 1/8	3 1/4	3 1/4	3 1/4
3/8	4	4	4	4 1/8	4 1/4	4 3/8	4 3/8	3/8	3 3/8	3 3/8	3 3/8	3 3/8	3 3/8	3 3/8	3 3/8
1/2	4 1/8	4 1/8	4 1/8	4 1/4	4 3/8	4 1/2	4 1/2	1/2	3 1/2	3 1/2	3 1/2	3 1/2	3 1/2	3 5/8	3 5/8
5/8	4 1/4	4 1/4	4 1/4	4 3/8	4 1/2	4 5/8	4 5/8	5/8	3 3/4	3 5/8	3 5/8	3 5/8	3 5/8	3 3/4	3 3/4
3/4	4 3/8	4 3/8	4 3/8	4 1/2	4 5/8	4 3/4	4 3/4	3/4	3 7/8	3 3/4	3 3/4	3 3/4	3 3/4	3 7/8	3 7/8
7/8	4 5/8	4 5/8	4 5/8	4 5/8	4 3/4	4 7/8	5	7/8	4	3 7/8	3 7/8	3 7/8	3 7/8	4	4

THREADED FASTENERS

Nominal bolt size, *D*	Bolt Dimensions, in Inches			Nut Dimensions, in Inches	
	Heavy Hexagon Structural Bolts			Heavy Semi-finished Hexagon Nuts	
	Width across flats *F*	Height, *H*	Thread length, *T*	Width across flats *W*	Height, *H*
1/2	7/8	5/16	1	7/8	31/64
5/8	1 1/16	25/64	1 1/4	1 1/16	39/64
3/4	1 1/4	15/32	1 3/8	1 1/4	47/64
7/8	1 7/16	35/64	1 1/2	1 7/16	55/64
1	1 5/8	39/64	1 3/4	1 5/8	63/64
1 1/8	1 13/16	11/16	2	1 13/16	1 7/64
1 1/4	2	25/32	2	2	1 7/32
1 3/8	2 3/16	27/32	2 1/4	2 3/16	1 11/32
1 1/2	2 3/8	15/16	2 1/4	2 3/8	1 15/32

Bolt marking ←Thread→
Nut marking
Nuts may be washer faced as in (a) or double chamfered as in (b)

253

TABLE 18 HUMAN SPACE STANDARDS

Walking between two high walls (space adequate for both men and women)

Two people passing (figure derived; twice the space for one person to walk between two high walls)

Walking between high wall and 30" high table (space adequate for both men and women)

Walking with elbows extended (space adequate for both men and women)

Kneeling on one knee (woman only)

Man bending at a right angle

Reaching, maximum height

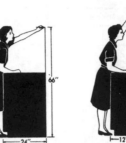

Reaching over obstruction, 24" deep and 36" high

Reaching over obstruction, 12" deep and 36" high (women only)

Maximum reach to back of shelf 12" deep (women only)

Using a conventional range

Using a wall oven

Using a refrigerator

Using a base cabinet

Using a front-opening dishwasher requires 4 inches more space than using other appliances in a kitchen

Using a cleaning closet

Foot extension, knees crossed, not at table

Arising from a card table

Rising from table, armless chair (armchair 2" more)

Edging past seated person

Walking past seated person

TABLE 18 *(continued)* HUMAN SPACE STANDARDS

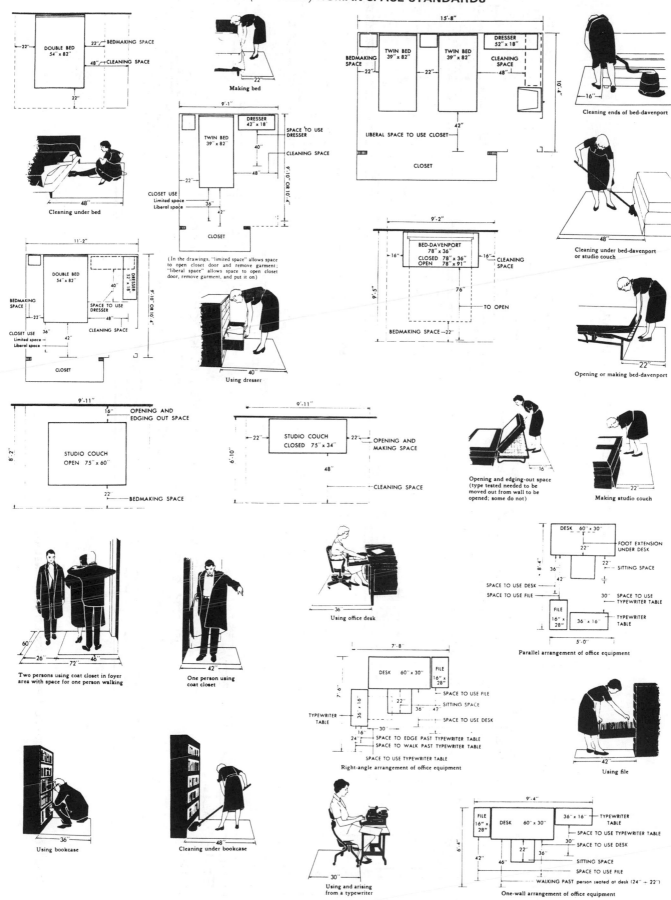

DOUBLE BED 54" x 82"
22" BEDMAKING SPACE
22"
48" CLEANING SPACE
22"

Making bed

BEDMAKING SPACE 22"
TWIN BED 39" x 82"
22"
TWIN BED 39" x 82"
DRESSER 52" x 18"
CLEANING SPACE 48"
15'-8"
10'-4"
42"
LIBERAL SPACE TO USE CLOSET
CLOSET

Cleaning ends of bed-davenport

16"

Cleaning under bed
48"

TWIN BED 39" x 82"
DRESSER 42" x 18"
SPACE TO USE DRESSER
CLEANING SPACE
40"
48"
22"
9'-1"
6'-10" OR 7'-4"
CLOSET USE
Limited space 36"
Liberal space 42"
CLOSET

(In the drawings, "limited space" allows space to open closet door and remove garment; "liberal space" allows space to open closet door, remove garment, and put it on)

Using dresser
40"

BED-DAVENPORT 78" x 36"
CLOSED 78" x 36"
OPEN 78" x 91"
16"
16" CLEANING SPACE
9'-2"
9'-5"
76"
TO OPEN
BEDMAKING SPACE 22"

Cleaning under bed-davenport or studio couch
48"

Opening or making bed-davenport
22"

DOUBLE BED 54" x 82"
DRESSER 52" x 18"
40"
SPACE TO USE DRESSER
48"
11'-2"
9'-10" OR 10'-4"
BEDMAKING SPACE
22"
CLEANING SPACE
CLOSET USE 36"
Limited space 42"
Liberal space
CLOSET

STUDIO COUCH OPEN 75" x 60"
16" OPENING AND EDGING OUT SPACE
9'-11"
8'-2"
22" BEDMAKING SPACE

STUDIO COUCH CLOSED 75" x 34"
22"
22"
9'-11"
6'-10"
OPENING AND MAKING SPACE
48"
CLEANING SPACE

Opening and edging-out space (type tested needed to be moved out from wall to be opened; some do not)
16"

Making studio couch
22"

Two persons using coat closet in foyer area with space for one person walking
60"
26"
72"
48"

One person using coat closet
42"

Using office desk
36"

DESK 60" x 30"
22"
36"
42"
FOOT EXTENSION UNDER DESK
22" SITTING SPACE
SPACE TO USE DESK
SPACE TO USE FILE
FILE 16" x 28"
36 x 16
30" SPACE TO USE TYPEWRITER TABLE
TYPEWRITER TABLE
5'-0"

Parallel arrangement of office equipment

DESK 60" x 30"
FILE 16" x 28"
22"
36" 42"
7'-8"
7'-6"
TYPEWRITER TABLE 36 x 16
30"
24" 16"
SPACE TO USE FILE
SITTING SPACE
SPACE TO USE DESK
SPACE TO EDGE PAST TYPEWRITER TABLE
SPACE TO WALK PAST TYPEWRITER TABLE
SPACE TO USE TYPEWRITER TABLE

Right-angle arrangement of office equipment

Using file
42"

Using bookcase
36"

Cleaning under bookcase
48"

Using and arising from a typewriter
30"

FILE 16" x 28"
DESK 60" x 30"
36" x 16"
TYPEWRITER TABLE
9'-4"
6'-4"
22"
46"
36"
42"
SPACE TO USE TYPEWRITER TABLE
30" SPACE TO USE DESK
SITTING SPACE
SPACE TO USE FILE
WALKING PAST person seated at desk (24" + 22")

One-wall arrangement of office equipment

TABLE 19 TYPICAL CONCRETE BEAM DETAIL

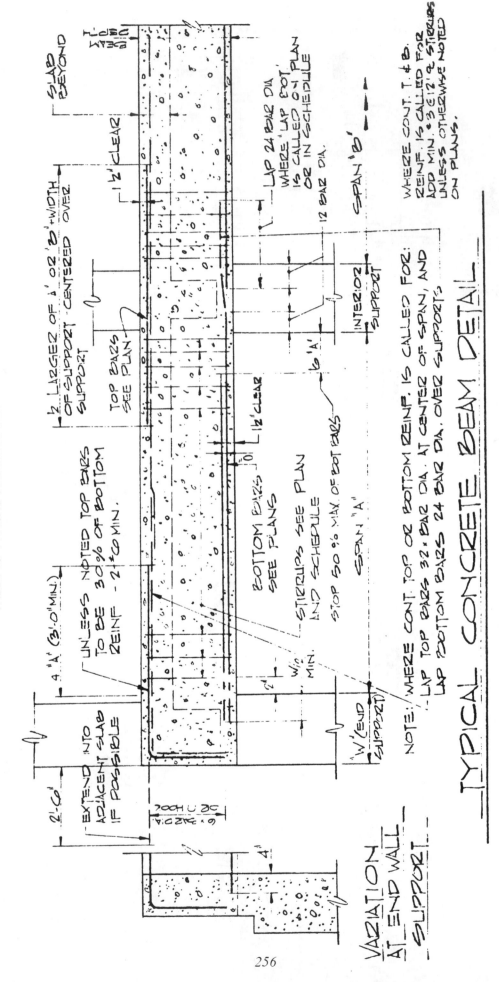

TYPICAL CONCRETE BEAM DETAIL

TABLE 20 TYPICAL ONE-WAY SLAB DETAIL

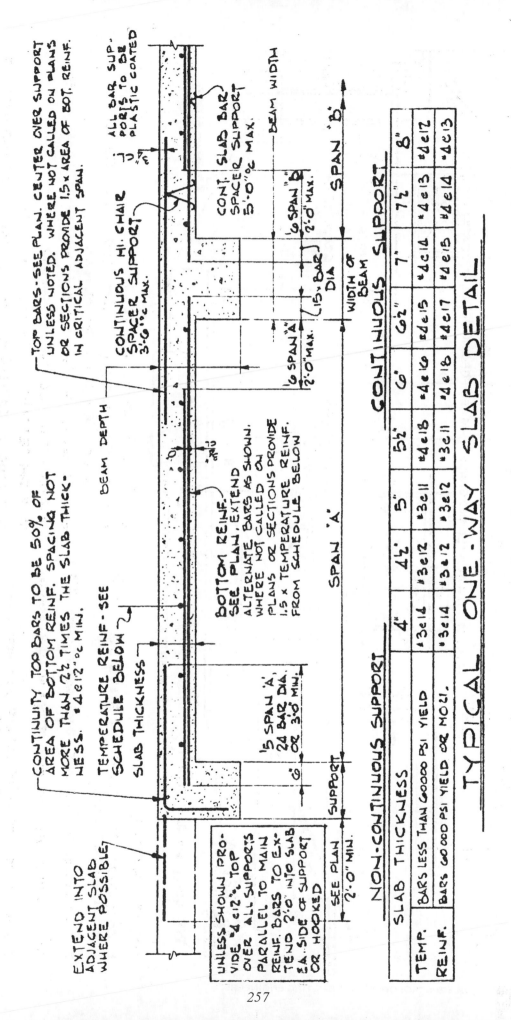

TYPICAL ONE-WAY SLAB DETAIL

NON-CONTINUOUS SUPPORT

SLAB THICKNESS	4"	4½"	5"	5½"	6"	6½"	7"	7½"	8"
TEMP. REINF. — BARS LESS THAN 60000 PSI YIELD	#3@14	#3@12	#3@11	#4@18	#4@16	#4@15	#4@14	#4@13	#4@12
TEMP. REINF. — BARS 60000 PSI YIELD OR MORE	#3@14	#3@12	#3@12	#3@11	#4@18	#4@17	#4@15	#4@14	#4@13

CONTINUOUS SUPPORT

(COURTESY OF PAULUS & SOKOLOWSKI - CONSULTING ENGINEERS)

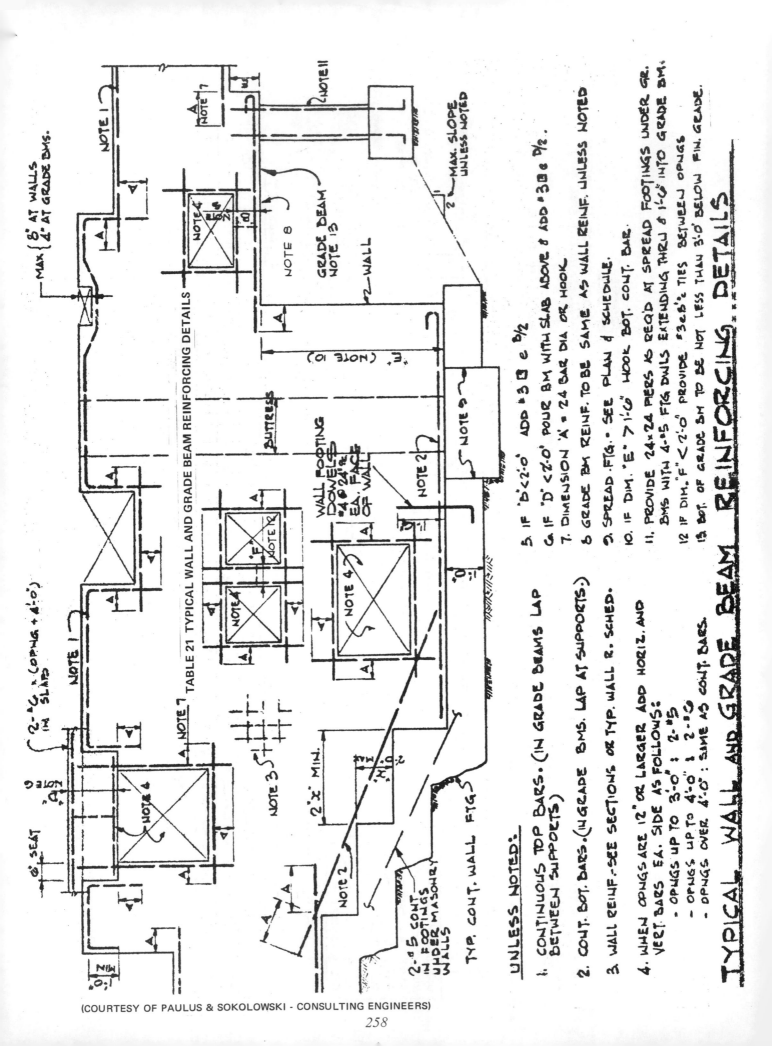

TABLE 21 TYPICAL WALL AND GRADE BEAM REINFORCING DETAILS

UNLESS NOTED:

1. CONTINUOUS TOP BARS. (IN GRADE BEAMS LAP BETWEEN SUPPORTS.)

2. CONT. BOT. BARS. (IN GRADE BMS. LAP AT SUPPORTS.)

3. WALL REINF.- SEE SECTIONS OR TYP. WALL R. SCHED.

4. WHEN OPNGS ARE 12" OR LARGER ADD HORIZ. AND VERT. BARS EA. SIDE AS FOLLOWS:
   - OPNGS UP TO 3'-0" : 2-#5
   - OPNGS UP TO 4'-0" : 2-#6
   - OPNGS OVER 4'-0" : SAME AS CONT. BARS.

5. IF "D"< 2'-0" ADD #3 ⊡ @ 9½

6. IF "D" < 2'-0" POUR BM WITH SLAB ABOVE & ADD #3 ⊡ @ 9½ .

7. DIMENSION "A" = 24 BAR DIA OR HOOK

8. GRADE BM. REINF. TO BE SAME AS WALL REINF. UNLESS NOTED

9. SPREAD FTG.- SEE PLAN & SCHEDULE.

10. IF DIM. "E" > 7'-6" HOOK BOT. CONT. BAR.

11. PROVIDE 24x24 PIERS AS REQ'D AT SPREAD FOOTINGS UNDER GR. BMS WITH 4-#5 FTG DWLS EXTENDING THRU 8 1'-6" INTO GRADE BM.

12. IF DIM. "F" < 2'-0" PROVIDE #3 @ 8" TIES BETWEEN OPNGS

13. BOT. OF GRADE BM TO BE NOT LESS THAN 3'-0 BELOW FIN. GRADE.

TYPICAL WALL AND GRADE BEAM REINFORCING DETAILS

TABLE 22 TYPICAL SLAB ON GROUND DETAILS

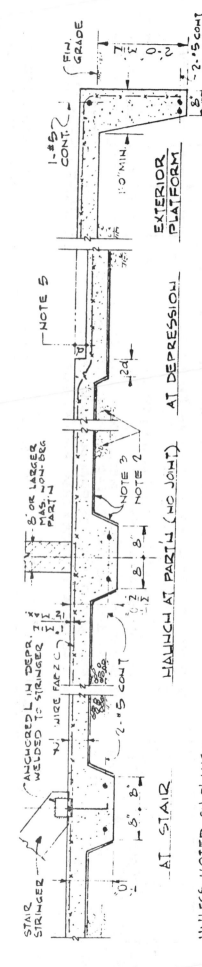

TYPICAL SLAB ON GROUND DETAILS

259

(COURTESY OF PAULUS & SOKOLOWSKI - CONSULTING ENGINEERS)

TABLE 23 TYPICAL PIER AND FOOTING DETAIL

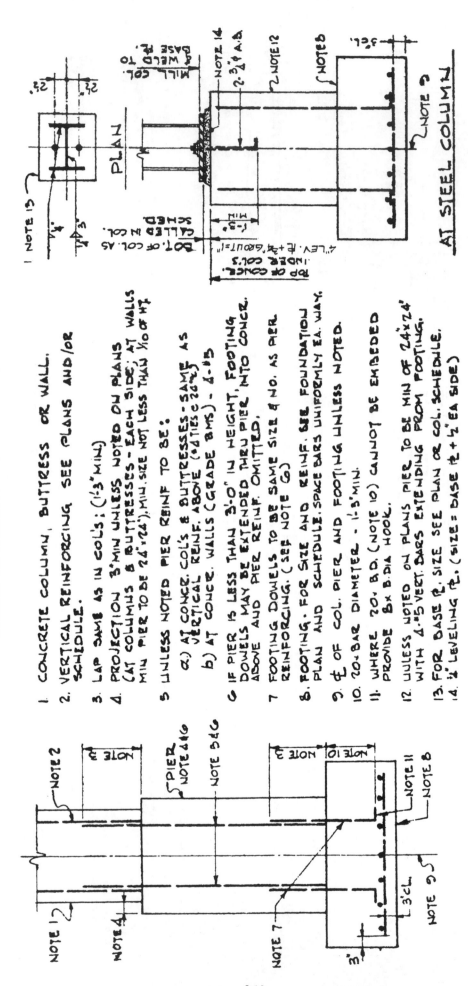

1. CONCRETE COLUMN, BUTTRESS OR WALL.

2. VERTICAL REINFORCING SEE PLANS AND/OR SCHEDULE.

3. LAP SAME AS IN COLS; (1'-3"MIN)

4. PROJECTION 3"MIN UNLESS NOTED ON PLANS (AT COLUMNS & BUTTRESSES-EACH SIDE; AT WALLS MIN PIER TO BE 24"×24").MIN SIZE NOT LESS THAN 1/10 OF HT

5. UNLESS NOTED PIER REINF TO BE:
   a.) AT CONCR. COLS & BUTTRESSES-SAME AS VERTICAL REINF. ABOVE (#4 TIES @ 24"±)
   b.) AT CONCR. WALLS (GRADE BMS) - 4-#5

6. IF PIER IS LESS THAN 3'-0" IN HEIGHT, FOOTING DOWELS MAY BE EXTENDED THRU PIER INTO CONCR. ABOVE AND PIER REINF. OMITTED.

7. FOOTING DOWELS TO BE SAME SIZE & NO. AS PIER REINFORCING. (SEE NOTE 6)

8. FOOTING. FOR SIZE AND REINF. SEE FOUNDATION PLAN AND SCHEDULE. SPACE BARS UNIFORMLY EA. WAY.

9. ℄ OF COL. PIER AND FOOTING UNLESS NOTED.

10. 20×BAR DIAMETER - 1'-5"MIN.

11. WHERE 20×B.D. (NOTE 10) CANNOT BE EMBEDDED PROVIDE B×B.DIA HOOK.

12. UNLESS NOTED ON PLANS PIER TO BE MIN OF 24"×24" WITH 4-#5 VERT. BARS EXTENDING FROM FOOTING.

13. FOR BASE ℄, SIZE SEE PLAN OR COL. SCHEDULE.

14. 1"LEVELING ℄. (SIZE = BASE ℄ + 2" EA SIDE)

AT STEEL COLUMN

TYPICAL PIER ≠ FOOTING DETAIL

(COURTESY OF PAULUS & SOKOLOWSKI - CONSULTING ENGINEERS)

260

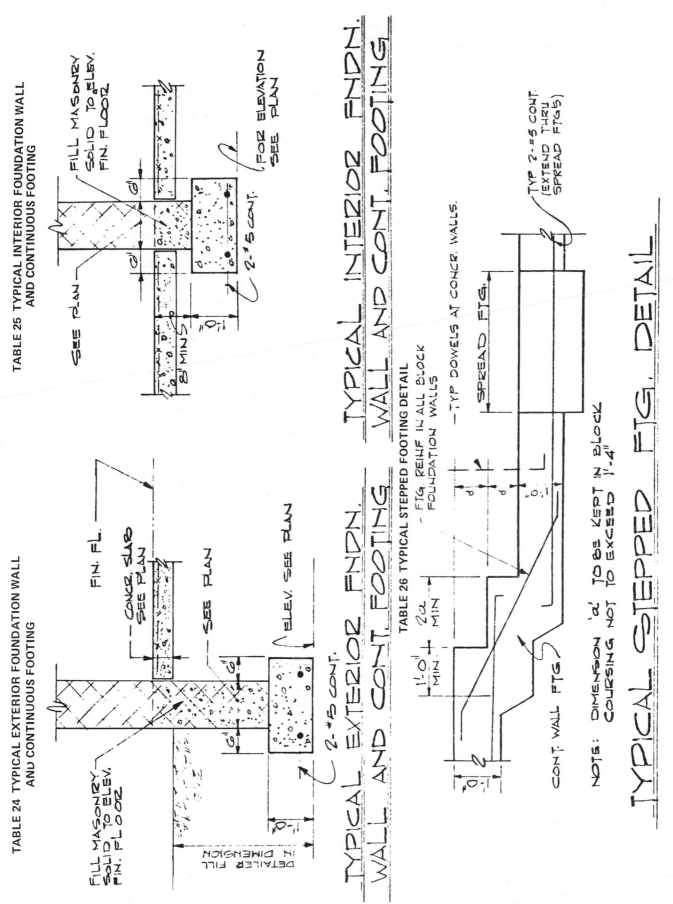

TABLE 25 TYPICAL INTERIOR FOUNDATION WALL
AND CONTINUOUS FOOTING

TABLE 24 TYPICAL EXTERIOR FOUNDATION WALL
AND CONTINUOUS FOOTING

TABLE 26 TYPICAL STEPPED FOOTING DETAIL

TYPICAL INTERIOR FNDN.
WALL AND CONT. FOOTING

TYPICAL EXTERIOR FNDN.
WALL AND CONT. FOOTING

TYPICAL STEPPED FTG. DETAIL

(COURTESY OF PAULUS & SOKOLOWSKI - CONSULTING ENGINEERS)

261

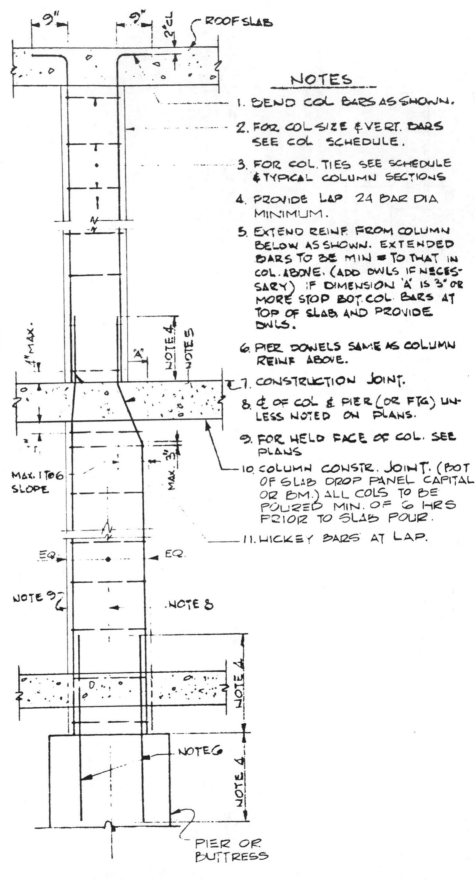

TABLE 27 TYPICAL CONCRETE COLUMN DETAIL

ROOF SLAB

NOTES

1. BEND COL BARS AS SHOWN.

2. FOR COL SIZE & VERT. BARS SEE COL SCHEDULE.

3. FOR COL. TIES SEE SCHEDULE & TYPICAL COLUMN SECTIONS

4. PROVIDE LAP 24 BAR DIA MINIMUM.

5. EXTEND REINF. FROM COLUMN BELOW AS SHOWN. EXTENDED BARS TO BE MIN # TO THAT IN COL. ABOVE. (ADD DWLS IF NECESSARY) IF DIMENSION 'A' IS 3" OR MORE STOP BOT. COL. BARS AT TOP OF SLAB AND PROVIDE DWLS.

6. PIER DOWELS SAME AS COLUMN REINF ABOVE.

7. CONSTRUCTION JOINT.

8. ℄ OF COL & PIER (OR FTG) UNLESS NOTED ON PLANS.

9. FOR HELD FACE OF COL. SEE PLANS

10. COLUMN CONSTR. JOINT. (BOT OF SLAB DROP PANEL CAPITAL OR BM.) ALL COLS TO BE POURED MIN. OF 6 HRS PRIOR TO SLAB POUR.

11. HICKEY BARS AT LAP.

MAX. 1 TO 6 SLOPE

EQ. EQ.

NOTE 9 NOTE 8

PIER OR BUTTRESS

TYPICAL CONCRETE COLUMN DETAIL

(COURTESY OF PAULUS & SOKOLOWSKI - CONSULTING ENGINEERS)

TABLE 28 COLUMN SECTIONS AND REINFORCING DETAILS

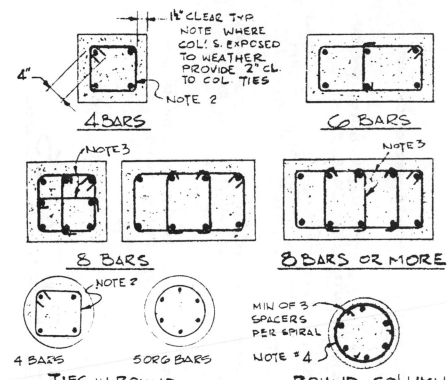

1½" CLEAR TYP
NOTE WHERE
COL'S. EXPOSED
TO WEATHER
PROVIDE 2" CL.
TO COL TIES
NOTE 2

4"

4 BARS

6 BARS

NOTE 3

NOTE 3

8 BARS

8 BARS OR MORE

NOTE 2

4 BARS   5 OR 6 BARS

MIN OF 3
SPACERS
PER SPIRAL

NOTE #4

TIES IN ROUND COLUMN

ROUND COLUMN WITH SPIRAL

1. FOR VERTICAL COL. REINF. SEE PLAN & COL. SCHEDULE
2. FOR COL. TIES SEE SCHEDULE BELOW
3. TIES & HOOKS TO BE SAME SIZE & SPACING
4. FOR SPIRAL SEE COL. SCHEDULE

SIZE AND SPACING OF COLUMN TIES

A \ B	8"	10"	12"	14"	16"	18"	20"	
#5	#3@8	#3@10	#3@10	#3@10				
#6	DO	DO	#3@12	#3@12	#3@12	#3@12	#3@12	
#7	DO	DO	DO	#3@14	#3@14	#3@14	#3@14	
#8	DO	DO	DO	DO	#3@16	#3@16	#3@16	
#9	DO	DO	DO	DO	DO	#3@18	#3@18	
#10	DO	DO	DO	DO	DO	DO	#3@18	
#11	DO	DO	DO	DO	DO	DO	#3@18	

A = SIZE OF VERTICAL REINFORCING

B = MINIMUM COLUMN SIZE.

COLUMN SECTIONS
AND REINFORCING DETAILS

(COURTESY OF PAULUS & SOKOLOWSKI - CONSULTING ENGINEERS)

TABLE 29 TYPICAL FLAT SLAB NOTES

FLAT SLAB NOTES

1. CONTINUITY TOP BARS FOR SIZE AND NUMBER SEE PLAN ("5 @ 15"2 MIN.). SPACE UNIFORMLY IN STRIP.

2. L TO BE L₁ OR L₂ WHICHEVER IS LARGER.

3. MIN. OF 50% OF BARS TO BE 30L. MAX. OF 50% OF BARS TO BE 25L.

4. SPACE COLUMN TOP BARS EQUALLY ACROSS COL. STRIP. ALTERNATE LONG & SHORT BARS.

5. CONTINUOUS HIGH CHAIR SUPPORT (ALL TOP BARS).

6. UNLESS NOTED TYPICAL BOTTOM MAT TO BE "6" EACH WAY. THRUOUT. LAP BARS 24 BAR DIA. NEAR ₵ OF COL. STRIP.

7. ALL BOTTOM BARS SHOWN THIS S ⟨10-"5B⟩ ON PLAN ARE ADDED BARS TO TYPICAL MAT (10= NO. OF BARS, "5 = 5#," B = BOTTOM). SPACE BARS UNIFORMLY IN STRIP BETWEEN AND IN THE SAME LAYER AS TYPICAL MAT BARS.

8. BOTTOM BARS IN OPPOSITE DIRECTION NOT SHOWN FOR CLARITY.

9. 3" CLEAR TOP & BOTTOM OUTER BARS. FOR DIRECTION OF OUTER BARS SEE PLAN.

10. TOP BARS CALLED THUS 11-"GT. (EX.) ON PLAN ARE TOTAL NUMBER OF TOP BARS IN THAT STRIP UNLESS NOTED. (11= NO OF BARS, "6= 5%"∮ T= TOP).

11. NOT MORE THAN 50% OF TOTAL BOTTOM BARS (MAT + ADDED) TO BE SHORT BARS. EXTEND PART OF ADDED BARS (AS REQ'D) AS SHOWN IN SECT. C-C.

12. CONTR. TO SUBMIT SEPARATE SHOP DWGS. FOR TOP & BOT. REINF. BARS.

TYPICAL FLAT SLAB DETAILS

(COURTESY OF PAULUS & SOKOLOWSKI - CONSULTING ENGINEERS)

TABLE 30 TYPICAL (POURED IN PLACE) CONCRETE JOIST DETAIL

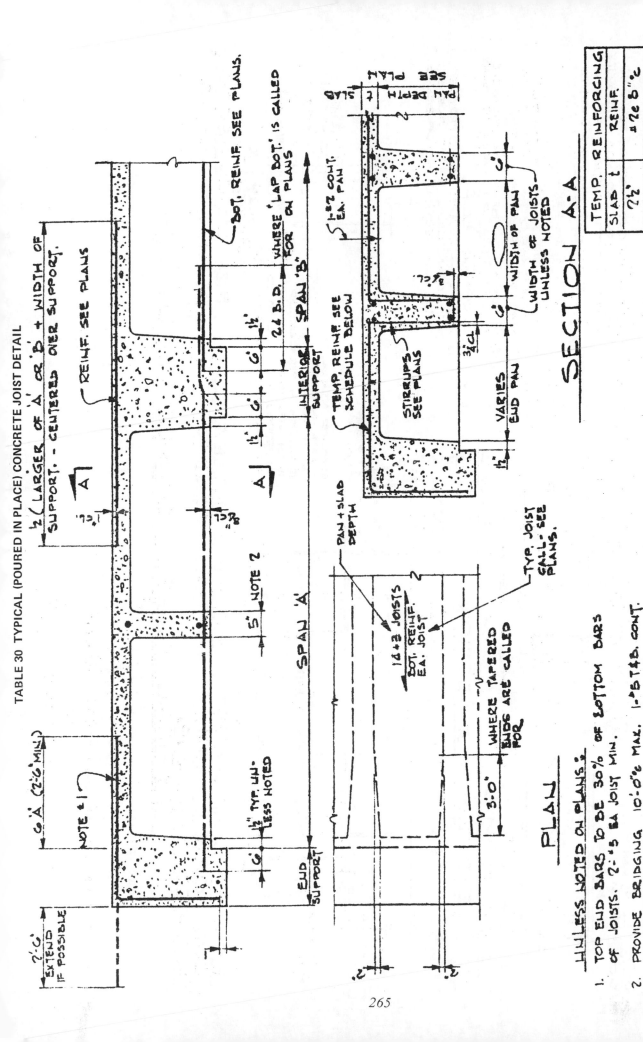

UNLESS NOTED ON PLANS:

1. TOP END BARS TO BE 30% OF BOTTOM BARS OF JOISTS. 2-#5 EA. JOIST MIN.

2. PROVIDE BRIDGING 10'-0"c MAX. 1-#5 T&B CONT.

3. FOR WIDTH OF JOISTS SEE PLAN

(COURTESY OF PAULUS & SOKOLOWSKI - CONSULTING ENGINEERS)

TYPICAL (POURED IN PLACE) CONCRETE JOIST DETAIL

SECTION A-A

PLAN

TEMP. REINFORCING	
SLAB t	REINF.
2½"	#2@ 8"c
3"	#3 @ 15"c
4"	#3@ 12"c

TABLE 31 TYPICAL STEEL CONNECTION DETAILS

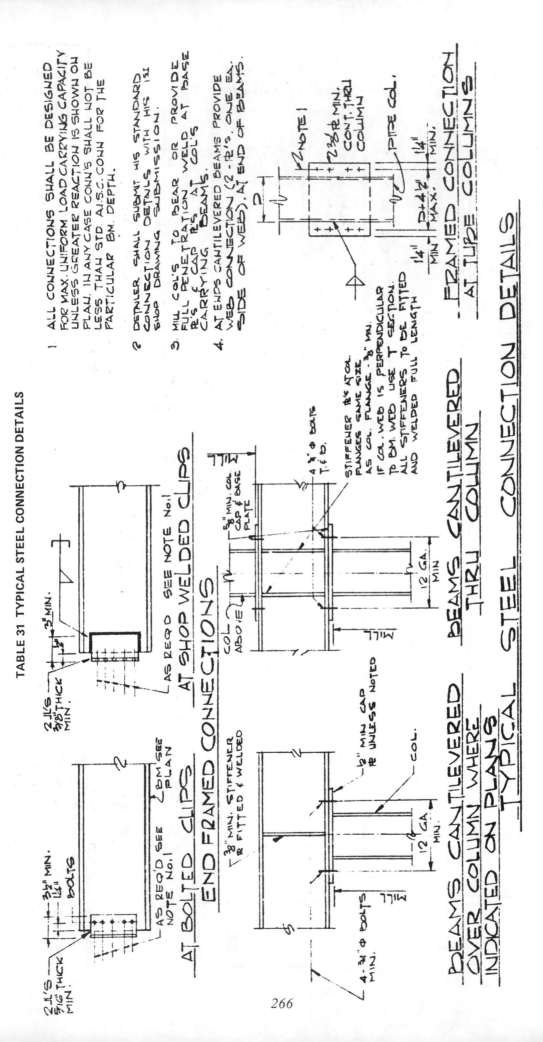

1. ALL CONNECTIONS SHALL BE DESIGNED FOR MAX. UNIFORM LOAD CARRYING CAPACITY UNLESS GREATER REACTION IS SHOWN ON PLAN. IN ANY CASE CONN'S SHALL NOT BE LESS THAN STD. A.I.S.C. CONN FOR THE PARTICULAR BM. DEPTH.

2. DETAILER SHALL SUBMIT HIS STANDARD CONNECTION DETAILS WITH HIS 1st SHOP DRAWING SUBMISSION.

3. MILL COL'S TO BEAR OR PROVIDE FULL PENETRATION WELD AT BASE PL'S & CAP PL'S AT COL'S CARRYING BEAMS.

4. AT ENDS CANTILEVERED BEAMS PROVIDE WEB CONNECTION (2 - PL'S, ONE EA. SIDE OF WEB), AT END OF BEAMS.

AT BOLTED CLIPS

AT SHOP WELDED CLIPS

END FRAMED CONNECTIONS

BEAMS CANTILEVERED OVER COLUMN WHERE INDICATED ON PLANS

BEAMS CANTILEVERED THRU COLUMN

FRAMED CONNECTION AT TUBE COLUMNS

TYPICAL STEEL CONNECTION DETAILS

(COURTESY OF PAULUS & SOKOLOWSKI - CONSULTING ENGINEERS)

266

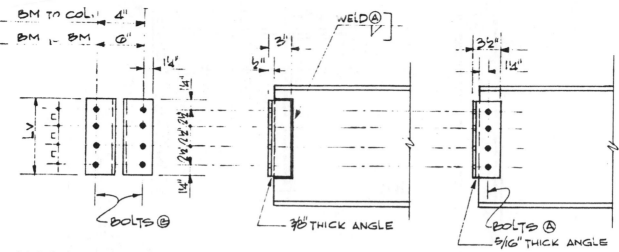

NOTES:

1. ANGLE THICKNESS 3/8" FOR WELDED CONN.
   5/16" FOR BOLTED CONN.

2. WELD Ⓐ BASED ON FOLLOWING MINIMUM WEB THICKNESS

E70 ⎱

WELD SIZE	WEB THICKNESS	WELD SIZE	WEB THICKNESS
3/16 △	.19"	3/16 △	.25"
1/4 △	.30"	1/4 △	.33"
5/16 △	.48"	5/16 △	.41"

⎰ E60

3. Lv = LENGTH OF ANGLE
4. π = PITCH OF BOLTS = 2½" MIN.
5. BOLTS 3/4"∅ (SEE BELOW)
6. HOLES 13/16"∅

DOUBLE ANGLE CONNECTIONS

LENGTH OF ANGLE (Lv)	NO. OF BOLTS IN (1) ROW	3/4"∅ BOLTS		WELDS		
		A325 (H.S.B)	A307 (MACH)	FILLET	E60 XX	E70 XX
3"	1	13.2	8.8	3/16 △	8.5	10.0
				1/4 △	12.0	14.0
				———	———	———
5"	2	26.5	17.7	3/16 △	13.8	18.4
				1/4 △	21.0	24.5
				5/16 △	26.3	30.7
7½"	3	39.8	26.5	3/16 △	24.1	28.1
				1/4 △	32.1	37.5
				5/16 △	40.1	46.9
10"	4	53.0	35.3	3/16 △	32.6	38.4
				1/4 △	43.9	51.2
				5/16 △	54.9	64.0
1'-0½"	5	66.3	44.2	3/16 △	42.1	49.1
				1/4 △	55.6	65.0
				5/16 △	70.2	81.9
1'-3"	6	79.5	53.0	3/16 △	51.5	60
				1/4 △	68.7	80.2
				5/16 △	85.9	100.4
1'-5½"	7	92.8	61.9	3/16 △	60.7	70.8
				1/4 △	80.9	94.4
				5/16 △	101.0	118.0
1'-8"	8	106.0	70.7	3/16 △	70.7	82.4
				1/4 △	94.2	110.0
				5/16 △	118.0	137.0

ALLOWABLE LOADS IN KIPS

TABLE 32 DOUBLE ANGLE CONNECTIONS

TABLE 33 TYPICAL FOUNDATION WALL AND GRADE BEAM REINFORCING SCHEDULE AND LAP DETAILS

AT CORNERS

AT INTERSECTIONS

UNLESS NOTED:

1. ALL HORIZONTAL BARS SHALL BE CONTINUOUS

2. ALL CONT. BARS SHALL BE LAPPED AT SPLICES AND BEND AROUND CORNERS.

3. ALL CONT. BOT. BARS TO BE SPLICED NEAR SUPPORTS (THAT IS WITHIN ⅕ OF SPAN LENGTH.)

4. ALL CONT. TOP BARS SHALL BE SPLICED BETWEEN SUPPORTS (WITHIN ⅕ OF SPAN FROM ℄ OF MIDSPAN.)

5. PROVIDE 24 BAR DIA LAP LENGTH AT SPLICES

6. INCREASE LAPS 50% IF MORE THAN 3 ADJACENT BARS ARE SPLICED WITHIN 3'-0" OF EACH OTHER.

WALL REINFORCING SCHEDULE

WALL THICKNESS	REINFORCING UNLESS NOTED	REMARKS
8", 9"	2-#6 TOP & BOT CONT.	CENTER OF WALL
	#5 e 14"c HORIZ. #4 e 15"c VERT.	
10", 11", 12"	2-#7 T&B. CONT.	EACH FACE
	#6 e 17"c HORIZ. #4 e 16"c VERT.	
13", 14"	2-#7 T & B CONT.	EACH FACE
	#6 e 17"c HORIZ. #4 e 16"c VERT.	
15", 16"	2-#7 T&B. CONT.	EACH FACE
	#5 e 15"c HORIZ. #4 e 16"c VERT.	
17", 18"	3-#7 T&B. CONT.	EACH FACE
	#5 e 14"c HORIZ. #4 e 15"c VERT.	

TYPICAL FOUNDATION WALL AND GRADE BEAM
REINFORCING SCHEDULE AND LAP DETAILS

TABLE 34 SWIMMING POOL DESIGNS AND DIMENSIONS

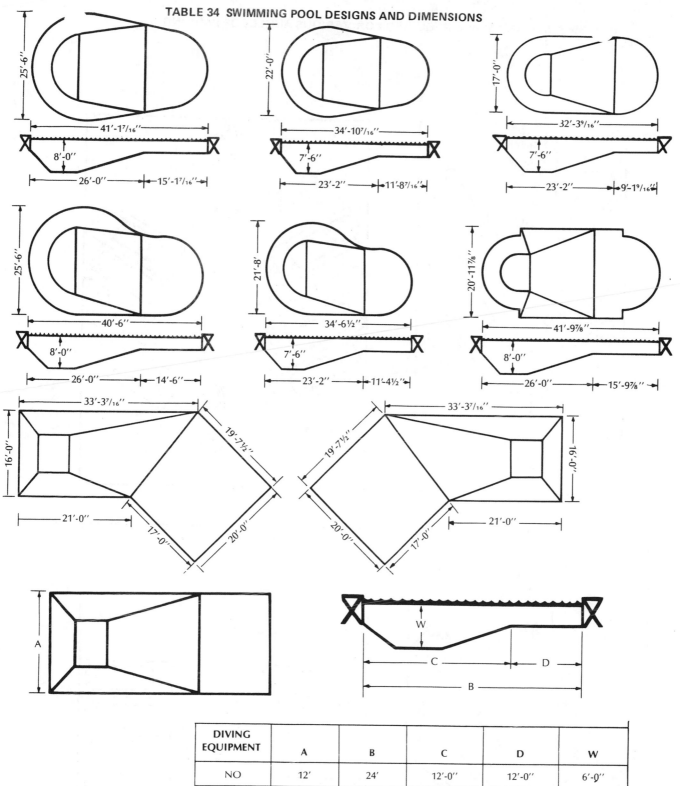

DIVING EQUIPMENT	A	B	C	D	W
NO	12'	24'	12'-0''	12'-0''	6'-0''
NO	12'	28'	15'-0''	13'-0''	6'-0''
YES	16'	32'	23'-0''	9'-0''	7'-6''
YES	16'	36'	23'-0''	13'-0''	7'-6''
YES	18'	36'	26'-0''	10'-0''	8'-0''
YES	20'	40'	28'-6''	11'-6''	8'-6''
YES	24'	40'	28'-6''	11'-6''	8'-6''
YES	24'	48'	31'-6''	16'-6''	9'-0''

TABLE 35 AISLE AND SPACE REQUIRED FOR VARIOUS ANGLES OF PARKING

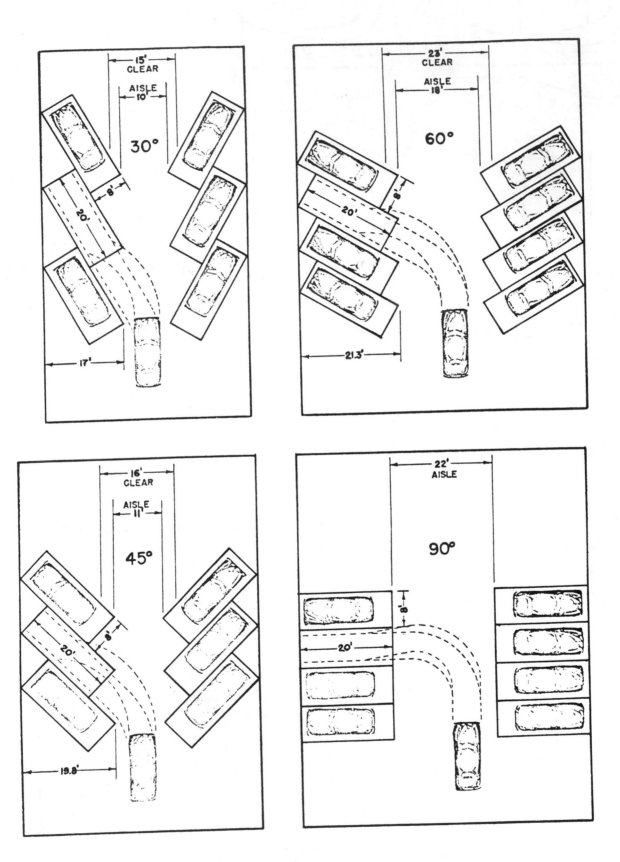

TABLE 36 CONCRETE MASONRY UNITS (METRIC MODULAR)

Load Bearing

W available in 190-240 & 290.
Available in 2 or 3 core.

Stretcher

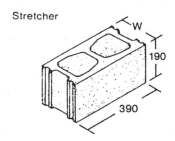

Non-Load Bearing

W available in 90 & 140.
Available in 2 or 3 core.

Partition
Stretcher

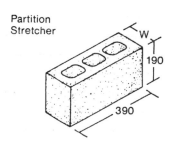

Floor Systems

D available in 100 to 250.

Celdex Unit.

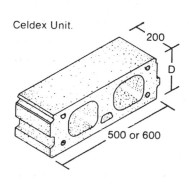

Veneers

H available in 40 to 190.
W available in 90 to 290.
Brick—available in various sizes.

Split Block.

Fluted

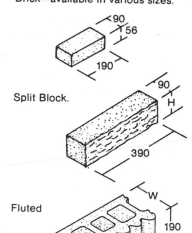

Structural

W available in 140 & 290.

Bond Beam.

Pilaster

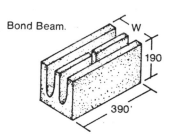
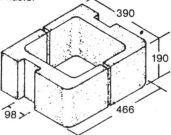

Pierced Design

W available in 90 & 190.

Random Shapes

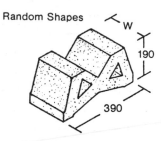

Available in 190-290 & 390

Square Units.

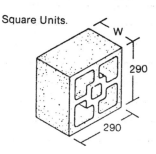

Profile

W available in 90 to 290.

Scored.

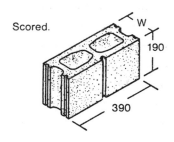

Hi-Lite

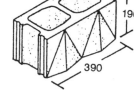

NOTES

NOTES

ALPHABETICAL
INDEX

CONVERSION FACTORS FOR UNITS

SAA MH1—1972

Conversion factors are taken to **six** significant figures where appropriate. **Bold** values denote exact conversions.

METRIC TO IMPERIAL			IMPERIAL TO METRIC		
Plane Angle:					
1 rad	= 57° 17′ 45″	degree	1 degree	= 0·017 453 3	rad
	= 57·2958	degree	1 minute		
	= 3437·75	minute	1 second	= 0·290 888 × 10⁻³	rad
	= 206 265	second		= 4·848 14 × 10⁻⁶	rad
Length:					
1 km	= 0·621 371	mile	1 mile	= **1·609 344**	km
	= 49·7097	chain	1 chain	= **20·1168**	m
1 m	= 1·093 61	yd	1 yd	= **0·9144**	m
	= 3·280 84	ft	1 ft	= **0·3048**	m
1 mm	= 0·039 370 1	in		= **304·8**	mm
			1 in	= **25·4**	mm
Area:					
1 km²	= 0·386 102	mile²	1 mile²	= 2·589 99	km²
1 ha	= 2·471 05	acre	1 acre	= 0·404 686	ha
1 m²	= 1·195 99	yd²		= 4046·86	m²
	= 10·7639	ft²	1 yd²	= 0·836 127	m²
1 mm²	= 0·001 550 00	in²	1 ft²	= 0·092 903 0	m²
			1 in²	= **645·16**	mm²
Volume, Capacity, Modulus of Section:					
1 m³	= 0·810 713 × 10⁻³	acre ft	1 acre ft	= 1233·48	m³
	= 1·307 95	yd³	1 yd³	= 0·764 555	m³
	= 35·3147	ft³	100 super ft	= 0·235 973	m³
	= 423·776	super feet	1 ft³	= 0·028 316 8	m³
1 mm³	= 61·0237 × 10⁻⁶	in³		= 28·3168	litre
1 litre (l)	= 0·035 314 7	ft³	1 in³	= 16 387·1	mm³
	= 0·219 969	gal		= 16·3871	ml
	= 1·759 76	pt	1 gal	= **4·546 09**	litre
1 ml	= 0·061 023 7	in³	1 pt	= 568·261	ml
	= 0·035 195 1	fl oz	1 fl oz	= 28·413 0	ml

Note: Australian Standard 1000 — 1970 defines the litre (l) as the volume of a cube with **100 mm** sides.

Second Moment of Area:					
1 mm⁴	= 2·402 51 × 10⁻⁶	in⁴	1 in⁴	= 416 231	mm⁴
				= 0·416 231 × 10⁻⁶	m⁴
Velocity, Speed:					
1 m/s	= 3·280 84	ft/s	1 ft/s	= **0·3048**	m/s
	= 2·236 94	mile/h	1 mile/h	= **1·609 344**	km/h
1 km/h	= 0·621 371	mile/h		= **0·447 04**	m/s
Acceleration:					
1 m/s²	= 3·280 84	ft/s²	1 ft/s²	= **0·3048**	m/s²
Volume Rate of Flow:					
1 m³/s	= 35·3147	ft³/s	1 ft³/s	= 0·028 316 8	m³/s
	= 19·0053	million gal/day	1 ft³/min	= 0·471 947	l/s
	= 0·810 713 × 10⁻³	acre ft/s	1 gal/min	= 0·075 768 2	l/s
1 l/s	= 2·118 88	ft³/min	1 gal/h	= 0·001 262 8	l/s
	= 13·198 2	gal/min	1 million		
	= 791·891	gal/h	gal/day	= 0·005 261 68	m³/s
			1 acre ft/s	= 1233·48	m³/s
Equivalent Temperature Value (°C = K — 273·15):					
°C	= 5/9 (°F — 32)		°F	= 9/5 °C + 32	
Temperature Interval:					
1 °C	= 1 K = 1·8 °F		1 °F	= 0·555 556 °C	
				= 5/9 °C = 5/9 K	
Mass:					
1 tonne (t)	= 0·984 207	ton	1 ton	= 1·016 05	t
	= 19·684 1	cwt	1 cwt	= 50·8023	kg
1 kg	= 2·204 62	lb	1 lb	= 0·453 592	kg
1 g	= 0·035 274	oz	1 oz	= 28·3495	g

USED IN THE CONSTRUCTION INDUSTRY

Mass/Unit Length:

1 kg/m	= 0·671 969	lb/ft	1 lb/ft	= 1·488 16	kg/m
1 g/m	= 3·547 99	lb/mile	1 lb/mile	= 0·281 849	g/m

Mass/Unit Area:

1 kg/m²	= 0·204 816	lb/ft²	1 lb/ft²	= 4·882 43	kg/m²
1 g/m²	= 0·029 494	oz/yd²	1 oz/yd²	= 33·9057	g/m²
	= 0·003 277 06	oz/ft²	1 oz/ft²	= 305·152	g/m²

Density (Mass/Unit Volume):

1 kg/m³	= 0·062 428	lb/ft³	1 lb/ft³	= 16·0185	kg/m³
	= 1·685 56	lb/yd³	1 lb/yd³	= 0·593 278	kg/m³
1 t/m³	= 0·752 48	ton/yd³	1 ton/yd³	= 1·328 94	t/m³

Mass/Unit Time:

1 kg/s	= 2·204 62	lb/s	1 lb/s	= 0·453 592	kg/s
1 t/h	= 0·984 207	ton/h	1 ton/h	= 1·016 05	t/h

Moment of Inertia:

1 kg·m²	= 23·7304	lb·ft²	1 lb·ft²	= 0·042 140 1	kg·m²
	= 3417·17	lb·in²	1 lb·in²	= 292·640	kg·mm²

Force:

1 MN	= 100·361	tonf	1 tonf	= 9·964 02	kN
1 kN	= 0·100 361	tonf	1 lbf	= 4·448 22	N
	= 224·809	lbf			
1 N	= 0·224 809	lbf			

Moment of Force, Torque:

1 N·m	= 0·737 562	lbf·ft	1 lbf·ft	= 1·355 82	N·m
	= 8·850 75	lbf·in	1 lbf·in	= 0·112 985	N·m
1 kN·m	= 0·329 269	tonf·ft	1 tonf·ft	= 3·037 03	kN·m
	= 0·737 562	kip·ft	1 kip·ft	= 1·355 82	kN·m

Force/Unit Length:

1 N/m	= 0·068 521 8	lbf/ft	1 lbf/ft	= 14·5939	N/m
1 kN/m	= 0·030 590 1	tonf/ft	1 tonf/ft	= 32·6903	kN/m

Pressure, Stress, Modulus of Elasticity (1 Pa = 1 N/m²):

1 MPa	= 0·064 749 0	tonf/in²	1 tonf/in²	= 15·4443	MPa
	= 9·323 85	tonf/ft²	1 tonf/ft²	= 107·252	kPa
	= 145·038	lbf/in²	1 lbf/in²	= 6·894 76	kPa
1 kPa	= 20·8854	lbf/ft²	1 lbf/ft²	= 47·8803	Pa

Work, Energy, Heat (1 J = 1 W·s):

1 MJ	= 0·277 778	kWh	1 kWh	= **3·6**	MJ
1 kJ	= 0·947 817	Btu	1 Btu	= 1·055 06	kJ
1 J	= 0·737 562	ft·lbf		= 1055·06	J
			1 ft·lbf	= 1·355 82	J

Power, Heat Flow Rate:

1 kW	= 1·341 02	hp	1 hp	= 0·745 700	kW
1 W	= 3·412 14	Btu/h		= 745·700	W
	= 0·737 562	ft·lbf/s	1 Btu/h	= 0·293 071	W
			1 ft·lbf/s	= 1·355 82	W

Intensity of Heat Flow (Heat Loss from Surfaces):

1 W/m²	= 0·316 998	Btu/(ft²·h)	1 Btu/(ft²·h)	= 3·154 59	W/m²

Thermal Conductance (Heat Transfer Coefficient):

1 W/(m²·K)	= 0·176 110	Btu/(ft²·h·°F)	1 Btu/(ft²·h·°F)	= 5·678 26	W/(m²·K)

Thermal Conductivity:

1 W/(m·K)	= 0·577 789	Btu/(ft·h·°F)	1 Btu/(ft·h·°F)	= 1·730 73	W/(m·K)

Calorific Value (Mass and Volume Basis):

1 kJ/kg	= 0·429 923	Btu/lb	1 Btu/lb	= **2·326**	kJ/kg
(1 J/g)					(J/g)
1 kJ/m³	= 0·026 839 2	Btu/ft³	1 Btu/ft³	= 37·2589	kJ/m³

Thermal Capacity (Mass and Volume Basis):

1 kJ/(kg·K)	= 0·238 846	Btu/(lb·°F)	1 Btu/(lb·°F)	= **4·1868**	kJ/(kg·K)
1 kJ/(m³·K)	= 0·014 910 7	Btu/(ft³·°F)	1 Btu/(ft³·°F)	= 67·0661	kJ/(m³·K)

Illumination:

1 lx	= 0·092 903	lm/ft²	1 lm/ft²	= 10·7639	lx

Luminance:

1 cd/m²	= 0·092 903	cd/ft²	1 cd/ft²	= 10·7639	cd/m²